INVESTIGATIONS

IN NUMBER, DATA, AND SPACE®

D1497662

GRADE 2 UNIT 5

HOW MANY TENS? HOW MANY HUNDREDS?

Addition, Subtraction, and the Number System 3

PEARSON

TERC

Glenview, Illinois • Boston, Massachusetts • Chandler, Arizona • New York, New York

Photographs

Photo locators denoted as follows: Top (T), Center (C), Bottom (B), Left (L), Right (R), Background (Bkgd)

All photographs ©Pearson Education.

Elaborations text ©Illustrative Mathematics.

The Investigations curriculum was developed by TERC, Cambridge, MA.

This material is based on work supported by the National Science Foundation ("NSF") under Grant No. ESI-0095450. Any opinions, findings, and conclusions or recommendations expressed in this material are those of the author(s) and do not necessarily reflect the views of the National Science Foundation.

PEARSON

ISBN-13: 978-0-328-85910-8
ISBN-10: 0-328-85910-9

DEVELOPERS

Investigations Curriculum Center
Education Research Collaborative at TERC

Cambridge, MA
investigations.terc.edu

T E R C

COLLABORATING TEACHERS

This group of dedicated teachers carried out extensive field testing in their classrooms, met regularly to discuss issues of teaching and learning mathematics, provided feedback to staff, welcomed staff into their classrooms to document students' work, and contributed both suggestions and written material that has been incorporated into the 2nd and 3rd editions of the curriculum.

Bethany Altchek	Susan Gillis	Deborah O'Brien
Linda Amaral	Steve Goldman*	Jolene O'Brien*
Lindsay Barton*	Diane Griggs*	Timothy O'Connor
Kimberly Beauregard	Danielle Harrington	Anne Marie O'Reilly
Barbara Bernard	Elaine Herzog	Mark Paige
Nancy Buell	Francine Hiller	Margaret Riddle
Carolyn Callender*	Kirsten Lee Howard	Karen Schweitzer
Katie Carr*	Liliana Klass	Elisabeth Seyferth
Rose Christiansen	Leslie Kramer	Susan Smith
Chris Colbath-Hess	Melissa Lee Andrichak	Debra Sorvillo
Lisette Colon	Kelley Lee Sadowski	Shoshanah Starr
Kim Cook	Gizelle Lev*	Stacy Sweeney*
Frances Cooper	Jennifer Levitan	Janice Szymaszek
Mary Elizabeth Cranton*	Mary Lou LoVecchio	Karen Tobin
Justin Cravens*	Kristen McEnaney	JoAnn Trauschke
Kathleen Drew	Maura McGrail	Ana Vaisenstein
Kathleen Earley*	Kathe Millett	Ashley Warlick*
Cailin Eaton*	Katrina Mills*	Yvonne Watson
Rebeka Eston Salemi	Florence Molyneaux	Jerilyn Willig*
Kerri Favreau*	Amy Monkiewicz	Lucy Wittenberg*
Thomas Fisher	Elizabeth Monopoli	Michelle Woods
Michael Flynn	Carol Murray	Mary Wright
Jen Gehling*	Robyn Musser	
Holly Ghazey	Christine Norrman	

*Collaborating teachers for *Investigations 3*

Investigations 3 is built on the work of many authors who contributed to the first, second, and third editions of the curriculum. We acknowledge the critical contributions of these authors in developing the content and pedagogy of *Investigations*.

AUTHORS

Joan Akers

Virginia Bastable

Michael T. Battista

Katie Hickey

Douglas H. Clements

Keith Cochran

Darrell Earnest

Karen Economopoulos

Arusha Hollister

Nancy Horowitz

Marlene Kliman

Erin Leidl

Jan Mokros

Megan Murray

Ricardo Nemirovsky

Young Oh

Beth W. Perry

Andee Rubin

Susan Jo Russell

Deborah Schifter

Kathy Sillman

Cornelia Tierney

Lucy Wittenberg

CONTRIBUTING AUTHORS

Mary Berle-Carman

Denise Baumann

Nancy Belkov

Lorraine Brooks*

Christopher Clancy*

Rebecca B. Corwin

Jennifer DiBrienza

Rebeka Eston

Claryce Evans

Hollee Freeman

Anne Goodrow

Paula Hooper

Cliff Konold

Chris Mainhart

Sue McMillen

Katrina Mills

Jerrie Moffet

Stephen Monk

Tracy Noble

Mary Beth O'Connor

Kim O'Neil

Mark Ogonowski

Julie Sarama

Amy Shulman Weinberg

Margie Singer

Katie Stokinger*

Judy Storeygard

Annie Sussman

Amy Taber*

Denise Treacy

Elizabeth Van Cleef

Virginia Woolley

Carol Wright

Tracey Wright

*Administrative Staff for *Investigations 3*

REVIEWERS

George Avrunin
Professor
Department of Mathematics and Statistics
University of Massachusetts Amherst

Ben Ford
Professor
Department of Mathematics and Statistics
Sonoma State University

Scott J. Hendrickson
Associate Teaching Professor
Mathematics Education
Brigham Young University

DeAnn Huinker
Professor, Mathematics Education
Director, Center for Mathematics and Science Education Research
University of Wisconsin-Milwaukee

Reva Kasman
Associate Professor
Mathematics
Salem State University

Elham Kazemi
Professor
Mathematics Education
University of Washington

Harriet Pollatsek
Professor Emerita
Mathematics
Mount Holyoke College

Edward Silver
Professor of Education & Mathematics
University of Michigan

Virginia C. Stimpson
Mathematics Educator
University of Washington

Lucy West
President and Founder
Metamorphosis Teaching Learning Communities

CONTENTS

UNIT 5 How Many Tens? How Many Hundreds?

INTRODUCTION AND OVERVIEW

INVESTIGATION 1
COMBINATIONS OF 100

INVESTIGATION 2
ADDING WITHIN 100 AND COUNTING TO 1,000

INVESTIGATION 3
FLUENCY WITHIN 100

PROFESSIONAL DEVELOPMENT

Content Focus

Each session has one Classroom Routine that is done outside of math time.

A full description of these Classroom Routine activities is available in Review and Practice in This Unit.

CLASSROOM ROUTINES

Fact Fluency
CCSS 2.OA.B.2

Today's Number
CCSS 2.NBT.A.1, 2.NBT.A.1b, 2.NBT.A.2, 2.NBT.A.3, 2.NBT.A.4, 2.NBT.B.5, 2.NBT.B.9, 2.MD.C.8

Quick Images
CCSS 2.NBT.A.1b, 2.NBT.A.2, 2.NBT.A.3, 2.NBT.B.5, Supports 2.NBT.B.8

How Many Pockets?
CCSS 2.OA.B.2, 2.NBT.B.5, 2.NBT.B.6

What Time Is It?
CCSS 2.MD.C.7

INVESTIGATION 1

Combinations of 100

Students add and subtract 10, 20, and 30 and 1, 2, and 3, to or from 2-digit numbers as they try to capture 5 chips scattered around a 100 chart. They solve 2-step story problems about money and stickers and figure out how much more they need in order to have 100 or $1.00. Students continue to review and practice addition and subtraction facts and consider the relationship between adding 9 and 10 and subtracting 9 and 10 when the +/−9 Fact Cards are added to their set.

Ways to Make One Dollar $1 $1.00
50¢ + 50¢ = $1.00
25¢ + 75¢ = $1.00
53¢ + 47¢ = $1.00
10¢ + 10¢ + 80¢ = $1.00
30¢ + 70¢ = $1.00
60¢ + 40¢ = $1.00
61¢ + 36¢ = $1.00

CCSS
2.OA.A.1, 2.OA.B.2, 2.NBT.B.5, 2.NBT.B.6, 2.NBT.B.8, 2.NBT.B.9, 2.MD.B.6, 2.MD.C.8

INVESTIGATION 2

Adding within 100 and Counting to 1,000

Students think about combinations that make 100 as they try to find pairs of 2-digit numbers that equal a number close to 100. They also revisit activities that extend the rote counting sequence to 1,000. They practice reading, writing, and comparing 3-digit numbers, skip counting within that range, and adding 10 or 100 to any 3-digit number. They use the sticker context to represent the composition of 3-digit numbers as hundreds, tens, and ones.

40 + 61 = 101   Score: 1
49 + 60 = 109   Score: 9
96 + 04 = 100   Score: 0

CCSS
2.OA.B.2, 2.NBT.A.1, 2.NBT.A.1a, 2.NBT.A.1b, 2.NBT.A.2, 2.NBT.A.3, 2.NBT.A.4, 2.NBT.B.5, 2.NBT.B.8, 2.NBT.B.9, 2.MD.C.8

INVESTIGATION 3

Fluency within 100

Students solve story problems, including comparison problems with a bigger unknown and problems with more than one step. They focus on developing efficient and accurate strategies for adding 2-digit numbers within 100, specifically those that involve adding tens and ones and adding on one number in parts.

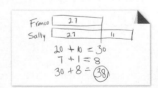

CCSS
2.OA.A.1, 2.OA.B.2, , 2.NBT.A.1, 2.NBT.A.1b, 2.NBT.A.2, 2.NBT.A.3, 2.NBT.B.5, 2.NBT.B.6, 2.NBT.B.8, 2.NBT.B.9, 2.MD.B.6

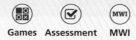
Session Structure

DAY	SESSION	CLASSROOM ROUTINES	ACTIVITY	DISCUSSION	MATH WORKSHOP	ASSESSMENT	SESSION FOLLOW-UP
1	1.1 Plus 9 or Minus 9 Bingo	●	● ● ●	●			●
2	1.2 Capture 5: Adding and Subtracting Tens and Ones	●	● ●	●			●
3	1.3 How Many Stickers? How Many More to Get 100?	●	●	●	●		●
4	1.4 Make a Dollar	●	● ● ● ●				●
5	1.5 How Much to $1.00? How Much to 100?	●		● ●			●
6	1.6 How Much More to $1.00?	●	●			●	●
7	2.1 Close to 100	●	● ● ●				●
8	2.2 Numbers to 1,000	●	●	●	●		●
9	2.3 Stickers: Hundreds, Tens, and Ones	●	●	●	●		●
10	2.4 Plus or Minus 10 or 100	●	●	●	●		●
11	2.5 What Do You Know about 345?	●	●	●	●		●
12	2.6 Ten Hundreds Make One Thousand	●		●	●	●	●
13	3.1 Strategies for Addition	●	● ●	●			●
14	3.2 Comparison Problems with the Bigger Amount Unknown	●	● ●	●			●
15	3.3 Capture 5 in the 1,000 Book	●	●	●	●		●
16	3.4 Adding Tens and Ones	●	●	●	●		●
17	3.5 Adding One Number On in Parts	●	●	●	●		●
18	3.6 Enough for the Grade?	●	●	●	●		●
19	3.7 Fluency with Addition	●		●	●	●	●
20	3.8 Adding within 100, Counting within 1,000	●				●	●

Unit Focus

How Many Tens? How Many Hundreds? is the fifth of eight units in the Grade 2 sequence and the third of five units in the Grade 2 Number and Operations strand of *Investigations*. This strand develops students' ideas about counting and quantity, place value and the structure of the base-10 number system, the meaning of operations with whole numbers, the development of computational fluency, and generalizations about numbers and operations.

This unit focuses on the place value of 3-digit numbers and operating on numbers within 100. Students come to see 100 as 10 tens and multiples of 100 as being made up of some number of hundreds. They solve a variety of types of story problems (e.g., put together/take apart with one or both addends unknown, add to and take from with result unknown, unknown change or an unknown start). They play games that involve combining amounts to get to 100 or $1. Work on fluency with addition and subtraction within 100 continues, with a focus on using known facts and knowledge of the operations. Fluency with addition within 100 is a benchmark in this unit. Students also identify, read, and write numbers to 1,000 and add and subtract 10 and 100 to numbers in that range. Fluency with addition within 100 is a benchmark in this unit.

CONNECTIONS: LOOKING BACK

This unit builds especially on the work in Units 1 and 3. In those units, students solved a variety of types of story problems (e.g., put together/take apart with one or both addends or the total unknown, add to and take from with result unknown, unknown change or an unknown start). They were introduced to a place-value context for modeling our base-10 number system and came to see 100 as 10 tens and multiples of 100 as being made up of hundreds. They began to develop fluency with addition, focusing on strategies that involved decomposing one or both numbers by place. Students played games involving 100 and worked with the counting sequence and composition of 3-digit numbers to 500. In all previous Grade 2 units, students have been working on developing fluency with sets of addition and subtraction facts.

This unit focuses on the following five main math ideas:

1 Understanding place value

Students extend their understanding of place value to 3-digit numbers. They look closely at how 3-digit numbers are composed and at how numbers change when 10 or 100 is added or subtracted. Using a familiar place-value context, they represent 3-digit numbers with sticker notation and think

about how the number of sheets, strips, and singles connects to the number of hundreds, tens, and ones and to the way a number is written in words, with numbers, and in expanded form. Students think about how the meaning of a digit changes when its place in a number changes and use that information to estimate, compare, and reason about 3-digit numbers.

Number	Sticker Notation	Sheets, Strips, Singles	Hundreds, Tens, Ones	Equation
407		4 Sheets 0 Strips 7 Singles	4 Hundreds 0 Tens 7 Ones	$400+0+7=407$
500		5 Sheets 0 Strips 0 Singles	5 Hundreds 0 Tens 0 Ones	$500+0=500$

MATH FOCUS POINTS IN SESSIONS

o Identifying the value that each digit in a 3-digit number represents

o Representing 3-digit numbers in expanded form

o Using a place-value model to represent 3-digit numbers as hundreds, tens, and ones

o Comparing 3-digit numbers by comparing like places (i.e., hundreds with hundreds, tens with tens, ones with ones)

o Using standard notation ($>$, $<$) to express the relationship between two quantities

o Working with the relationship between 1, 10, 100, and 1,000

o Noticing how the digit in the tens place changes when the addends in the ones place sum to greater than 10

o Adding 10 or 100 to and subtracting 10 or 100 from a given number and describing what part of the number changes

MATH FOCUS POINTS IN CLASSROOM ROUTINES

o Reasoning about the place value of 3-digit numbers

o Expressing a 3-digit number in expanded form

o Determining the quantity represented by a given number of hundreds

o Using an equation to represent a 3-digit multiple of 100 as the sum of hundreds (e.g., $300 = 100 + 100 + 100$)

o Noticing and comparing how a quantity changes when tens are added or when ones are added to a number

o Using standard notation ($<$, $>$) to express the relationship between quantities

2 Using knowledge of place value to add and subtract

Understanding the base-10 number system, specifically that numbers are composed of hundreds, tens, and ones and can be decomposed and recomposed flexibly, is foundational to the development of addition and subtraction strategies based on place value. This, along with a growing understanding of the operations of addition and subtraction and some of their properties, is the basis of the fluent strategies—efficient and accurate ways to add and subtract 2-digit numbers and ways to notate them in clear and understandable ways—that students develop by the end of Grade 2.

In this unit, students work specifically on adding by place (i.e., add the tens, add the ones, then add the results) and adding on one number in parts, either by place or in useful parts (i.e., adding 26 to 48 by first adding 2 from the 26 to make 50 and then adding the remaining 24 to 50. Students encounter a range of problems including those that require them to regroup 10 ones as 1 ten or to regroup 1 ten as 10 ones. Students develop clear and efficient ways to model and represent their strategies (e.g., sticker notation, number lines, equations, and vertical notation).

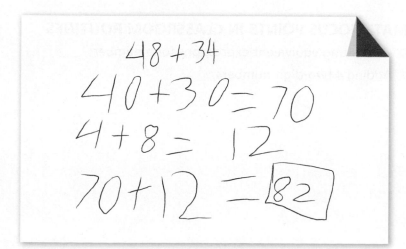

$$52$$
$$+39$$
$$91$$
$$52 + 30 = 82$$
$$82 + 9 = 91$$

[Adding On in Parts]

$$48 + 34$$
$$40 + 30 = 70$$
$$4 + 8 = 12$$
$$70 + 12 = \boxed{82}$$

[Adding by Place]

MATH FOCUS POINTS IN SESSIONS

○ Adding and subtracting a number of tens and/or ones to/from a 2- or 3-digit number

○ Relating the single-digit combinations of 10 (e.g., $8 + 2$) to multiple of 10 combinations of 100 (e.g., $80 + 20$)

○ Using knowledge of place value to find pairs of 2-digit numbers that add to 100 or a number close to 100

○ Using known pairs of 2-digit numbers that add to 100 to find related pairs that add to 100 or a number close to 100 (for example: $80 + 20 = 100$, so $79 + 21 = 100$)

○ Developing efficient strategies for adding 2-digit numbers

○ Developing efficient methods for notating addition strategies

○ Solving 2-digit addition problems using accurate and efficient strategies

MATH FOCUS POINTS IN CLASSROOM ROUTINES

○ Adding and subtracting a number of tens and/or ones to/from a 2-digit number

○ Using knowledge of place value to find pairs of 2-digit numbers that add to 100 or a number close to 100

○ Estimating the sum of two 2-digit numbers using known combinations, place value, and properties of operations

3 Understanding, representing, and solving problems involving addition and subtraction

Students continue to solve the story problem types introduced in Units 1 and 3 and encounter new ones as well. Investigation 1 focuses on problems with one addend unknown, with a total of 100. Some are framed within the context of a two-step problem (e.g., Franco has 35¢. Sally has 37¢. They want to buy a comic book that costs $1.00. How much more money do they need?). While most students combine 35 and 37 (which means they are also solving an add to problem with result unknown) and then find the difference between the total and 100, a few may start with a dollar and subtract 35 and 37. As students work on these problems and discuss various approaches to thinking about and solving them, they are deepening their understanding about the operations of addition and subtraction and the relationship between the two. They are also refining their addition and subtraction strategies and working towards accurate and efficient strategies that can be generalized to greater numbers.

MATHEMATICS IN THIS UNIT

In Investigation 3, students are introduced to comparison problems with a bigger unknown that also ask them to solve an add to problem:

> **Kira and Jake both collect shark stickers. Kira has 30 shark stickers in her sticker book. Jake has 23 more shark stickers than Kira.**
>
> **Does Jake have more stickers than Kira or fewer?**
>
> **How do you know?**
>
> **How many stickers does Jake have?**
>
> **If Kira and Jake combined their stickers, how many would they have in all?**

> **Franco and Sally collected cans for a recycling project. Franco collected 35 cans. He collected 20 fewer cans than Sally.**
>
> **How many cans did Sally collect?**
>
> **How many cans did Franco and Sally collect together?**

As students consolidate work with addition in Investigation 3, Enough for the Grade? problems, an extension of Enough for the Class? problems (Unit 1), provide practice with many of the types of problems students have solved thus far.

> **The Pine Hill School has two Grade 2 classrooms. Room 2A has 19 students. Room 2B has 7 more students than Room 2A. How many students are in Room 2B?**
>
> **The gym teacher at the Pine Street School has a basket of bean bags.**
>
> **He has 38 green bean bags and 18 yellow bean bags.**
>
> **Are there enough bean bags for the grade?**

Work with addition and subtraction is not solely focused on solving story problems. In this unit, students play a variety of games that focus on the composition of 100 and reinforce strategies for adding and subtracting 1- and 2-digit numbers. These games include *Close to 100*, which involves selecting two 2-digit addends from several possible choices that sum to as close to 100 as possible; *Make a Dollar*, where students find combinations of coins that equal $1.00; and *Capture 5*, which involves strategically adding and subtracting multiples of tens and groups of ones to/from 2-digit numbers to land on certain numbers on the 100 chart.

$40 + 61 = 101$	Score: 1
$49 + 60 = 109$	Score: 9
$96 + 04 = 100$	Score: 0

MATH FOCUS POINTS IN SESSIONS

- Finding the difference between two 2-digit numbers
- Finding the difference between a 2- or 3-digit number and 100
- Solving 2-step problems
- Adding two 2-digit numbers, and determining the difference between the sum and 100
- Finding combinations of coins that equal $1.00
- Recognizing and using coin equivalencies
- Visualizing, representing, and solving add to story problems with the result unknown
- Visualizing, representing, and solving comparison problems with a bigger unknown (more than/fewer than)
- Solving 2-step story problems that involve comparison and finding the difference

MATH FOCUS POINTS IN CLASSROOM ROUTINES

- Generating equivalent expressions for a number
- Adding 4 two-digit numbers

4 Fluency within 20

Students continue to work towards the goal of knowing the single-digit addition and subtraction facts within 20, reviewing the facts in their envelope of "Facts I Know" and practicing the ones in their "Facts I Am Still Working On" envelope. In this unit, students receive the Plus 9 and Minus 9 fact cards and think about how adding or subtracting 9 relates to adding or subtracting 10. Later, they add cards for the remaining addition facts and the subtraction facts that are related to them. For example:

$6 + 8$ $8 + 6$ Clue: _____	$14 - 8$ Clue: _____

$14 - 6$ Clue: _____

Discussion focuses on using known facts as "clues" to learn facts that might be hard to remember. For example, some students think about $6 + 8$ as $6 + 6 + 2$ or as $6 + 4 + 4$, using a doubles fact or a Make 10 fact that they already know to make sense of a less familiar fact. Some students relate subtraction facts to a known addition fact and use their knowledge about the relationship between addition and subtraction (e.g., $6 + 8 = 14$, so $14 - 8 = 6$), while others use 10 as a useful stopping-off point (e.g., $14 - 6 = 14 - 4 - 2$). In each of these examples and with all facts, fluency is based on what students know and understand rather than on memorization.

MATH FOCUS POINTS IN SESSIONS

○ Developing fluency with addition and subtraction within 20

○ Relating the Plus 10/Minus 10 facts to the Plus 9/Minus 9 facts

○ Using cubes and the number line to show the relationship between adding (or subtracting) 9 and adding (or subtracting) 10 to/from a number

MATH FOCUS POINTS IN CLASSROOM ROUTINES

○ Developing fluency with addition and subtraction within 20

○ Relating unknown facts to known ones
  (e.g., $8 + 6 = 8 + 2 + 4$, or using $8 + 6 = 14$ to solve $14 - 8$)

5 Understanding and extending the counting sequence

Students extend the rote counting sequence to 1,000. They find and use patterns in the sequence of numbers in a 1,000 Book made up of five charts, each displaying 200 numbers in rows of 10 (i.e., 1–200, 201–400, etc.) and use it to play *Guess My Number, Capture 5,* and *Plus or Minus 10 or 100.* They also use it to explore the counting by 5s and 10s sequences and to think about 10 or 100 more or less than a given 3-digit number. Many of these activities ask students to read and write 3-digit numbers.

MATH FOCUS POINTS IN SESSIONS

○ Reading and writing 3-digit numbers

○ Reasoning about the magnitude of and relationship between 2- and 3-digit numbers

○ Skip counting and writing multiples of 5 and 10 within 1,000 and noticing patterns in the number sequence

MATH FOCUS POINTS IN CLASSROOM ROUTINES

○ Counting by 5s within 1,000

○ Counting by 10s within 1,000

○ Identifying patterns in the skip counting sequence of 5s

The following content is also included in this unit:

MATH FOCUS POINTS IN CLASSROOM ROUTINES

○ Collecting, counting, representing, and comparing data

The Mathematical Practices, Classroom Routines, Homework, and Practice pages are also a critical part of the mathematics of this unit. See the **Mathematical Practices in This Unit** and **Review and Practice in This Unit** for more information.

CONNECTIONS: LOOKING FORWARD

Students continue to build on and extend their work with number and operations in the final three units of Grade 2. They apply their understanding of the operations of addition and subtraction as they solve story problems that involve combining and comparing lengths (Unit 6), and comparison problems with a smaller unknown (Unit 8). The *Enough for the Grade?* context continues in Unit 8, providing students with opportunities to review and practice a variety of story problem types. In Unit 8, students also achieve fluency with subtraction within 100, and apply their addition and subtraction strategies for 2-digit numbers and their knowledge of place value as they solve problems with 3-digit numbers. Students continue to review and practice addition and subtraction facts within 20 in Units 6 and 7, demonstrating fluency with these facts in Unit 8.

The eight Mathematical Practices are a critical part of students' mathematics learning. Mathematical Practice Notes are included throughout the unit to indicate opportunities for engaging students in these practices. Each unit focuses specifically on two Mathematical Practices.

In this unit, the highlighted practices are MP4, Model with mathematics, and MP7, Look for and make use of structure. This essay describes each of these practices and provides examples from the unit of how to engage Grade 2 students in them.

MP4 Model with mathematics.

When given a problem in a contextual situation, mathematically proficient students at the elementary grades can identify the mathematical elements of a situation and create a mathematical model that shows those mathematical elements and relationships among them. The mathematical model might be in the form of numbers and symbols, geometric figures, pictures or physical objects used to abstract the mathematical elements of the situation, or a mathematical diagram such as a number line, a table, or a graph, or students might use more than one of these to help them interpret the situation. . . .

Mathematically proficient students are able to identify important quantities in a contextual situation and use mathematical models to show the relationships of those quantities, particularly in multistep problems or problems involving more than one variable. . . .

Mathematically proficient students use their model to analyze the relationships and draw conclusions. They interpret their mathematical results in the context of the situation and reflect on whether the results make sense, possibly improving the model if it has not served its purpose.

As students model situations with mathematics, they are choosing tools appropriately (MP.5). As they decontextualize the situation and represent it mathematically, they are also reasoning abstractly (MP.2).

(Illustrative Mathematics, *Standards for Mathematical Practice: Commentary and Elaborations for K–5*)

In Grade 2, students are introduced to a variety of story problem types and are asked to write equations for the problem. An equation is one form of a mathematical model: To write an equation, students abstract the mathematical elements from the context and show the relationships among those quantities. In discussions of their equations, students discover that often there is more than one possible equation that models the story. For example, consider the following scenario, in which students have solved this problem: *Kira has 56 star stickers. How many more stickers does she need to fill a page that holds 100 stickers?*

Teacher:	We've seen different strategies for solving this problem, and we all agree that the answer is 44. What equation did you write for this problem?
Lonzell:	$56 + 44 = 100$.
Holly:	Mine was different. I wrote $100 - 56 = 44$.

The teacher writes both problems on the board.

Teacher:	This is very interesting. Lonzell wrote an addition equation, and Holly wrote a subtraction equation. Which one is right, or are they both right?
Juanita:	I know that Lonzell is right. Kira had 56 stickers on her page, so you start with 56 and add on what's empty to get to 100.
Leo:	(pointing to a representation of the sticker page the class had used earlier in the discussion) It's blue plus white equals 100. $56 + 44 = 100$.

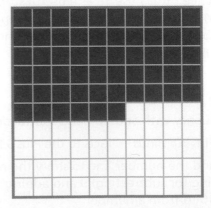

Luis:	I did it Holly's way. $100 - 56$, and I got 44.
Rochelle:	Me, too. You have the whole page. Take away the blue, and you get the white.
Teacher:	What does the blue stand for in this representation?
Rochelle:	Blue is Kira's stickers. 56. White is the stickers she still needs to get.
Tia:	I think both equations are right.

After most of the class concurs that both equations model the problem, the teacher poses another question.

Teacher: I wonder if this happens with other stories? When can we have both an addition equation and a subtraction equation for the same story?

In this discussion, students consider two equations (two models) for the story problem they have solved. In response to the teacher's questions, students return to the context to defend the equation they had written. They also turn back to yet another model—an array of 100 squares that show the number of stickers Kira already has in blue and the number of stickers Kira has yet to buy in white—to explain why their model makes sense. The class concludes that both equations fit the story.

Looking at these three models—two equations and an array of squares—brings to light a significant mathematical concept: the relationship between addition and subtraction. Any problem solved by subtraction can also be solved by finding a missing addend and vice versa. Understanding of this idea, which arises in a variety of situations in second grade, is deepened through examining different models of story problems.

The following chart shows where Mathematical Practice Notes specifically address MP4 and when that mathematical practice is assessed.

MP4 Model with mathematics.		
SESSION	MPN	ASSESSMENT CHECKLIST
1.3	●	●
1.5		●
1.6		●
3.1	●	●
3.2	●	●
3.3		●
3.4		●
3.5		●
3.6		●
3.7		●

🔍 MP7 Look for and make use of structure.

Mathematically proficient students at the elementary grades use structures such as place value, the properties of operations, other generalizations about the behavior of the operations (for example, the less you subtract, the greater the difference), and attributes of shapes to solve problems. In many cases, they have identified and described these structures through repeated reasoning (MP.8).

(Illustrative Mathematics, *Standards for Mathematical Practice: Commentary* and *Elaborations for K–5*)

Central to our system of numbers is its base-10 structure. A component of almost all efficient multi-digit computation procedures involves decomposing numbers by place and working with the single digits that represent the number of ones, tens, hundreds, etc. The compactness of this system is what makes it powerful, but that very compactness means that it is dense with ideas that young students must put together. That learning begins in the primary grades.

In this unit, students identify, read, and write numbers to 1,000 and add and subtract 10 and 100 in that range. They come to see 100 as 10 tens and multiples of 100 as being made up of some number of hundreds. Students also use the structure of tens (and eventually hundreds) as they operate with multidigit numbers.

In the following scenario, the class is discussing strategies for adding 35 + 27. In order to solve a problem like this, students decompose the numbers in order to work with parts that are easier to compute and then put the results together to solve the original problem. There are different ways to decompose the numbers, but almost all efficient strategies make use of the structure of tens. Consider the strategies of Leigh, Amaya, Travis, and Anita.

$$\textbf{Leigh} \qquad \begin{aligned} 30 + 20 &= 50 \\ 5 + 7 &= 12 \\ 50 + 12 &= 62 \end{aligned}$$

Leigh decomposed 35 and 27 into tens and ones, added the tens, added the ones, and added the results.

$$\textbf{Amaya} \qquad \begin{aligned} 35 + 20 &= 55 \\ 55 + 7 &= 62 \end{aligned}$$

Amaya decomposed 27 into tens and ones and then added those parts to 35 in stages, first adding the tens, then the ones.

$$\textbf{Travis} \qquad \begin{aligned} 35 + 5 &= 40 \\ 40 + 22 &= 62 \end{aligned}$$

Travis decomposed 27 into 5 + 22 so that at the first step he created a multiple of 10. "40 + 22 is easy," he said.

Anita $35 + 27$

   Take 3 from 35, and add it to the 27.

   $32 + 30 = 62$

Anita thought in terms of subtracting 3 and adding 3 to create an equivalent problem that's easier to solve. She chose 3 in order to create a multiple of 10.

These students have all learned how to add multiples of 10 to 2-digit numbers. In each of their strategies, they make use of that structure in one of two ways:

1. They decompose one or both of the addends into tens and ones.

2. They add to, or subtract from, one of the addends to create a multiple of 10. After having made that first step, they combine parts to solve the original problem.

The following chart shows where Mathematical Practice Notes specifically address MP4 and when that mathematical practice is assessed.

SESSION	MPN	ASSESSMENT CHECKLIST
MP7 Look for and make use of structure.		
1.1	●	
1.2	●	
1.3	●	●
1.4	●	
1.5	●	●
1.6	●	●
2.1	●	
2.2	●	
2.3	●	
2.5	●	
2.6	●	
3.1	●	●
3.2		●
3.3	●	●
3.4	●	●
3.5	●	●
3.6		●
3.7		●

SESSION	BENCHMARK 1	BENCHMARK 2	BENCHMARK 3	BENCHMARK 4	BENCHMARK 5	BENCHMARK 6	BENCHMARK 7	MP4	MP7	PORTFOLIO
INVESTIGATION 1										
1.1										
1.2										
1.3								•	•	•
1.4										•
1.5								•	•	•
1.6	•							•	•	•
INVESTIGATION 2										
2.1										•
2.2										•
2.3										•
2.4										•
2.5										•
2.6		•	•	•						•
INVESTIGATION 3										
3.1								•	•	•
3.2								•	•	•
3.3								•	•	•
3.4								•	•	•
3.5								•	•	•
3.6								•	•	•
3.7		•	•	•	•		•	•	•	•
3.8			•		•	•	•			•

Assessing the Benchmarks

Opportunities for assessment are carefully woven throughout the unit. These opportunities, which include written assessments and observations of students at work, provide an in-depth portrait of each student's understandings of and proficiencies with key mathematical concepts. Observing students as they engage in activities and conversation about their ideas is a primary means of assessing students' learning. Such formative assessment opportunities are built into every session, particularly in the **Ongoing Assessment: Observing Students at Work** feature, which offers questions to consider as students work.

Assessments are tied to Unit Benchmarks that set clear expectations for what students should know and be able to do. These assessments include:

○ **Embedded Assessments** Students solve problems and show or explain their solution strategies. These assessments are accompanied by Teacher Notes that provide examples of student work.

○ **Quizzes** Quizzes are short assessments that also serve to monitor students' progress.

○ **Assessment Checklists** Assessment Checklists focus on particular Benchmarks and/or Mathematical Practices. These checklists are used to record notes about what students understand as you observe them at work.

All assessments are available as print and digital resources.

Present   Videos   Tools   Games   Assessment   MWI   Portfolio   eText   PDF

Benchmarks

Benchmark 1: Solve a 2-step story problem that involves finding the difference between a 2-digit number and 100

How Much More to $1.00?* ** (Resource Masters, A39) in Session 1.6

Benchmark 2: Understand that 3-digit numbers represent amounts of hundreds, tens, and ones

Quiz 1 (Resource Masters, A40) in Session 2.6

Quiz 2 (Resource Masters, A41–A42) in Session 3.7

Benchmark 3: Read, write, count, and compare numbers to 1,000

Quiz 1 (Resource Masters, A40) in Session 2.6

Quiz 2 (Resource Masters, A41–A42) in Session 3.7

Skip Counting Strips (Resource Masters, A45) in Session 3.8

Benchmark 4: Add/subtract 10 or 100 to/from numbers within 1,000

Quiz 1 (Resource Masters, A40) in Session 2.6

Quiz 2 (Resource Masters, A41–A42) in Session 3.7

Benchmark 5: Add fluently within 100

Quiz 2 (Resource Masters, A41–A42) in Session 3.7

How Many Points?* ** (Resource Masters, A43–A44) in Session 3.8

Benchmark 6: Solve comparison story problems with a bigger unknown

How Many Points?* ** (Resource Masters, A43–A44) in Session 3.8

Benchmark 7: Count by 5s, 10s, and 100s within 1,000

Quiz 2 (Resource Masters, A41–A42) in Session 3.7

Skip Counting Strips (Resource Masters, A45) in Session 3.8

* Throughout *Investigations*, students are asked to show their work. As they describe their strategies, they are often asked to consider/explain why these strategies work. See the cited session (and related Assessment Teacher Note) for details.

**When students solve problems about combining, comparing, or removing, some use the number line to represent the problem, solve the problem, and/or show their work. See the cited session (and related Assessment Teacher Note) for details.

Mathematical Practices

Assessment Checklist: MP4 and MP7 (Resource Masters, A38) Use in Session 1.3 and again in Sessions 1.5–1.6 and 3.1–3.7.

This is the second of two formal opportunities to assess these math practices. The first opportunity to assess MP4 was in Unit 4. The first opportunity to assess MP7 was in Unit 2.

Portfolio Opportunities

In addition to all written assessments and quizzes, the following student work is appropriate for a portfolio:

How Many Stickers? How Many More to 100? (*Student Activity Book*, pages 298–299) in Session 1.3

Ways to Make a Dollar (*Student Activity Book*, page 305) in Session 1.4

How Many More to 100? How Much More to $1.00? (*Student Activity Book*, pages 307–310) in Session 1.5

How Many Stickers? (*Student Activity Book*, pages 318–319) in Session 2.3

Find the Number (*Student Activity Book*, pages 325–326) in Session 2.5

Example of *Make a Dollar* Recording Sheet (Resource Masters, G34) in Sessions 1.4–1.6, 2.2

Example of *Close to 100* Recording Sheet (Resource Masters, G36) in Sessions 2.1–2.6 and 3.3–3.7

Addition Problems, Set 1 (*Student Activity Book*, pages 335–336) in Session 3.1

Comparison and Addition Problems (*Student Activity Book*, pages 343–344) in Session 3.2

Comparison and Addition Problems 2 (*Student Activity Book*, pages 347–348) in Session 3.3

Solving Problems by Adding Tens and Ones (*Student Activity Book*, pages 351–352) in Session 3.4

Solving Problems by Adding On in Parts (*Student Activity Book*, pages 357–358) in Session 3.5

Today's Number: 200 (*Student Activity Book*, page 365) in Session 3.6

Example of *Enough for the Grade* problem in Sessions 3.6 and 3.7

SESSION	CR: Fact Fluency	CR: Today's Number	CR: Quick Images	CR: How Many Pockets?	CR: What Time Is It?	DAILY PRACTICE	HOMEWORK	GAMES	MATH WORDS AND IDEAS
INVESTIGATION 1									
1.1					•	•		•	•
1.2			•			•		•	•
1.3		•				•	•	•	•
1.4		•				•		•	•
1.5		•				•	•	•	•
1.6		•				•		•	•
INVESTIGATION 2									
2.1	•					•	•	•	•
2.2			•			•		•	•
2.3				•		•		•	•
2.4		•				•	•	•	•
2.5		•				•		•	•
2.6		•				•	•	•	
INVESTIGATION 3									
3.1					•	•	•		•
3.2		•				•			•
3.3	•					•	•	•	•
3.4		•				•		•	•
3.5		•				•	•	•	•
3.6		•				•		•	•
3.7				•		•		•	•
3.8		•				•			

Review and Practice

Review and practice play an integral role in helping students develop proficiency with mathematical skills and concepts. Students have frequent opportunities to review and practice mathematical ideas over the course of a unit and grade.

Daily opportunities for review and practice are found in the following activities or features:

○ **Classroom Routines (CR)**, to be done in ten minutes outside of math class, are introduced in a unit and repeated throughout the grade. Specific directions for the day's activity are included in each session.

○ The **Session Follow-Up** includes a **Daily Practice** page for every session and **Homework** approximately 2 times per week. The Daily Practice pages provide both reinforcement of the content in the unit and ongoing review of previously covered topics. The Homework pages are most often an extension of the work done in class.

○ **Games** are a central part of the *Investigations* curriculum. They provide engaging opportunities for students to develop concepts and to practice skills.

○ **Math Words and Ideas** provide illustrations of important words and ideas that students encounter in math class. Students can also review words and ideas that they encountered in previous units or grades.

All of these activities and features are available as print and digital resources.

Classroom Routines

For the full description and variations of the Classroom Routines activities, see *Implementing Investigations in Grade 2*.

Fact Fluency

Students add cards for the Plus Nine and Minus Nine Facts and receive a final set of remaining facts. They review the "Facts I Know," practice the "Facts I Am Still Working On," and write clues for the facts they are finding hard to remember.

MATH FOCUS POINTS

○ Developing fluency with addition and subtraction within 20

○ Relating unknown facts to known ones
(e.g., $8 + 6 = 8 + 2 + 4$, or using $8 + 6 = 14$ to solve $14 - 8$)

Today's Number

Students estimate the sum of two 2-digit numbers, compare their estimate to either 50 or 100, and add to find Today's Number. They generate 3-digit numbers and compare the numbers to find Today's Number. They practice skip counting by 5s or 10s and generate expressions using only multiples of 5 and 10.

MATH FOCUS POINTS

○ Estimating the sum of two 2-digit numbers using known combinations, place value, and properties of operations

○ Using standard notation (<, >) to express the relationship between quantities

○ Generating equivalent expressions for a number

○ Reasoning about the place value of 3-digit numbers

○ Expressing a 3-digit number in expanded form

○ Counting by 5s and 10s within 1,000

○ Identifying patterns in the skip counting sequence of 5s and 10s

○ Generating equivalent expressions for a number

Quick Images

Students see images made of tens and ones and think about what happens when you add or subtract 1, 2, or 3 tens or 1, 2, or 3 ones. Later, they look at groups of hundreds, building an image of 1,000 as ten hundreds.

MATH FOCUS POINTS

○ Adding and subtracting a number of tens and/or ones to/from a 2-digit number

○ Noticing and comparing how a quantity changes when tens are added or when ones are added to a number

○ Determining the quantity represented by a given number of hundreds

○ Using an equation to represent a 3-digit multiple of 100 as the sum of hundreds (e.g., $300 = 100 + 100 + 100$)

How Many Pockets?

Four groups of students determine and then share the total number of pockets they are wearing. Using the four subtotals, individuals then determine the total number of pockets the class is wearing.

MATH FOCUS POINTS

○ Collecting, counting, representing and comparing data

○ Adding four 2-digit numbers

What Time Is It?

Students practice telling and notating time to the quarter hour. Given a time, they figure out what time it will be in 15 minutes.

MATH FOCUS POINTS

○ Naming, notating, and telling time to the hour, half hour, and quarter hour using analog and digital formats

○ Determining what time it will be when given start and elapsed times that are multiples of 15 minutes

Session Follow-Up

Practice Practice opportunities in this unit provide review of adding and subtracting 9, 100, and multiples of 10, finding combinations that equal a given number, word problems, determining time to the quarter hour, comparing 3-digit numbers, place-value notation, and counting by 5s and 10s.

Homework Homework in this unit provides practice with addition and subtraction facts, finding combinations that equal a given number, and writing and solving story problems.

Games

In this unit, students play the following games:

○ *Plus 9 or Minus 9 Bingo* introduced in Session 1.1

○ *Capture 5* introduced in Session 1.2

○ *Make a Dollar* introduced in Session 1.4

○ *Close to 100* introduced in Session 2.1

○ *Guess My Number* introduced in Session 2.2

○ *Plus or Minus 10 or 100* introduced in Session 2.4

Math Words and Ideas

Students and families may wish to review math words and ideas related to this unit.

SESSION	INTERVENTION	PRACTICE	EXTENSION	ELL SUPPORT
INVESTIGATION 1				
1.1	● ●			●
1.2	● ●			●
1.3	● ● ■		● ● ●	● ■
1.4	● ●			●
1.5	● ●	■	● ■	● ■ ■
1.6	●			●
INVESTIGATION 2				
2.1	● ●			●
2.2	●		●	●
2.3	● ● ● ■		●	● ■
2.4	● ●	■	● ● ■	● ■ ■
2.5	●		● ●	●
2.6			●	
INVESTIGATION 3				
3.1	● ■	■	●	● ■ ■
3.2	●			●
3.3			● ■	● ■
3.4	●		●	●
3.5	● ●		● ●	
3.6	●		●	●
3.7			● ●	
3.8				●

● Session-level support
■ Expanded Differentiation Activity

Supporting the Range of Learners

See *Implementing Investigations in Grade 2* for more information.

The *Investigations* program is designed to engage and support the range of learners. Throughout the unit, you will find session-specific suggestions for Intervention and Extension in the **Differentiation: Supporting the Range of Learners** feature.

Each Intervention or Extension is labeled with a specific strategy to support students with the content of the session. These strategies include:

- Adapt the Learning Situation
- Adapt the Problem
- Adapt a Material
- Clarify the Problem
- Vary the Problem
- Scaffold a Solution
- Extend Thinking
- Suggest a Tool

At the end of each investigation, you will find three different **Expanded Differentiation Activities** to address the needs of the range of learners.

- **Intervention** activities are designed to support the students who are having difficulty with a particular concept.
- **Practice** activities provide additional opportunities for students to practice important ideas and concepts.
- **Extension** activities support and engage students who are ready for additional challenges.

Supporting English Language Learners (ELL)

See *Implementing Investigations in Grade 2* for more information.

In each of the **Expanded Differentiation Activities** and in some sessions, you will find embedded ELL support, again labeled with a specific strategy. These strategies include:

- Model Thinking Aloud
- Partner Talk
- Provide Vocabulary Support
- Provide Sentence Stems
- Repeat and Clarify
- Provide a Sequence
- Provide Opportunities for Practice
- Allow Varied Responses

| Present | Videos | Tools | Games | Assessment | MWI | Portfolio | eText | PDF |

Previewing Unit Content for English Language Learners

Modeling and Sharing Strategies English Language Learners may need support when asked to explain their strategies and reasoning for solving addition and subtraction problems. Look for opportunities to model explaining strategies so students hear the vocabulary they can use to explain their own work. Support English Language Learners by asking questions about their work. Provide opportunities for students to practice sharing their strategies verbally with you or a peer prior to class discussions. If students need additional support, provide words and/or sentence stems that they can use to explain their steps, or write what students say and let them practice reading it.

Story Problems To help English Language Learners understand what is happening in the story problems, demonstrate with pictures, sketches, manipulatives, and/or act out the problems. Rephrase story problems using simpler language. Have students retell the information in their own words before they begin to solve a problem individually. For example, given a 2-step problem (e.g., Session 1.5), have students identify the first step and the second step before they begin to solve it. If students need additional support, ask questions to help them identify what they know from reading or listening to the problem. Write the information for students so they can refer to it as they solve the problem.

Money In Session 1.4, students will use coins to find combinations that make $1.00. Students used coins in Unit 1, but some English Language Learners may need to review U.S. coins and their values. Use *How Many Pennies?* (T3) to show students a picture of each coin (*penny, nickel, dime, quarter*) and its value. Prior to Session 1.4, work with students in a small-group setting to review the value of each coin, and have students practice making different amounts using coins. Also, provide pictures of coin combinations that can be used to make a given amount (e.g., To make 25¢, show 2 dimes and 1 nickel, 1 dime and 3 nickels, and 5 nickels). Use the *Math Words and Ideas* Coin Value and Coin Equivalency digital resource for additional support.

Vocabulary Preview new and/or difficult vocabulary with English Language Learners. For example, prior to Session 2.2, preview place-value terms (e.g., *hundreds, tens,* and *ones*, as well as *hundreds place, tens place, ones place*) and the terms *greater than, less than,* and *between*. Make a vocabulary word chart with definitions, sketches, and labels for students to reference as needed. Use the terms throughout instruction and encourage students to use the terms during class discussions. Use the *Math Words and Ideas* digital resource for additional support.

Expanded Differentiation Activities

These activities, which take between 15 and 30 minutes, can be done in small groups, pairs, or with individuals. It may be appropriate for some students to complete more than one of the activities within an investigation or unit.

INVESTIGATION 1 Combinations of 100

Intervention: **Solving 2-Step Sticker Problems**
Use anytime after Session 1.3.

Practice: **Problems about 100: Representing Strategies on the Number Line**
Use anytime after Session 1.5.

Extension: ***Make 2 or More Dollars***
Use anytime after Session 1.5.

INVESTIGATION 2 Adding within 100 and Counting to 1,000

Intervention: **Representing 3-Digit Numbers with Stickers and Equations**
Use anytime after Session 2.3.

Practice: **How Many Stickers? How Many Hundreds, Tens, and Ones?**
Use anytime after Session 2.4.

Extension: **Sticker Combinations**
Use anytime after Session 2.4.

INVESTIGATION 3 Fluency within 100

Intervention: **Adding Tens and Ones**
Use anytime after Session 3.1.

Practice: **Adding On in Parts**
Use anytime after Session 3.1.

Extension: ***Close to 100* with Wild Cards**
Use anytime after Session 3.3.

INVESTIGATION

COMBINATIONS OF 100

Main Math Ideas

○ Fluency within 20

○ Understanding, representing, and solving problems involving addition and subtraction

○ Understanding place value

○ Using knowledge of place value to add and subtract

Combinations of 100

	SESSION 1.1	SESSION 1.2
	PLUS 9 OR MINUS 9 BINGO Students think about the relationship between adding 10 and adding 9 to a number and the relationship between subtracting 10 and subtracting 9 from a number. They learn and play a new game, *Plus 9 or Minus 9 Bingo*, and then add these fact cards to their sets.	**CAPTURE 5: ADDING AND SUBTRACTING TENS AND ONES** Students learn, play, and discuss *Capture 5*, a game that provides practice adding and subtracting tens and ones.
Professional Development	**TEACHER NOTES 1–2** **DIALOGUE BOX 1**	
Materials to View Ahead of Time	**TEACHER PRESENTATIONS:** 📺 **Classroom Routine** *What Time is It? What Time Will It Be?: Quarter Hours* 📺 **Discussion** Related Problems ▦ **Activity** Introducing *Plus 9 or Minus 9 Bingo* 📺 **Activity** Plus 9, Minus 9 Fact Cards ◉ **DIFFERENTIATION: ENGLISH LANGUAGE LEARNERS** See **Differentiation in This Unit** for session content to preview with students.	**TEACHER PRESENTATIONS:** 📺 **Classroom Routine** *Quick Images: Stickers* ▦ **Activity** Introducing *Capture 5* ▦ **Discussion** *Capture 5*
Materials to Gather	**Demonstration clock** (optional) 🔧 **Student clocks** (1 per student) **Blank paper** (1 sheet per student) 🔧 **Connecting cubes** (optional) 🔧 **Counters such as coins, buttons, or beans** (25 per pair) **Students' envelopes of "Facts I Know" and "Facts I Am Still Working On"** (from Unit 4)	**Translucent colored chips** (12 per pair) **Game pieces** (1 per pair) **Envelope of stickers** (for display, from Unit 3: 8 sheets, 14 strips, and 42 singles) **Note that in Session 2.6 (and, optionally in Sessions 2.2–2.3) you will need 10 sheets of 100. Use T13–14 and T25 to replenish, as needed.** (optional)
Materials to Prepare	📄 **C50, 0–20 Cards** Make copies and cut out. (1 deck per pair with Wild Cards removed; 1 deck for display, optional) 📄 **G29,** *Plus 9 or Minus 9 Bingo* **Gameboard** Make copies. (1 per pair) 📄 **G30,** *Plus 9 or Minus 9 Bingo* **Directions** Make copies. 📄 **C51–C52, Fact Cards: Set 5** Make copies, on cardstock if possible, and cut out. (1 set per student)	📄 **C53–C54, Change Cards** Make copies and cut out. (1 deck per pair) 📄 **G31,** *Capture 5* **Gameboard** Make copies. (1 per pair) 📄 **G32,** *Capture 5* **Recording Sheet** Make copies. (1 per student per game) 📄 **G33,** *Capture 5* **Game Directions** Make copies.
Common Core State Standards	**Classroom Routines:** 2.MD.C.7 **Session:** 2.OA.B.2, 2.NBT.B.5, 2.MD.B.6 **Daily Practice:** 2.OA.B.2, 2.NBT.B.5	**Classroom Routines:** 2.NBT.A.3, 2.NBT.B.5, Supports 2.NBT.B.8 **Session:** 2.NBT.B.5, 2.NBT.B.6, Supports 2.NBT.B.8 **Daily Practice:** 2.NBT.B.5, 2.NBT.B.6

	SESSION 1.3	SESSION 1.4
	HOW MANY STICKERS? HOW MANY MORE TO GET 100? Students solve 2-step problems that involve adding two 2-digit numbers and then finding the difference between that sum and 100. Math Workshop focuses on these problems, *Capture 5*, and the Plus 9 and Minus 9 Facts. Discussion focuses on one set of sticker story problems, with a particular focus on adding two 2-digit numbers with more than 10 ones between them.	**MAKE A DOLLAR** Students review coin values and equivalencies and find and record combinations of coins that equal one dollar.
Professional Development	**TEACHER NOTES 3–5**	**DIALOGUE BOX 2**
Materials to View Ahead of Time	**TEACHER PRESENTATIONS:** **Classroom Routine** *Today's Number: More or Less?* **Activity** Introducing How Many Stickers? How Many More to Get 100? **Discussion** Why Isn't the Answer in the 20s?	**TEACHER PRESENTATIONS:** **Classroom Routine** *Today's Number: More or Less?* **Activity** Introducing Combinations That Make a Dollar **Activity** Introducing *Make a Dollar* **DIFFERENTIATION: ENGLISH LANGUAGE LEARNERS** See **Differentiation in This Unit** for session content to preview with students.
Materials to Gather	**Envelopes of stickers for students** (from Unit 3) **Connecting cubes in towers of 10** (as needed) **Materials for *Capture 5*** (from Session 1.2) **A second game piece for *Capture 5*** (optional) **Materials for *Plus 9 or Minus 9 Bingo*** (from Session 1.1) **Wild Cards from C50** (optional; for the Extension) **Counters in a second color** (optional)	**Coin and Dollar Sets** (1 per pair) **Self-stick notes** (optional; for the Intervention) **T3, How Many Pennies?** (from Unit 1; optional; for the English Language Learners)
Materials to Prepare	**A38, Assessment Checklist: MP4 and MP7** Make copies. (as needed) **T43, 100 Grids** Make copies. (1 for display plus others, as needed) **C50, 0–20 Cards** Make copies and cut out. (1 deck per student with Wild Cards removed; for use at home)	**Chart: "Ways to Make a Dollar"** Title a piece of chart paper "Ways to Make a Dollar." **C55–C58, *Make a Dollar* Cards** Make copies. (1 deck per pair; 1 deck for display) **G34, *Make a Dollar* Recording Sheet** Make copies. (1 per student per game; 1 for display) **G35, *Make a Dollar* Directions** Make copies.
Common Core State Standards	**Classroom Routines:** 2.NBT.B.5, 2.NBT.B.9, Supports 2.NBT.A.4 **Session:** 2.OA.A.1, 2.OA.B.2, 2.NBT.B.5, 2.NBT.B.6, 2.NBT.B.9, Supports 2.NBT.B.8 **Daily Practice:** 2.OA.A.1, 2.NBT.B.5	**Classroom Routines:** 2.NBT.B.5, 2.NBT.B.9, 2.MD.C.8, Supports 2.NBT.A.4 **Session:** 2.NBT.B.5, 2.MD.C.8 **Daily Practice:** 2.NBT.B.5, 2.MD.C.8

Combinations of 100

	SESSION 1.5	SESSION 1.6
	HOW MUCH TO $1.00? HOW MUCH TO 100? Students discuss strategies for playing *Capture 5*. In Math Workshop, they play *Make a Dollar, Capture 5,* and *Plus 9 or Minus 9 Bingo* and solve 2-step problems about combining two amounts of money and finding the difference between the sum and $1.00. Discussion focuses on strategies for solving these problems.	**HOW MUCH MORE TO $1.00?** Students are introduced to the remaining addition facts and related subtraction facts. Math Workshop focuses on practicing these facts and completing any remaining activities begun in previous Math Workshops. As an assessment, students solve a problem about combining two amounts of money and finding the difference between that sum and $1.00.
Professional Development	DIALOGUE BOX 3	TEACHER NOTE 6
Materials to View Ahead of Time	**TEACHER PRESENTATIONS:** 🎦 **Classroom Routine** *Today's Number: More or Less?* 🎦 **Discussion** Strategies for *Capture 5* 🎦 **Discussion** How Much More to $1.00? 🎦 DIFFERENTIATION: ENGLISH LANGUAGE LEARNERS See **Differentiation in This Unit** for session content to preview with students.	**TEACHER PRESENTATIONS:** 🎦 **Classroom Routine** *Today's Number: More or Less?* 🎦 **Activity** The Remaining Addition Facts and Related Subtraction Facts
Materials to Gather	☑️📄 **A38, Assessment Checklist: MP4 and MP7** (from Session 1.3) 📄 **T43, 100 Grids** (from Session 1.3; optional; for the Intervention) **Materials for *Make a Dollar*** (from Session 1.4) **Materials for *Capture 5*** (from Sessions 1.2 and 1.3) **Materials for *Plus 9 or Minus 9 Bingo*** (from Sessions 1.1 and 1.3) 🔧 **Coins, stickers, cubes** (as needed)	☑️📄 **A38, Assessment Checklist: MP4 and MP7** (from Session 1.3) 🔧 **Connecting cubes** **Students' envelopes of "Facts I Know" and "Facts I Am Still Working On"** (from Session 1.1) **Materials for How Many More to 100? How Much More to $1.00?** (from Session 1.5) **Materials for *Make a Dollar*** (from Sessions 1.4 and 1.5) **Materials for *Capture 5*** (from Sessions 1.2 and 1.3)
Materials to Prepare		📄 **C59–C61, Fact Cards: Set 6** Make copies, on cardstock if possible, and cut out (1 set per student; 1 for display) ☑️📄 **A39, How Much More to $1.00?** Make copies or use the Online Assessment.
Common Core State Standards	**Classroom Routines:** 2.NBT.A.4, 2.NBT.B.5, 2.NBT.B.9 **Session:** 2.OA.A.1, 2.OA.B.2, 2.NBT.B.5, 2.NBT.B.9, 2.MD.B.6, 2.MD.C.8, Supports 2.NBT.B.8 **Daily Practice:** 2.OA.A.1, 2.NBT.B.5	**Classroom Routines:** 2.NBT.A.4, 2.NBT.B.5, 2.NBT.B.9, 2.MD.C.8 **Session:** 2.OA.A.1, 2.OA.B.2, 2.NBT.B.5, 2.NBT.B.8, 2.MD.C.8 **Daily Practice:** 2.MD.C.7

Plus 9 or Minus 9 Bingo

MATH FOCUS POINTS

○ Relating the Plus 10/Minus 10 facts to the Plus 9/Minus 9 facts

○ Using cubes and the number line to show the relationship between adding (or subtracting) 9 and adding (or subtracting) 10 to/from a number

○ Developing fluency with the Plus 9 and Minus 9 facts

VOCABULARY

○ Plus 9 Facts

○ Minus 9 Facts

TODAY'S PLAN	MATERIALS
(10) Class **CLASSROOM ROUTINES: REVIEW AND PRACTICE** *What Time Is It? What Time Will It Be?: Quarter Hours*	Teacher Presentation (or use the demonstration clock) Student clocks (1 per student) Blank paper (1 sheet per student)
(20) Class **1 DISCUSSION** **Related Problems**	Teacher Presentation (or use connecting cubes)
(10) Class **2 ACTIVITY** **Introducing *Plus 9 or Minus 9 Bingo***	*Plus 9 or Minus 9 Bingo* (or use one set of game materials; see Activity 3)
(20) Pairs **Groups** **3 ACTIVITY** **Playing *Plus 9 or Minus 9 Bingo***	C50* G29–G30* Counters such as coins, buttons, or beans (25 per pair)
(10) Class **Individuals** **4 ACTIVITY** **Plus 9, Minus 9 Fact Cards**	Teacher Presentation (or use C51–C52*) Students' envelopes of "Facts I Know" and "Facts I Am Still Working On" (from Unit 4)
SESSION FOLLOW-UP: REVIEW AND PRACTICE **Daily Practice**	*Student Activity Book*, pp. 293, 295–296

* See *Materials to Prepare* in the Investigation 1 Planner.

Common Core State Standards	**Classroom Routines:** 2.MD.C.7 **Session:** 2.OA.B.2, 2.NBT.B.5, 2.MD.B.6	**Daily Practice:** 2.OA.B.2, 2.NBT.B.5

What Time Is It? What Time Will It Be?: Quarter Hours

MATH FOCUS POINTS

○ Naming, notating, and telling time to the hour, half hour, and quarter hour using analog and digital formats

○ Determining what time it will be when given start and elapsed times that are multiples of 15 minutes

Ask students to set their clocks to 8:00 and to record the time in digital format. Display the Teacher Presentation (or set the demonstration clock to 8:00), and ask "In 15 minutes what time will it be?"

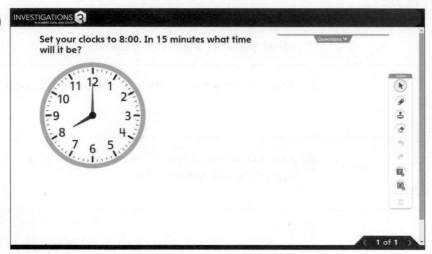

Pairs set their clocks, record the new time, and discuss how they knew. Emphasize counting by 5s as a way of determining 15 minutes. Record the new time (8:15) on the board, and ask "In 15 minutes what time will it be?" Students set their clocks, record the time (8:30), and discuss with their partner how they knew. Repeat with start times of 8:45 and 9:00. MWI

1 DISCUSSION

Related Problems

MATH FOCUS POINTS FOR DISCUSSION

○ Relating the Plus 10/Minus 10 facts to the Plus 9/Minus 9 facts

○ Using cubes and the number line to show the relationship between adding (or subtracting) 9 and adding (or subtracting) 10 to/from a number

MATH WORDS AND IDEAS

MWI Telling Time to the Quarter Hour

Display the Teacher Presentation (or write 4 + 10 on the board).

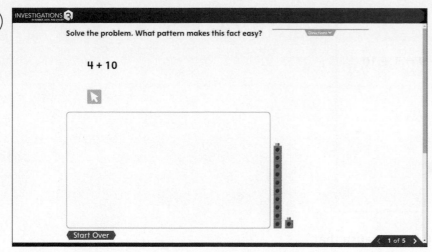

Begin by asking students to solve 4 + 10. Most "just know" the Plus 10 facts. Encourage them to explain the pattern that helps make these facts easy. Then, pose the related problem 4 + 9, and ask students to solve it mentally. **MN** **MPN1**

$$4 + 10 = 14$$
$$4 + \ \ 9 =$$

How can you use what you know about 4 + 10 to help you solve 4 + 9? **PD** **MPN2**

 STUDENTS MIGHT SAY 🟦

"I took 1 from the 4 and gave it to the 9. That made 3 + 10, and I just know that's 13."

"I know 4 + 10 is 14. 4 + 9 is 1 less, so the answer is 1 less, or 13."

Model students' strategies with cubes and the number line.

Let's look at [Malcolm]'s strategy with cubes. [He] started with 4 + 9 but turned the problem into 3 + 10. [Malcolm], can you show us that with cube towers?

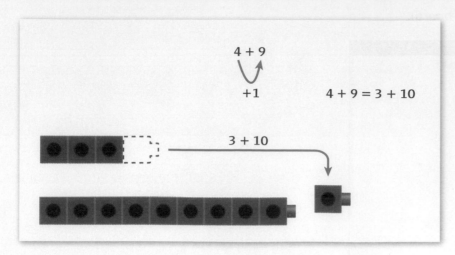

[Malcolm] turned the Plus 9 fact into an equivalent Plus 10 fact because that was easier for [him] to solve.

[Tia] also used a Plus 10 fact. [She] used what [she] knew about 4 + 10 to solve 4 + 9. Let's look at that strategy on the number line. **MPN**

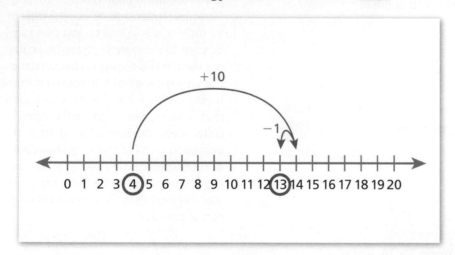

I see a plus 10 and a minus 1 on the number line. But the problem is 4 plus 9. Where's the plus 9?

As students respond, highlight the plus 9 by drawing a dotted or different-colored line from 4 to 13 on the same number line.

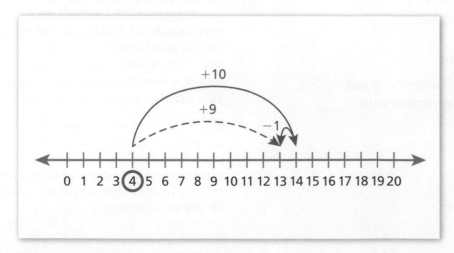

If any students counted on 9 from 4, ask them to demonstrate to reinforce that all of these strategies result in the same answer. **PD**

MATH PRACTICE NOTE

MPN 🔍 **MP7 Look for and make use of structure.** The relationship between 3 + 10 and 4 + 9 involves a generalization discussed earlier in the year: If you subtract 1 from one addend and add 1 to the other, the total remains the same. The relationship between 4 + 10 and 4 + 9 involves another generalization discussed earlier in the year: If you add 1 to an addend, the total increases by 1. If you subtract 1 from an addend, the total decreases by 1. For more information about the former, see **Teacher Note 1: Algebra Connections in This Unit.**

PROFESSIONAL DEVELOPMENT

PD DIALOGUE BOX 1: Adding Nine

Present another pair of related problems, writing the equations: $6 + 10 = \_\_$ and $6 + 9 = \_\_$. Ask students about the relationship between the problems and their strategies for solving them. Use cubes and/or the number line to model students' thinking.

Finally, pose a set of problems in which 10 and 9 are the first addends in the pair of equations.

$$10 + 8 =$$
$$9 + 8 =$$

Discuss how students can figure out the answer to the second problem, focusing on the relationship between the two problems in the set. **MN**

Next pose the problems $14 - 10$ and $10 - 9$. Most students "just know" the Minus 10 facts. Encourage them to explain what makes these facts easy.

How can you use what you know about $14 - 10$ to help you solve $14 - 9$?

Ask students to solve the problem mentally. Discuss and model students' strategies using cubes and then a number line.

Here are 14 cubes. In the first problem, we subtracted 10. So, you could think about removing this whole tower of 10. What happens when the problem is $14 - 9$?

Often, students are unsure whether to add 1 to or subtract 1 from 4. A cube model can help students make sense of why the answer to $14 - 9$ is one more than $14 - 10$. **MPN**

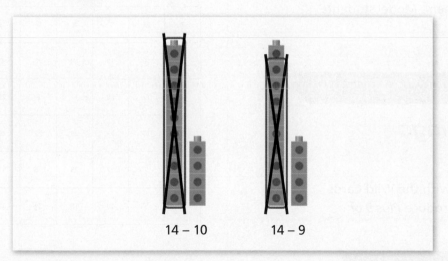

$14 - 10$ $14 - 9$

[Roshaun] said [he] subtracted 10 from 14 first. $14 - 10 = 4$. Then [he] added 1 because [he] was only supposed to subtract 9. Why do you think [he] added 1? Let's look at [Roshaun]'s strategy on the number line. How much did [he] end up subtracting in all?

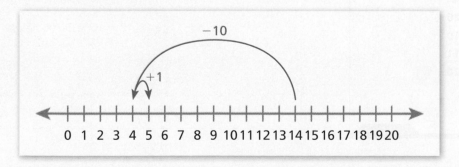

MATH NOTE

MN **Order Impacts Strategy** For some students, the reversal of the order changes the strategy they use to solve a problem. For example, they may use $8 + 10$ to think about $8 + 9$ but use near-doubles to solve $9 + 8$ or think about $9 + 6$ as $9 + 1 + 5$. This is fine as long as students recognize that because of the commutative property of addition, they *could* use the strategy that you have been discussing.

MATH PRACTICE NOTE

MPN 🔍 **MP7 Look for and make use of structure.** Students are often surprised that generalizations that apply to addition may not apply to subtraction. By modeling problems with cubes or other representations, students can make sense of how subtraction problems are related.

STUDENTS MIGHT SAY

"If you subtract 10, you take away 1 too many, so you have to add 1 back on."

"[Roshaun] subtracted 9 in all. I can see it on the number line. First [he] took away 10, but [he] added 1 back on, so [he] really took away 9 in all."

As students respond, highlight the 9 by drawing a dotted or different-colored line from 14 to 5 on the same number line.

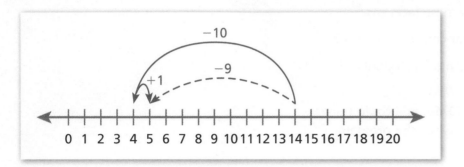

Follow the same process with another pair of related problems, writing 17 − 10 = __ and 17 − 9 = __. Continue to ask students about the relationship between the problems and their strategies for solving them. Model students' thinking using cubes and/or the number lines.

2 ACTIVITY

Introducing *Plus 9 or Minus 9 Bingo*

Display the Game Presentation (or a deck of 0–20 cards with the Wild Cards removed (C50), a gameboard (G29), and counters) to introduce *Plus 9 or Minus 9 Bingo*.

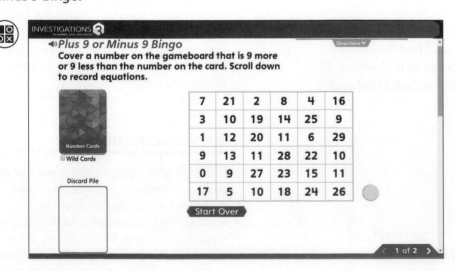

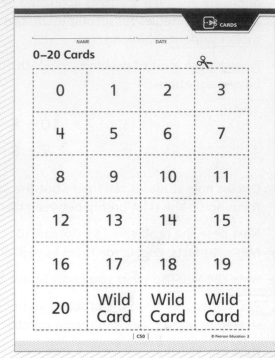

RESOURCE MASTERS, C50

CARDS

NAME   DATE

0–20 Cards

0	1	2	3
4	5	6	7
8	9	10	11
12	13	14	15
16	17	18	19
20	Wild Card	Wild Card	Wild Card

| C50 | © Pearson Education 2

RESOURCE MASTERS, G29

GAMES

NAME   DATE

Plus 9 or Minus 9 Bingo Gameboard

7	21	2	8	4	16
3	10	19	14	25	9
1	12	20	11	6	29
9	13	11	28	22	10
0	9	27	23	15	11
17	5	10	18	24	26

| G29 | © Pearson Education 2

Explain that in this game, players turn over a card, decide whether to add 9 to or subtract 9 from that number, and cover the answer on the gameboard. Partners work together to cover an entire row on the gameboard, vertically, horizontally, or diagonally. Demonstrate a few rounds.

Our first card is 10. What number can we cover if we add 9? What if we subtract 9?

Record equations that show the two possible problems, and decide as a class whether to cover 1 or 19 on the gameboard.

$$10 + 9 = 19$$
$$10 - 9 = 1$$

Next, demonstrate a turn with a card less than 9.

Our next card is 7. Record the two equations. What number do we get if we add 9? What if we subtract 9?

$$7 + 9 = \square$$
$$7 - 9 = \square$$

〝 STUDENTS MIGHT SAY 〞

"There's not enough numbers to take 9 from 7."

"You would end up below zero."

"If you owe someone 9, but you only have 7 to give them, you still owe them some."

We can think about subtracting 9 from 7, but we won't get an answer that's on our gameboard. When that happens, your only option is to add 9. `TN`

Cover 16 on the gameboard, and continue until students understand how to play.

Explain that if both possible answers are already covered on the gameboard, players should turn over a new card. If players run out of cards, they should shuffle the discarded cards and reuse them.

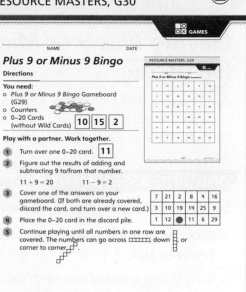

RESOURCE MASTERS, G30

Plus 9 or Minus 9 Bingo

TEACHING NOTE

TN Negative Numbers Some students might know that subtracting a greater number from a lesser one results in a negative number. Others may have never heard of such numbers. Acknowledge that students will learn more about these numbers when they are older. For now, it is important to know that $7 - 9$ does not yield an answer on their gameboard.

3 ACTIVITY

Playing *Plus 9 or Minus 9 Bingo*

Partners play *Plus 9 or Minus 9 Bingo*, working together to cover one full row. Each pair needs a gameboard (G29), a deck of 0–20 Cards without the Wild Cards (C50), and a set of 25 counters. The directions are available on G30.

ONGOING ASSESSMENT Observing Students at Work

Students practice the Plus 9 and Minus 9 Facts within 20.

○ **How fluent are students with adding 9?** Do they use the relationship between adding 10 and adding 9 to solve these problems? 📖 **MP7**

○ **How fluent are students with subtracting 9?** Do they use the relationship between subtracting 10 and subtracting 9 to solve these problems? 📖 **MP7**

○ **How do students decide whether to add 9 or subtract 9?** Are they strategizing?

Students get repeated practice with the Plus 9 and Minus 9 Facts by playing *Plus 9 or Minus 9 Bingo*.

 DIFFERENTIATION Supporting the Range of Learners

INTERVENTION Adapt the Learning Situation Students who are counting on or back by ones may benefit from playing the game together with you in a small group. As you play, discuss and model the same strategies for adding and subtracting 9 that you introduced in the discussion earlier in the session.

ENGLISH LANGUAGE LEARNERS Repeat and Clarify Before students begin to play the game, confirm that they understand what it means to *cover an entire row on the gameboard*. Display the gameboard (G29), and say: **You need to cover a row.** Use counters to demonstrate as you trace your fingers across a row, down a column, and along a diagonal to demonstrate the different ways to *cover an entire row* as you say: **You can go *across, down,* or *corner-to-corner* to cover a row.**

4 ACTIVITY

Plus 9, Minus 9 Fact Cards

Display the Teacher Presentation (or use several Fact Cards from Set 5 (C51–C52), and ask students what they notice.

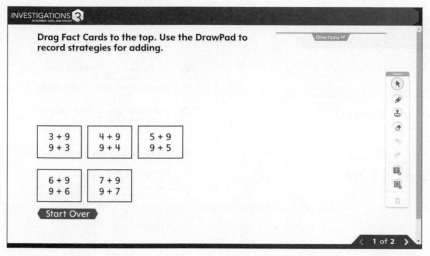

INVESTIGATIONS

Drag Fact Cards to the top. Use the DrawPad to record strategies for adding.

Directions ⌄

| 3 + 9 / 9 + 3 | 4 + 9 / 9 + 4 | 5 + 9 / 9 + 5 |
| 6 + 9 / 9 + 6 | 7 + 9 / 9 + 7 | |

Start Over

< 1 of 2 >

These are the Plus 9 Facts and Minus 9 Facts. [Carla] noticed that these problems are very similar to the problems she solved when playing *Plus 9 or Minus 9 Bingo*. What are some strategies that you used when playing *Plus 9 or Minus 9 Bingo* that could help someone practice these facts? MWI1 MWI2

Display several Plus 9 Facts, and solve them together as a class, briefly reviewing the strategy of adding 10 and subtracting 1. Also display several Minus 9 Facts, and review the strategy of subtracting 10 and adding 1.

Then distribute the 12 new cards in Fact Cards: Set 5 (C51–C52) to each student. Remind them *not* to write the answers on the cards and to label the back of each card with their initials.

Students go through the new set of cards to figure out which problems they know and which they still need to work on. They can add clues to the cards they do not yet know and put them in their "Facts I Am Still Working On" envelope. They can also look through their "Facts I Am Still Working On" envelope and see if any of those are Plus 9 Facts or Minus 9 Facts.

ONGOING ASSESSMENT Observing Students at Work

Students practice the Plus 9 and Minus 9 Facts.

○ **How fluent are students in adding 9 to any single-digit number?** Do they use what they know about adding 10 to solve Plus 9 problems? 🔍 MP7

○ **How fluent are students in subtracting 9 from a 2-digit number?** Do they use Minus 10 Facts to solve the Minus 9 Facts? 🔍 MP7

RESOURCE MASTERS, C51

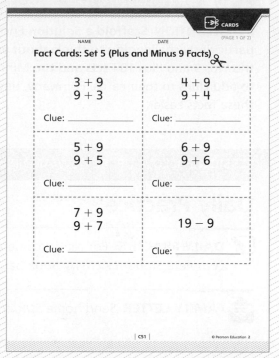

CARDS (PAGE 1 OF 2)
NAME   DATE
Fact Cards: Set 5 (Plus and Minus 9 Facts)

3 + 9 / 9 + 3 Clue: ___	4 + 9 / 9 + 4 Clue: ___
5 + 9 / 9 + 5 Clue: ___	6 + 9 / 9 + 6 Clue: ___
7 + 9 / 9 + 7 Clue: ___	19 − 9 Clue: ___

| C51 | © Pearson Education 2

RESOURCE MASTERS, C52

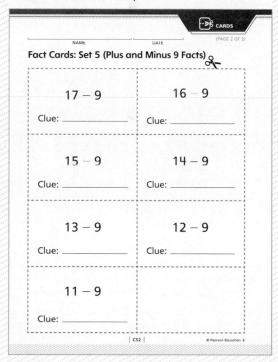

CARDS (PAGE 2 OF 2)
NAME   DATE
Fact Cards: Set 5 (Plus and Minus 9 Facts)

17 − 9 Clue: ___	16 − 9 Clue: ___
15 − 9 Clue: ___	14 − 9 Clue: ___
13 − 9 Clue: ___	12 − 9 Clue: ___
11 − 9 Clue: ___	

| C52 | © Pearson Education 2

MATH WORDS AND IDEAS

MWI1 Learning Subtraction Facts

MWI2 Learning Addition Facts

DIFFERENTIATION Supporting the Range of Learners

INTERVENTION Scaffold a Solution Encourage students who find these facts particularly challenging to think about and model the relationship between the Plus 9 and Plus 10 Facts and the Minus 9 and Minus 10 Facts as they work to add clues to their cards. For many, understanding this relationship makes these facts easier.

SESSION FOLLOW-UP: REVIEW AND PRACTICE

Daily Practice

 DAILY PRACTICE For reinforcement of this unit's content, students complete *Student Activity Book* page 293.

 FAMILY LETTER Send home *Student Activity Book* pages 295–296.

STUDENT ACTIVITY BOOK, P. 293

Plus 9 or Minus 9 Bingo **Problems**

Kira and Jake are playing *Plus 9 or Minus 9 Bingo.* Below are some of their turns.

1. Kira flipped over a 10. What numbers can she cover? **19; 1** Choose one and cover it on the board.

7	10	2	8
26	21	19	14
1	12	20	11
9	29	5	3

2. Jake flipped over a 12. What numbers can he cover? **21; 3** Choose one and cover it on the board.

3. Kira flipped over a 17. What numbers can she cover? **26; 8** Choose one and cover it on the board.

4. Jake flipped over a 20. What numbers can he cover? **29; 11** Choose one and cover it on the board.

5. What cards would Kira and Jake need to turn over to get 4 in a row? **Answers will vary.**

NOTE
Students solve problems about the game *Plus 9 or Minus 9 Bingo.*

UNIT 5 293 SESSION 1.1   © Pearson Education 2

Capture 5: Adding and Subtracting Tens and Ones

MATH FOCUS POINTS

○ Adding and subtracting a number of tens and/or ones to/from a 2-digit number

○ Finding the difference between two 2-digit numbers

TODAY'S PLAN		MATERIALS
10 Class	**CLASSROOM ROUTINES: REVIEW AND PRACTICE** *Quick Images: Stickers*	Teacher Presentation (or use 6 strips and 4 singles from the envelope of stickers from Unit 3*)
10 Class	**1 ACTIVITY** **Introducing** *Capture 5*	*Capture 5* (or use one set of *Capture 5* game materials; see Activity 2)
40 Pairs	**2 ACTIVITY** **Playing** *Capture 5*	C53–C54* G31–G33* Translucent colored chips (12 per pair) Game pieces (1 per pair)
10 Class	**3 DISCUSSION** *Capture 5*	*Capture 5* (or use one set of *Capture 5* game materials; see Activity 2)
	SESSION FOLLOW-UP: REVIEW AND PRACTICE **Daily Practice**	*Student Activity Book*, p. 297

* See *Materials to Prepare* in the Investigation 1 Planner.

| Common
Core State
Standards | **Classroom Routines:** 2.NBT.A.3, 2.NBT.B.5,
Supports 2.NBT.B.8
Session: 2.NBT.B.5, 2.NBT.B.6, Supports 2.NBT.B.8 | **Daily Practice:** 2.NBT.B.5, 2.NBT.B.6 |

CLASSROOM ROUTINES: REVIEW AND PRACTICE

Quick Images: Stickers

MATH FOCUS POINTS

○ Adding and subtracting a number of tens and/or ones to/from a 2-digit number

○ Noticing and comparing how a quantity changes when tens are added or when ones are added to a number

Display the Teacher Presentation (or use paper stickers from Unit 3).

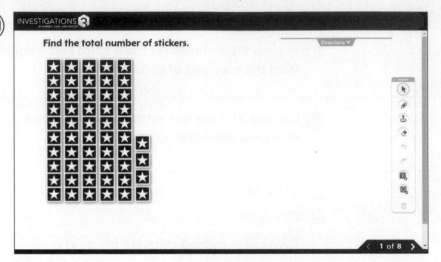

Display five strips of 10 stickers and 4 single stickers. Follow the basic *Quick Images* routine to establish that there are 54 stickers, recording $54 = 50 + 4$ in the process. **TN**

Then, with the stickers displayed, pose a series of questions about adding and subtracting strips of 10 and single stickers.

We agree there are 54 stickers. With the stickers still displayed, add a strip of 10. **I added a strip of 10. How many do we have now? MPN**

We agree there are 64 stickers. With the stickers still displayed, remove three strips of 10. **I took away 3 strips of 10. How many do we have now?**

We agree there are 34 stickers. With the stickers still displayed, add two strips of 10. **I added two strips of 10. How many do we have now?**

Throughout, encourage students to think about what's changing and what's staying the same in the number of stickers.

Then, using 54 as the base amount, pose a similar series of problems about adding or subtracting one, two, or three singles and thinking about the impact on the total number of stickers. Discuss which part of the number stays the same, which part changes, and why.

TEACHING NOTE

TN *Quick Images* Routine

○ Briefly show the image.

○ Students think about what they saw.

○ Show the image again, briefly.

○ Students revise their thinking.

○ With the image showing, volunteers share how many stickers they saw, how they were arranged, and how they remembered.

MATH PRACTICE NOTE

MPN 🔍 **MP7 Look for and make use of structure.** By connecting the image of strips and singles with symbols, students make sense of the structure of place value. In this Classroom Routine, students consider why adding or subtracting a number of groups of 10 results in the tens digit increasing or decreasing by that number.

1 ACTIVITY

Introducing *Capture 5*

Display the Game Presentation (or use G31 with 12 transparent chips—one covering 62 and the others placed on random numbers, a game piece, a deck of Change Cards, and G32). Place a game piece on 32.

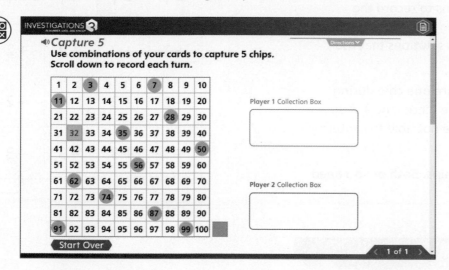

Today we're going to learn a game called *Capture 5*. In this game, you and your partner move a game piece around the 100 chart gameboard to "capture" chips.

Show students the various cards in the deck of Change Cards, and explain that these cards tell what combination of moves can be made on the 100 chart. Deal 5 cards, and play a few rounds with the class.

$+10$	$+20$	-2

-10	$+30$

You can use any number of your Change Cards to make a move. My game piece is on 32, and I want to capture one of the chips on the 100 chart. What if I wanted to move from 32 to 62?

Give students time to think and then to talk to a partner. Then, collect solutions, asking pairs to explain how they chose their cards. Use equations to record and model (or ask students to model) the two possible moves on the 100 chart.

$$32 + 10 + 20 = 62 \qquad 32 + 30 = 62$$

GAMES

NAME   DATE

Capture 5 Gameboard

1	2	3	4	5	6	7	8	9	10
11	12	13	14	15	16	17	18	19	20
21	22	23	24	25	26	27	28	29	30
31	32	33	34	35	36	37	38	39	40
41	42	43	44	45	46	47	48	49	50
51	52	53	54	55	56	57	58	59	60
61	62	63	64	65	66	67	68	69	70
71	72	73	74	75	76	77	78	79	80
81	82	83	84	85	86	87	88	89	90
91	92	93	94	95	96	97	98	99	100

| G31 | © Pearson Education 2

GAMES

NAME   DATE

Capture 5 Recording Sheet

Record your starting number, the change cards you use, and your ending number for each move, like this:

$16 + 10 + 10 + 2 = 38$

| G32 | © Pearson Education 2

We found two different ways to use the Change Cards to get from 32 to the chip on 62. If my partner and I chose 32 + 10 + 20 = 62, we would each record that as an equation, take the chip, and then discard and replace those 2 cards. **MPN1** **MPN2**

Model how to record the equation on the Recording Sheet. Remove the captured chip and the Change Cards used, and deal two new Change Cards. Remind students that they should always have 5 Change Cards to work with.

Continue playing, having students suggest, model, and explain combinations of Change Cards that capture another chip. Use equations to record the moves on the Recording Sheet. Play several rounds, being sure that students see solutions that involve using tens *and* ones, as well as solutions that use addition *and* subtraction.

Make sure students understand that they can only capture one chip during a turn (and it must be on the last square where the game piece lands). Also explain that if they can move, they must, even if they are not able to capture a chip on that turn.

You and your partner will work together to capture 5 chips. Both of you need to record an equation for each turn.

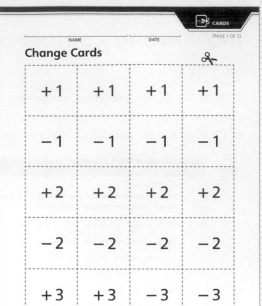

RESOURCE MASTERS, C53

2 ACTIVITY

Playing *Capture 5*

Pairs play *Capture 5*, working together to combine tens and ones to capture 5 chips on a 100 chart. Each pair needs a gameboard (G31), 12 translucent chips, a deck of Change Cards (C53–C54), and a game piece. Each student needs a copy of the *Capture 5* Recording Sheet (G32). The directions are available on G33.

ONGOING ASSESSMENT Observing Students at Work

Students practice adding and subtracting a number of tens and/or ones to/from a 2-digit number.

○ **How do students move on the gameboard?** Do they fluently add or subtract 10 or multiples of 10 to or from a number and then move their piece, or do they make jumps of 10 on the gameboard? 🔍 **MP7**

○ **How do students capture a chip?** By trial and error? Or do they determine the distance from their game piece to a chip and look for combinations of Change Cards that will make up that distance? 🔍 **MP7**

○ **Can students write equations that accurately reflect their moves from one number to another?** 🔍 **MP7**

○ **Are students demonstrating knowledge of the effect of combining forward and backward moves (e.g., using + 30 and − 10 cards to move forward 20 spaces)?** 🔍 **MP7**

MATH PRACTICE NOTES

MPN1 🔍 **MP7 Look for and make use of structure.** *Capture 5* reinforces two aspects of structure: 1) How adding and subtracting ones and/or groups of ten are reflected in changes of the digits of the original number and how these actions are represented as moves on the 100 chart; and 2) How equivalent expressions can be substituted into an equation, e.g., 34 + 20 = 54 can become 34 + 30 − 10 = 54.

MPN2 **MP2 Reason abstractly and quantitatively.** Representing moves on the 100 chart with addition and subtraction equations deepens students' understanding of the operations.

As students play *Capture 5*, they add and subtract multiples of 10.

 DIFFERENTIATION Supporting the Range of Learners

INTERVENTION **Scaffold a Solution** Help students who count by 1s think about larger jumps. Remind them of the work they've done thinking about patterns on the 100 chart. Also, thinking about cubes or stickers may help them add and subtract tens. **I see you have a + 10 Change Card. That makes me think of stickers. If you had 32 stickers and added a strip, how many would you have?** Helping students break multiples of 10 into tens can also help. **You have a + 20 card. How many strips would you have to add to add 20? What if you added one strip of 10? Can you find that number on the 100 chart? What if you added another strip of 10?** MWI

INTERVENTION **Scaffold a Solution** Help students who make their moves by trial and error consider number relationships to determine the best moves. **Your game piece is on 76, and you want to capture the chip on 58. How far apart are those numbers? Is there a combination of cards you can use that will let you move back that many spaces?**

ENGLISH LANGUAGE LEARNERS **Model Thinking Aloud** Play a couple of rounds with students. Model taking a turn. For example, use gestures to reinforce your words: **The game piece is on [28]. I want to *capture* the chip on [48]. I have [+ 20, − 5, − 10, + 15, + 5]. Which card or cards can I use? I can use the [+ 20] card because [28 + 20 = 48].** Are there other cards I could use? As students take turns, have them reason aloud as they act out each step. If they need additional support, ask questions to guide them. For example: **What number is the game piece on? What chip do you want to *capture*? What cards do you have? Which card or cards can you use to get to [48]?**

3 DISCUSSION

Capture 5

MATH FOCUS POINT FOR DISCUSSION

○ Adding and subtracting a number of tens and/or ones to/from a 2-digit number

---

RESOURCE MASTERS, C54

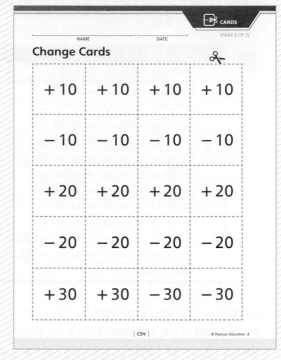

RESOURCE MASTERS, G33

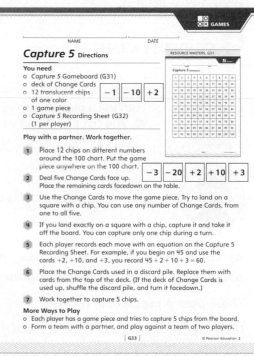

MATH WORDS AND IDEAS

MWI 100 Chart

Gather students to play a round or two of *Capture 5* together. Display the Game Presentation (or use a set of game materials with a game piece on 40 and a chip on 62).

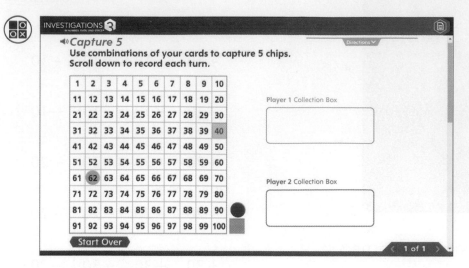

Suppose that you are playing *Capture 5*, and your game piece is on 40. You want to capture the chip that's on 62. Look at my Change Cards. Do you see a combination of cards you could use to get from 40 to 62?

Give students time to think and then to talk to a partner. Then collect suggestions. **TN**

STUDENTS MIGHT SAY

"I can use a plus 10 card to get to 50, another plus 10 card to get to 60, and the plus 2 card to get to 62."

"40 plus 20 gets me to 60, plus 2 gets me to 62."

As students respond, record their suggestions in the form of equations. Model or ask volunteers to model moving the game piece on the 100 chart.

Then, pose a problem in reverse.

Now my piece is on 62. What if I told you that I used a – 10 and a – 2 card to capture a chip? Where was the chip?

Again, discuss students' strategies and model them on the 100 chart.

SESSION FOLLOW-UP: REVIEW AND PRACTICE

Daily Practice

 DAILY PRACTICE For reinforcement of this unit's content, students complete *Student Activity Book* page 297.

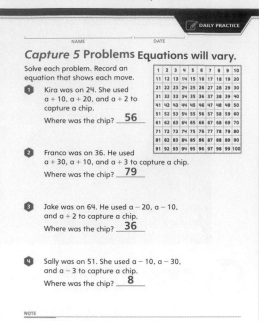

Capture 5 Problems Equations will vary.

Solve each problem. Record an equation that shows each move.

1. Kira was on 24. She used $a + 10$, $a + 20$, and $a + 2$ to capture a chip.
Where was the chip? __56__

2. Franco was on 36. He used $a + 30$, $a + 10$, and $a + 3$ to capture a chip.
Where was the chip? __79__

3. Jake was on 64. He used $a - 20$, $a - 10$, and $a + 2$ to capture a chip.
Where was the chip? __36__

4. Sally was on 51. She used $a - 10$, $a - 30$, and $a - 3$ to capture a chip.
Where was the chip? __8__

NOTE
Students solve problems related to the *Capture 5* game.
100 Chart

UNIT 5 | 297 | SESSION 1.2   © Pearson Education 2

TEACHING NOTE

TN **Strategies for *Capture 5*** Some students start by looking at their Change Cards. They might see where a [+30] would land their game piece, consider how close that is to a chip, and work from there. Others begin by determining the distance between their game piece and the number under a chip and then reason about whether there's a combination of cards that can get them there. Still others, particularly on the first day playing this game, use a trial-and-error approach, making random moves in an effort to capture a chip. Discussing possible moves and hearing and seeing others' strategies can help students begin to play more strategically.

SESSION 1.3

How Many Stickers? How Many More to Get 100?

MATH FOCUS POINTS

- Solving 2-step problems
- Adding two 2-digit numbers and determining the difference between the sum and 100
- Adding and subtracting a number of tens and/or ones to/from a 2-digit number
- Developing fluency with the Plus 9 and Minus 9 facts
- Noticing how the digit in the tens place changes when the addends in the ones place sum to greater than 10

VOCABULARY

- sum
- tens place
- estimate
- ones place

TODAY'S PLAN	MATERIALS
CLASSROOM ROUTINES: REVIEW AND PRACTICE ***Today's Number: More or Less?***	 Teacher Presentation
1 ACTIVITY **Introducing How Many Stickers? How Many More to Get 100?**	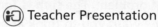 Teacher Presentation (or use an envelope of stickers and T43*)
(30) **2** MATH WORKSHOP **Addition and Subtraction with Tens and Ones** **2A** How Many Stickers? How Many More to Get 100? **2B** *Capture 5* **2C** *Plus 9 or Minus 9 Bingo*	**2A** *Student Activity Book*, pp. 298–299 A38* T43* Envelopes of stickers, cubes in towers of 10 (optional; for the Intervention) **2B** Materials from Session 1.2 A second game piece (optional; for the Extension) **2C** Materials from Session 1.1 Wild Cards (from Session 1.1, optional; for the Extension) Counters in a second color (optional)
3 DISCUSSION **Why Isn't the Answer in the 20s?**	Teacher Presentation (or use *Student Activity Book* p. 298 and T43) *Student Activity Book*, p. 298 (completed, from Activity 2A) Connecting cubes
SESSION FOLLOW-UP: REVIEW AND PRACTICE **Daily Practice and Homework**	*Student Activity Book*, pp. 300–301, 303–304 C50*

* See *Materials to Prepare* in the Investigation 1 Planner.

Common Core State Standards	**Classroom Routines:** 2.NBT.B.5, 2.NBT.B.9, Supports 2.NBT.A.4 **Session:** 2.OA.A.1, 2.OA.B.2, 2.NBT.B.5, 2.NBT.B.6, 2.NBT.B.9, Supports 2.NBT.B.8	**Daily Practice:** 2.OA.A.1, 2.NBT.B.5

Today's Number: More or Less?

MATH FOCUS POINTS

○ Estimating the sum of two 2-digit numbers using known combinations, place value, and properties of operations

○ Using standard notation (< , >) to express the relationship between quantities

○ Generating equivalent expressions for a number

Explain that you're going to introduce a new variation of *Today's Number*.

I'm going to display an addition problem. The sum is Today's Number. Before we figure out the exact answer, I want you to think about whether Today's Number is more or less than 50.

Display the Teacher Presentation (or write 22 + 35 on the board).

 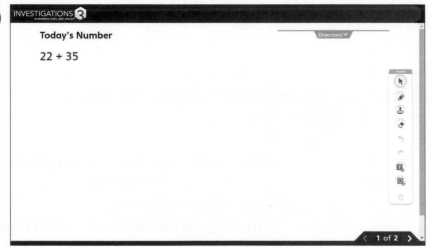

Students think about the problem individually, discuss their thinking with a partner, and then share strategies as a class.

What did you pay attention to when you were thinking about whether 22 + 35 was more or less than 50?

Listen for evidence that students' reasoning about the sum is based on the number of tens (e.g., there are 5 tens, and that's 50) or the sum of the tens (e.g., 20 + 30 = 50) and that they are also considering the number of ones.

Several of you said that you looked at the number of tens, or the number in the tens place in both numbers. You looked at the 2 in 22 and the 3 in 35 to make your estimate. Then you had to also look at the number of ones, or the numbers in the ones place.

CLASSROOM ROUTINES: REVIEW AND PRACTICE

Once students agree that the sum is greater than 50, determine the exact amount as a class. Use equations to record.

$$22 + 35 =$$
$$20 + 30 = 50$$
$$2 + 5 = 7$$
$$50 + 7 = 57$$
$$22 + 35 = 57$$

Finally, use symbols to compare Today's Number to 50.

$$57 > 50 \qquad 50 < 57$$

Display $27 + 12$, and repeat the above steps. Once again, students think on their own and then with a partner. Discuss strategies as a class, highlighting the importance of looking first at the number of tens and then at the number of ones. Find the exact answer as a class, using equations to record, and then use notation to compare that number to 50.

If time permits, students generate equations for one of Today's Numbers: 57 or 39. Alternatively, they can work on Today's Number at some other point in the day or for homework.

1 ACTIVITY

Introducing How Many Stickers? How Many More to Get 100?

Display the Teacher Presentation (or write the following story problem).

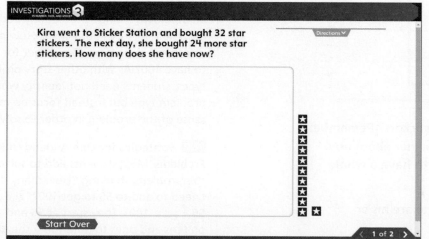

Kira went to Sticker Station and bought 32 star stickers. The next day, she bought 24 more star stickers. How many does she have now?

Read the problem together as a class. Ask volunteers to tell you how to show those amounts in stickers. Display 3 strips and 2 single stickers next to 2 strips and 4 single stickers. **PD1** **PD2**

PROFESSIONAL DEVELOPMENT

PD1 TEACHER NOTE 3: Stickers: A Context for Place Value

PD2 TEACHER NOTE 5: Place Value in Second Grade

How many star stickers does Kira have? How do you know?

Use this as an opportunity to briefly reintroduce ways to use sticker notation to record a strategy.

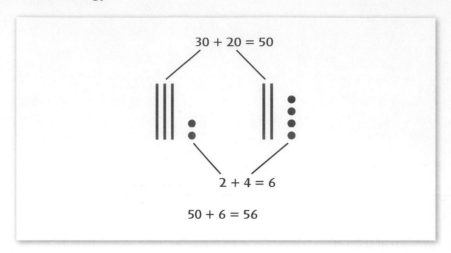

Next, display a copy of 100 Grids (T43), and remind students about sticker books, introduced in Unit 3.

What if Kira decided to put all of her star stickers on a blank page in her sticker book? What would the page look like?

Follow students' suggestions, shading or drawing a line through 5 complete rows and 6 squares in the next row. Remind students that in this work, it's not important to show the detail of the stickers.

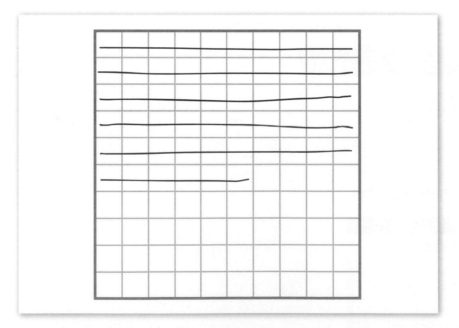

56 squares have stickers. How many squares don't have stickers? Remember a page in a sticker book holds 100 stickers. Talk with a partner about how you would figure out how many star stickers Kira needs to have a whole page. TN1 TN2

Once students have had time to think, ask a volunteer to share his or her thinking.

RESOURCE MASTERS, T43

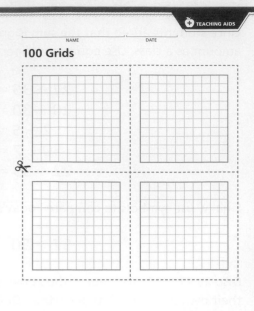

100 Grids

TEACHING NOTES

TN1 Problems with One Addend Unknown This is an example of a put together/take apart problem with one addend unknown. Students know how many are in one group and the total number; they must figure out how many are in the other group. In other words, Kira has 56 stickers. How many does she need to have 100? See **Teacher Note 4:** Types of Story Problems. Note that some students conceptualize this problem as an unknown change problem by adding an action: Kira has 56 stickers. How many would her mom have to give her for her to have 100? As with other story problem types, students need not identify which problem type but instead focus on making sense of the problem in order to solve it.

TN2 Strategies for One Addend Unknown Problems Most students add to solve this problem, thinking "How many do I need to add to 56 to get 100?" (i.e., $56 + \_\_ = 100$). They start at 56 and add on tens and ones to determine the answer. Note that this problem can also be solved by subtracting the 56 stickers she has from 100 (i.e., $100 - 56 = \_\_$) or by starting at 100 and subtracting until you reach 56 (i.e., $100 - \_\_ = 56$).

" **STUDENTS MIGHT SAY** „

"There are 4 empty in that row. Then there are 1, 2, 3, 4 rows of 10. 10, 20, 30, 40 and 4 more is 44."

"We saw the 4 empty rows and knew that's 40. Then we counted the others: 41, 42, 43, 44."

As students share, use the page in the sticker book to model the strategies and emphasize thinking of the blank squares as tens and ones. Summarize the problem in a way that highlights its structure, recording equations that represent what the problem is asking:

This page holds 100 stickers. Kira had 56 star stickers. To figure out how many more stickers she needs to fill the page, [Yama] and [Leo] figured out how many squares didn't have stickers in them.

$100 = 56 + \underline{\quad}$ $56 + \underline{\quad} = 100$ **TN**

Explain that students will be solving problems like these in Math Workshop. Explain that they should find ways to use equations and/or number lines to show their work and that 100 grids are available, as needed. **MPN**

2 MATH WORKSHOP

Addition and Subtraction with Tens and Ones

(30)

Students choose among the following activities.

---

2 A   How Many Stickers? How Many More to Get 100?

Students solve the problems on *Student Activity Book* pages 298–299 and show their work. Have copies of T43, 100 Grids, available as needed.

The addition and subtraction problems in this unit provide an opportunity to observe whether and how students model with mathematics (MP4) and make use of structure (MP7), the two highlighted math practices in this unit. Use **Assessment Checklist:** MP4 and MP7 (A38) to keep track of your observations over the course of the unit. The first two columns ask how students represent problems with stories, pictures, other representations, and equations (MP4); the second two columns ask whether students use strategies that rely on the structure of place value (MP7).

TEACHING NOTE

TN **Writing Equations That Represent the Problem** Most students see this problem as an addition problem with an unknown addend: $56 + \underline{\quad} = 100$. Note that $100 - 56 = \underline{\quad}$ and $100 - \underline{\quad} = 56$ are also equations that can be used to conceptualize and solve this problem.

MATH PRACTICE NOTE

MPN 🔍 **MP4 Model with mathematics;** and 🔍 **MP7 Look for and make use of structure.** In this unit, students encounter story problems that can be modeled with a missing addend equation or a subtraction equation. Students can also solve the problems by moving forward or backward on the number line. Coming to recognize how the same context can be seen as addition or subtraction supports students' understanding of the relationship between addition and subtraction.

RESOURCE MASTERS, A38

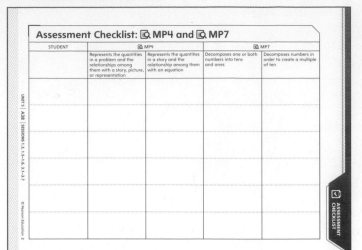

ONGOING ASSESSMENT Observing Students at Work

Students solve 2-step problems that involve adding two 2-digit numbers and then find the difference between that sum and 100.

○ **How do students add two 2-digit numbers?** Do they combine tens with tens, ones with ones, and then add those totals? Do they add one number on to the other in parts? Do they adapt the problem to make it easier to solve (e.g., thinking "If I take 2 from 24 and give it to 18, I've got 22 + 20" to solve 24 + 18)? How do they show their work? Do they use sticker notation? Equations? A number line?

○ **What strategies do students use to find the difference between a 2-digit number and 100?** Do they represent the sum and then find the total number of empty squares on a 100 grid? Do they add up from (or subtract back to) the given number? Do they add (or subtract) amounts that get them to multiples of 10 (e.g., add 8 to 42 first to get to 50, an easy number to work with)? Do they use multiples of 10? Do any students subtract the given amount from 100? How do they show their work? Do they use a 100 grid? A number line? Equations?

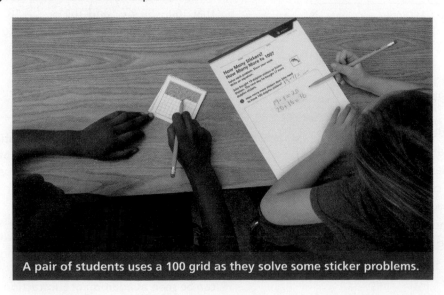

A pair of students uses a 100 grid as they solve some sticker problems.

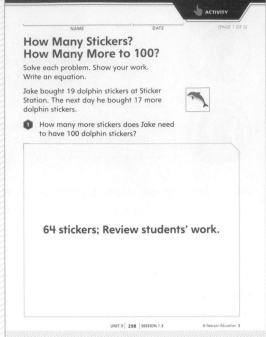 **STUDENT ACTIVITY BOOK, P. 298**

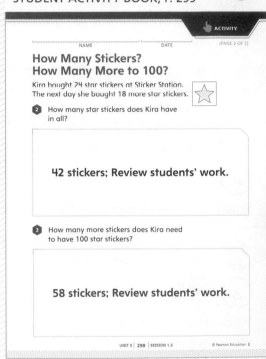 **STUDENT ACTIVITY BOOK, P. 299**

DIFFERENTIATION Supporting the Range of Learners

INTERVENTION **Suggest a Tool** Some students benefit from using cubes or strips and singles to represent the two quantities they need to combine. Seeing these quantities organized in tens and ones can help students see and use groups in their work. **MWI**

INTERVENTION **Clarify the Problem** Some students need support making sense of the situation. Use a 100 grid to discuss and represent the known information, as well as to talk about what is unknown.

> For a more comprehensive Intervention activity to be done outside of class, see *Solving 2-Step Sticker Problems* at the end of this investigation.

ENGLISH LANGUAGE LEARNERS **Provide Opportunities for Practice** To help students prepare for the class discussion, ask them to explain their strategies for adding the two numbers and how they found the difference between that sum and 100. Provide a vocabulary word list that students can use as needed. Include terms such as *added, subtracted, rows, columns, tens, ones, strips,* and *singles*. If students point to information or use one- or two-word responses, then provide a sequence that they can use. *First, I _____. Next, I _____. Then, I _____.* Model using the sequence, as needed.

---

2 B   *Capture 5*

For complete details on this activity, see Session 1.2.

 DIFFERENTIATION Supporting the Range of Learners

EXTENSION **Vary the Problem** Pairs ready for more challenge can play competitively, each using his or her own game piece. The first player to collect 5 chips wins.

---

2 C   *Plus 9 or Minus 9 Bingo*

For complete details on this activity, see Session 1.1.

 DIFFERENTIATION Supporting the Range of Learners

EXTENSION **Adapt the Problem** Students who fluently add and subtract 9 can play with Wild Cards added to the deck. A Wild Card can represent any number.

EXTENSION **Vary the Problem** Pairs ready for more challenge can play competitively on the same gameboard, each using a counter of one color or type. This introduces the strategy of blocking an opponent's move. The first to complete a row wins.

MATH WORDS AND IDEAS

MWI Sticker Station: Tens and Ones

3 DISCUSSION

Why Isn't the Answer in the 20s?

MATH FOCUS POINTS FOR DISCUSSION

○ Adding two 2-digit numbers and determining the difference between the sum and 100

○ Noticing how the tens place changes when the digits in the ones place sum to greater than 10

Display the Teacher Presentation (or use *Student Activity Book* page 298 and T43). **TN**

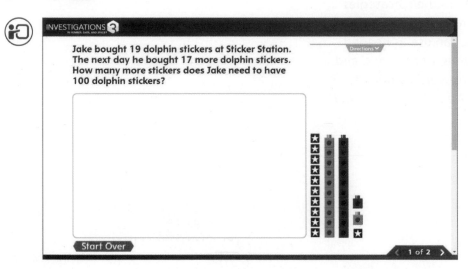

Because this problem doesn't explicitly ask how many dolphin stickers Jake bought, begin by asking students to retell the story and explain what it's asking.

Some students fill in 19 and then 17 stickers on a 100 grid and then figure out how many empty squares there are, without ever finding the total number of stickers Jake bought. If a student used this strategy, model it, pausing once the stickers are shaded.

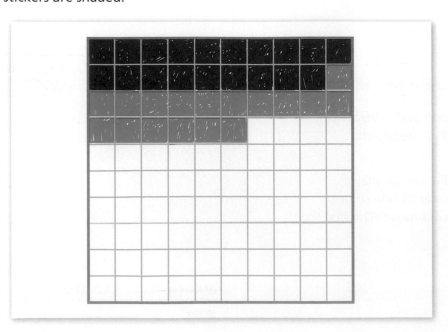

TEACHING NOTE

TN **The Size of the Numbers** The numbers are purposefully kept small so that students can focus on what happens when you add two 2-digit numbers that, between them, have more than 10 ones.

How many stickers did Jake buy at the store? [Lonzell] colored in a 100 grid to show the stickers. Did anyone do it another way?

Discuss and model other strategies for combining 19 and 17. `TN`

❝ STUDENTS MIGHT SAY ❞

"First I added the tens. 10 + 10 = 20. Then I added the singles. 7 + 9 is 16. Then I had to add the 16 onto 20. I know 20 + 10 = 30 and 6 more is 36."

"I drew stickers. 2 strips are 20. I crossed out one of the 7 singles and put it with the 9 and that gave me another 10. Then I had 3 strips of 10, which is 30, and 6 singles left over. That's 36 stickers in all."

"I did it differently. I started with 19 and then added the 17 on in parts. 19 + 10 = 29. Then 1 more is 30, plus 6 is 36."

Because there are more than 10 ones in this problem, spend some time on issues that commonly arise in this kind of problem. `MN`

I noticed something interesting. This problem was about 19 + 17. And like [Alberto] and [Holly] said, there's 1 strip or 1 ten in each number. 19 and 17 both have a 1 in the tens place. We know that two tens is 20. But everyone agrees that the answer is 36. Why is that? How come our answer isn't in the 20s?

Can we look at this with cubes? I think it's a little easier to see and move the cubes than with lots of single stickers.

Ask volunteers to build 19 and 17 with cube towers. Then place them side-by-side.

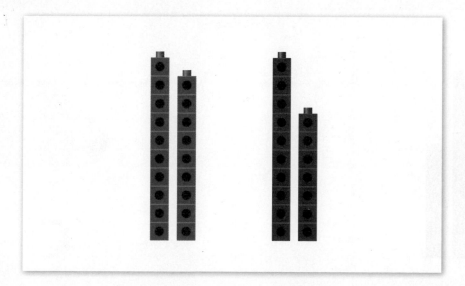

TEACHING NOTE

`TN` **Plus 9** Because this problem involves 9 and 7 ones, it provides an opportunity to see whether and how students are using the strategies discussed in Session 1.1. Do they see that these strategies can be used in a 2-digit addition problem? Do any students use what they know about adding 10 to add 9?

MATH NOTE

`MN` **More Than Nine Ones** When students use a strategy based on place value to add 2-digit numbers (i.e., add the tens, add the ones, then add the results), they will encounter situations where the total number of ones is greater than 9. For example, 19 + 17 results in 2 tens and 16 ones. When this happens there are two ideas that come into play in order to find the single quantity that represents the total. First, 10 of those 16 ones can be seen as 1 ten, with 6 ones remaining. Second, 1 ten can be grouped with the other 2 tens. Written in symbols, 20 + 16 = 20 + (10 + 6) = (20 + 10) + 6 = 30 + 6 = 36. Implicit in this move is the associative property of addition.

[Alberto] and [Holly] both talked about adding the tens. So I'm going to take the two towers of 10 and put them together. How much do we have here? (20) Now what? We have a tower with 9 and a tower with 7.

STUDENTS MIGHT SAY

"You can take one off the 7 and put it on the 9. Then you've got another 10. That's why it's not in the 20s!"

"It's like using a clue on a fact card. You know, 9 plus 7 is the same as $10 + 6$!"

"You can do the opposite. Make the 7 into a 10. And see how many are left."

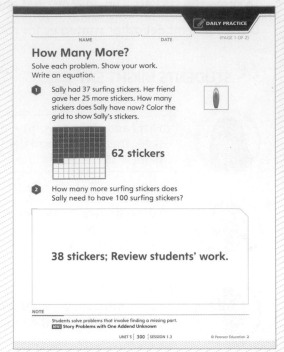

DAILY PRACTICE

NAME   DATE   (PAGE 1 OF 2)

How Many More?
Solve each problem. Show your work.
Write an equation.

1. Sally had 37 surfing stickers. Her friend gave her 25 more stickers. How many stickers does Sally have now? Color the grid to show Sally's stickers.

62 stickers

2. How many more surfing stickers does Sally need to have 100 surfing stickers?

38 stickers; Review students' work.

NOTE
Students solve problems that involve finding a missing part.
Story Problems with One Addend Unknown

UNIT 5 | 300 | SESSION 1.3   © Pearson Education 2

Model one way to show this strategy with sticker notation.

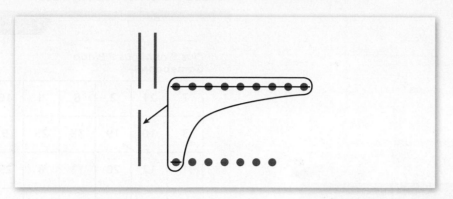

[Luis] and [Nadia] combined the group of 7 ones and the group of 9 and made another group of 10. So now there are 3 groups of 10 and a group of 6. How much is that?

Record 19 + 17 = 36, and once again look at the numbers in the tens and ones places.

Ask students to explain why the answer has a 3 in the tens place rather than a 2. Listen for evidence that they are connecting the 3 with the additional group of 10 that resulted from the 16 ones.

Finally, model ways to notate this strategy numerically. **TN**

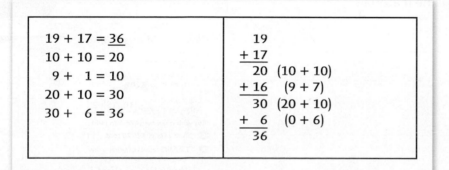

End by going back to the context of a page in a sticker book.

We agree Jake has 36 dolphin stickers. How many more stickers does he need to have 100? How could we use [Lonzell]'s 100 grid to figure it out? MWI

❝ STUDENTS MIGHT SAY ❞

"You have to find out how many blank squares. There's 4 in this row. Then count by 10s 1, 2, 3, 4, 5, 6 times. Six 10s is 60. 60 + 4 = 64, so he needs 64 more stickers."

"I would say 4 more to 40, and then I know 40 plus 60 is 100, so he needs 64 more stickers to fill the page."

STUDENT ACTIVITY BOOK, P. 301

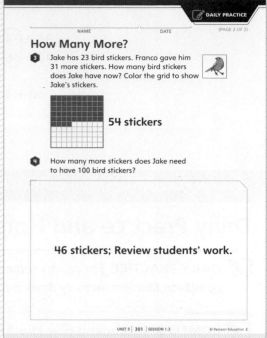

DAILY PRACTICE

NAME   DATE   [PAGE 2 OF 2]

How Many More?

3   Jake has 23 bird stickers. Franco gave him 31 more stickers. How many bird stickers does Jake have now? Color the grid to show Jake's stickers.

54 stickers

4   How many more stickers does Jake need to have 100 bird stickers?

46 stickers; Review students' work.

UNIT 5 | 301 | SESSION 1.3   © Pearson Education 2

TEACHING NOTE

TN Forms of Notation Students should become familiar with both vertical and horizontal forms of notating strategies, and see correspondences between the two. When students share a tens and ones strategy, show them how to record it using both types of notation. The steps recorded with equations in the horizontal notation (9 + 7 = 16, 10 + 10 = 20, 20 + 16 = 36) can also be recorded vertically. Side-by-side recording can highlight that these are just two different ways to show the same adding-by-place strategy. Notating strategies vertically in this way is a first step in unmasking the concise notation of the U.S. standard algorithm for addition, which is also an adding-by-place strategy.

MATH WORDS AND IDEAS

MWI Story Problems with One Addend Unknown

Use equations to show the steps of such a strategy.

$$36 + \boxed{4} = 40$$
$$40 + \boxed{60} = 100$$
$$60 + 4 = \boxed{64}$$

SESSION FOLLOW-UP: REVIEW AND PRACTICE

Daily Practice and Homework

DAILY PRACTICE For reinforcement of this unit's content, have students complete *Student Activity Book* pages 300–301.

HOMEWORK Students play *Plus 9 or Minus 9 Bingo* with someone outside school. They will need a deck of 0–20 cards without the Wild Cards (C50), a copy of the gameboard (*Student Activity Book* page 303), and a copy of the directions (*Student Activity Book* page 304). Encourage students to find a place at home to keep all of the game materials together.

STUDENT ACTIVITY BOOK, P. 303

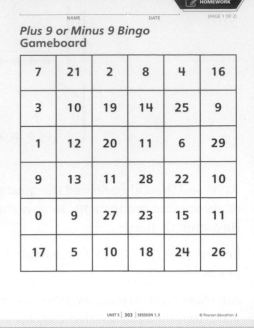

STUDENT ACTIVITY BOOK, P. 304

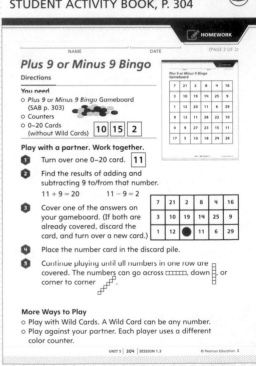

Make a Dollar

MATH FOCUS POINTS

○ Finding combinations of coins that equal $1.00
○ Recognizing and using coin equivalencies

VOCABULARY

○ sum
○ cents
○ dime
○ penny
○ nickel
○ quarter
○ dollar

TODAY'S PLAN	MATERIALS
CLASSROOM ROUTINES: REVIEW AND PRACTICE 10 Class *Today's Number: More or Less?*	Teacher Presentation
1 ACTIVITY 10 Class **Introducing Combinations That Make a Dollar**	Teacher Presentation (or use a Coin and Dollar Set) Chart: "Ways to Make a Dollar"*
2 ACTIVITY 10 Pairs **Combinations That Make a Dollar**	*Student Activity Book*, p. 305 Coin and Dollar Sets (1 per pair)
3 ACTIVITY 10 Class **Introducing *Make a Dollar***	*Make a Dollar* (or use C55–C58* and G34*)
30 Pairs **4 ACTIVITY** *Make a Dollar*	G34–G35*(1 per student per game) T3 (optional; for the English Language Learners) *Make a Dollar* Cards (1 deck per pair) Coin and Dollar Sets (as needed) Self-stick notes (optional; for the Intervention)
SESSION FOLLOW-UP: REVIEW AND PRACTICE **Daily Practice**	*Student Activity Book*, p. 306

* See *Materials to Prepare* in the Investigation 1 Planner.

Common Core State Standards	Classroom Routines: 2.NBT.B.5, 2.NBT.B.9, 2.MD.C.8, Supports 2.NBT.A.4 Session: 2.NBT.B.5, 2.MD.C.8	Daily Practice: 2.NBT.B.5, 2.MD.C.8

CLASSROOM ROUTINES: REVIEW AND PRACTICE

Today's Number: More or Less?

MATH FOCUS POINTS

○ Estimating the sum of two 2-digit numbers using known combinations, place value, and properties of operations

○ Using standard notation ($<$, $>$) to express the relationship between quantities

○ Generating equivalent expressions for a number

I'm going to display an addition problem. The sum is Today's Number. Just like yesterday, before we figure out the exact answer, we're going to estimate. Today, your job is to think about whether Today's Number is more or less than 50 cents.

Display the Teacher Presentation (or write 25¢ + 23¢ on the board).

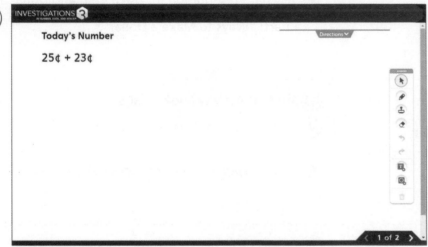

Students think about the problem individually, discuss their thinking with a partner, and then share strategies as a class.

What did you pay attention to when you were thinking about whether 25¢ + 23¢ is more or less than 50¢?

Listen for evidence that students' reasoning about the sum is based on what they know about money (e.g., "Two quarters make 50¢, and 23¢ is smaller than a quarter.") or place value (e.g., "There are 4 dimes and that's 40, and there's not enough pennies to make another dime." or "20 + 20 = 40, and 5 and 3 won't take you past 50.") **MPN**

Highlight the numbers in both the tens place and the ones place. Once students agree that the sum is less than 50, determine the exact amount as a class. Use equations to record.

$$25 + 23 =$$
$$20 + 20 = 40$$
$$5 + 3 = 8$$
$$40 + 8 = 48$$

MATH PRACTICE NOTE

MPN 🔍 **MP7 Look for and make use of structure.** Students' reasoning is based on mathematical structure, using what they know about the role of the tens digit in a number or comparing 23 + 25 to the familiar sum, 25 + 25.

CLASSROOM ROUTINES: REVIEW AND PRACTICE

Finally, use symbols to compare Today's Number to 50¢:

$$48¢ < 50¢ \qquad 50¢ > 48¢$$

Display 28¢ + 26¢ and repeat the above steps. Once again, students think on their own and then with a partner. Discuss students' strategies, which will likely include reasoning about quarters (e.g., 25¢ + 25¢ = 50¢, and "Both numbers are bigger than 25¢."). Find the exact answer as a class, recording with equations, and then use notation to compare that number to 50.

$$28 + 26 =$$
$$25 + 25 = 50 \qquad 54¢ > 50¢ \qquad 50¢ < 54¢$$
$$3 + 1 = 4$$
$$50 + 4 = 54$$

If time permits, students generate equations for one of Today's Numbers: 48 or 54. Alternatively, they can work on Today's Number at some other point in the day or for homework.

---

1 ACTIVITY

Introducing Combinations That Make a Dollar

Display the Teacher Presentation (or use a set of coins) to briefly review coin names, values, and equivalencies. **MWI1** **MWI2**

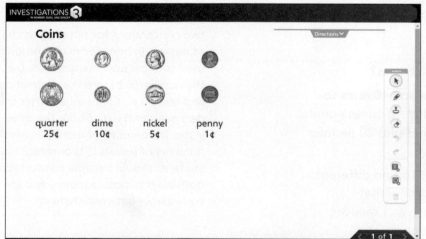

STUDENT ACTIVITY BOOK, P. 305

ACTIVITY

NAME DATE

Ways to Make a Dollar

Use the space below to record as many combinations of coins that make $1.00 as you can.

Answers will vary.

UNIT 5 | 305 | SESSION 1.4 © Pearson Education 2

MATH WORDS AND IDEAS

MWI1 Money

MWI2 Coin Values and Equivalencies

What is the name of this coin? Can you show us a dime? A penny? Which coin is worth 5¢? (the nickel) 25¢? (the quarter) Which coins could we put together to make 25¢? How much is the largest coin worth? Which coins could we combine to make 50¢?

Then, display the "Ways to Make a Dollar" chart.

Which coins could we combine to make a dollar? We've been thinking a lot about numbers that make 100. Can that help us think about combinations of coins that make a dollar?

Use equations to list a few of the combinations students suggest. Take the opportunity to review notation for dollars and cents. Remind students that one dollar can be shown as 100¢, $1, or as $1.00. **MN**

Ways to Make
One Dollar $1 $1.00

$$50¢ + 50¢ = \$1.00$$
$$25¢ + 75¢ = \$1.00$$
$$53¢ + 47¢ = \$1.00$$
$$10¢ + 10¢ + 80¢ = \$1.00$$
$$30¢ + 70¢ = \$1.00$$
$$60¢ + 40¢ = \$1.00$$
$$64¢ + 36¢ = \$1.00$$

2 ACTIVITY

Combinations That Make a Dollar

Distribute Coin and Dollar Sets to each pair. Partners find as many combinations of coins that add to a dollar as they can. Individuals record the combinations on *Student Activity Book* page 305. **MPN**

ONGOING ASSESSMENT ▶ Observing Students at Work

Students find combinations of coins that equal a dollar.

○ **Do students know coin names, values, and basic equivalencies?**

○ **Do students use knowledge of the equivalence of 1 ten and 10 ones to find multiple solutions?** For example, do they reason that 10 dimes equal 1 dollar, so 9 dimes plus 10 pennies equal 1 dollar, 8 dimes plus 20 pennies equal 1 dollar, and so on? 🔍 **MP7**

○ **Do students use knowledge of other coin equivalencies to find different combinations that make a dollar?** For example, if they know that 50¢ + 50¢ = $1.00, do they use coins that equal 50¢—such as 1 quarter, 2 dimes, and 1 nickel—to come up with another combination (50¢ + 25¢ + 10¢ + 10¢ + 5¢ = $1.00)? 🔍 **MP7**

○ **How do students record their combinations?** Do they use notation for money (e.g., ¢ and $)?

RESOURCE MASTERS, C55

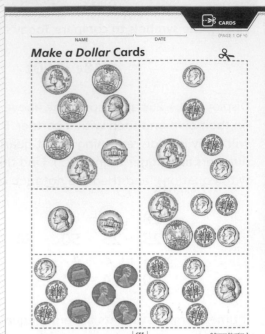

MATH NOTE

MN **Notation for Money** There are two conventions for notating amounts of money. In one, decimal notation is used to show how many dollars (i.e., the number(s) before the decimal point) and cents (i.e., the numbers after the decimal point) e.g., $1.00. The other states the amount of money in whole numbers of dollars ($1) or cents (100¢). Students should become comfortable with both ways to notate money and see the equivalency between them.

MATH PRACTICE NOTE

MPN 🔍 **MP7 Look for and make use of structure.** Using their knowledge of coin equivalencies, students can substitute groups of coins of equal value to create new combinations.

DIFFERENTIATION Supporting the Range of Learners

INTERVENTION Adapt the Problem Some students benefit from first finding combinations that make 25¢ or 50¢. These students may benefit from additional time working with the Coin and Dollar Sets outside of math time (e.g., see *Collect 50¢* in Unit 1 and *Collect $1* in Unit 3).

3 ACTIVITY

Introducing *Make a Dollar*

We are going to learn a new game called *Make a Dollar*. The object of the game is to find pairs of cards that together make *exactly* one dollar. To start, deal 8 *Make a Dollar* Cards, facing up.

Display the Game Presentation (or use 8 *Make a Dollar* Cards (C55–C58), including at least two pairs that combine to make a dollar).

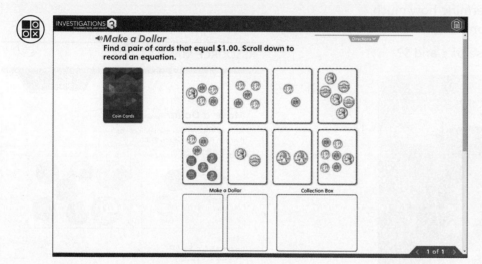

Can you find two groups of coins that together equal one dollar?

As students find pairs of cards with coins that add to a dollar, place the two cards next to each other, and ask a couple of students to verify that the sets of coins equal one dollar.

Demonstrate how to record these combinations on the *Make a Dollar* Recording Sheet (G34). Remove the cards that make the combination, and replace them with new cards. Play one or two rounds to make sure that students understand the rules of the game.

RESOURCE MASTERS, C56

RESOURCE MASTERS, C57

4 ACTIVITY

Make a Dollar

Pairs play *Make a Dollar*, finding pairs of *Make a Dollar* Cards (C55–C58) that add to a dollar. Each player records those combinations on G34. Remind students that the "Ways to Make a Dollar" chart can serve as a reference as they play. The directions are available on G35.

ONGOING ASSESSMENT Observing Students at Work

Students find combinations of coins that equal one dollar.

○ **How do students determine the amounts on each card?** Do they recognize some combinations of coins? Do they add like coins first? Do they count on?

○ **What strategies do students use to find pairs of cards that add to a dollar?** Do they total the individual cards first and then look for known combinations? Do they choose one card and then determine how much more is needed? How do they make that determination? **PD**

○ **How do students record?** Are they accurate in their use of ¢ and $?

Students work in pairs to find combinations of *Make a Dollar* Cards that equal a dollar.

As you observe, ask questions to learn more about students' thinking and to help them develop strategies:

○ **How much money is on this card? How did you add up the coins?**

○ **I see that you have one card that is worth [60 cents]. How much more money do you need to make exactly one dollar? What coins might equal that amount?**

○ **Are there any combinations that make one dollar that you "just know" without adding the coins?**

RESOURCE MASTERS, C58

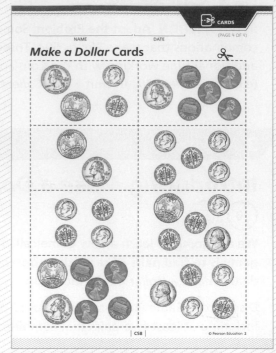

RESOURCE MASTERS, G34

Make a Dollar Recording Sheet

Write an equation for each pair of cards that you find that add to $1.00. Use the ¢ and $ signs.

Example:
45¢ + 55¢ = $1.00

Score (number of dollars collected): _____

PROFESSIONAL DEVELOPMENT

PD DIALOGUE BOX 2: Strategies for *Make a Dollar*

DIFFERENTIATION Supporting the Range of Learners

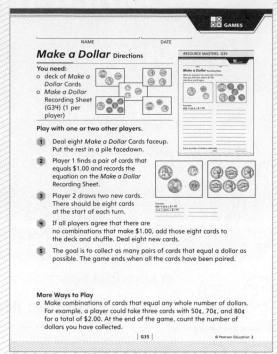

INTERVENTION **Suggest a Tool** Some students benefit from using tools such as coins for counting or 100 charts or grids for determining combinations that make 100. Some students have difficulty figuring out the totals on the cards and finding pairs that equal a dollar at the same time. Encourage them to find the amount on each card, write that amount on a self-stick note, and place it on the card. After they have labeled each card with the amount, they can better concentrate on finding the pairs of cards that add to a dollar.

ENGLISH LANGUAGE LEARNERS **Repeat and Clarify** Before students begin to play the game independently, confirm that they understand the game rules and how to *Make a Dollar*. Display 8 *Make a Dollar* cards. **You need to find two cards that make $1.00. $1.00 is the same as 100 cents. Are there two cards that total 100 cents? Which cards?** Review and discuss examples and non-examples with students. Play a round or two of the game with students. Also, display *How Many Pennies?* (T3), which shows a picture of each coin (*penny, nickel, dime, quarter*) and its value. Remind students to refer to T3 as needed.

SESSION FOLLOW-UP: REVIEW AND PRACTICE

Daily Practice

 DAILY PRACTICE For reinforcement of this unit's content, students complete *Student Activity Book* page 306.

RESOURCE MASTERS, G35

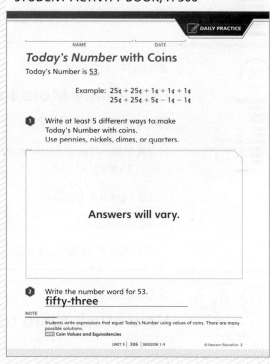

STUDENT ACTIVITY BOOK, P. 306

How Much to $1.00? How Much to 100?

MATH FOCUS POINTS

○ Solving 2-step problems

○ Adding two 2-digit numbers and determining the difference between the sum and 100

○ Finding combinations of coins that equal $1.00

○ Adding and subtracting a number of tens and/or ones to/from a 2-digit number

○ Developing fluency with the Plus 9 and Minus 9 facts

TODAY'S PLAN	MATERIALS

 10 Class

CLASSROOM ROUTINES: REVIEW AND PRACTICE

Today's Number: More or Less?

 Teacher presentation

---

15 Class

1 DISCUSSION

Strategies for *Capture 5*

Capture 5 (or one set of *Capture 5* game materials from Session 1.2)

G31 (1 per pair)

Translucent colored chips (2 per pair)

30

2 MATH WORKSHOP

How Many More to 100? How Much More to $1.00?

    2A How Many More to 100? How Much More to $1.00?

    2B *Make a Dollar*

    2C *Capture 5*

    2D *Plus 9 or Minus 9 Bingo*

2A *Student Activity Book*, pp. 307–310

 A38 (from Session 1.3)

T43 (from Session 1.3; optional; for the Intervention)

Coins, stickers, cubes (as needed)

2B Materials from Session 1.4

2C Materials from Sessions 1.2 and 1.3

2D Materials from Sessions 1.1 and 1.3

---

 15 Class

3 DISCUSSION

How Much More to $1.00?

Teacher Presentation

Student Activity Book, p. 307 (completed, from Math Workshop 2A)

SESSION FOLLOW-UP: REVIEW AND PRACTICE

Daily Practice and Homework

Student Activity Book, pp. 311–312

Common Core State Standards	**Classroom Routines:** 2.NBT.A.4, 2.NBT.B.5, 2.NBT.B.9 **Session:** 2.OA.A.1, 2.OA.B.2, 2.NBT.B.5, 2.NBT.B.9, 2.MD.B.6, 2.MD.C.8, Supports 2.NBT.B.8	**Daily Practice:** 2.OA.A.1, 2.NBT.B.5

CLASSROOM ROUTINES: REVIEW AND PRACTICE

Today's Number: More or Less?

MATH FOCUS POINTS

○ Estimating the sum of two 2-digit numbers using known combinations, place value, and properties of operations

○ Using standard notation ($<$, $>$) to express the relationship between quantities

○ Generating equivalent expressions for a number

I'm going to display an addition problem. The sum is Today's Number. Today, before we figure out the exact answer, I want you to think about whether Today's Number is more or less than 100.

Display the Teacher Presentation (or write 35 + 63 on the board).

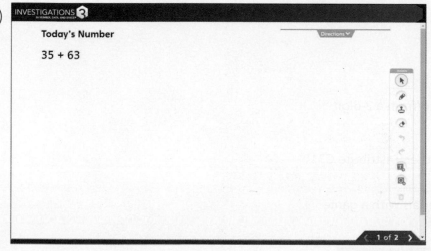

Students think about the problem individually, discuss their thinking with a partner, and then share strategies as a class.

What did you pay attention to when you were thinking about whether or not 35 + 63 was more or less than 100?

Listen for evidence that students' reasoning about the sum is based on the number of tens (e.g., "There are 9 tens, and that's 90.") or the sum of the tens (e.g., 30 + 60 = 90) and that they are also considering the number of ones. Once students agree that the sum is less than 100, determine the exact amount as a class. Use equations to record.

$$35 + 63 = \underline{}$$
$$30 + 60 = 90$$
$$5 + 3 = 8$$
$$90 + 8 = 98$$

Finally, use symbols to compare Today's Number to 100:

$$98 < 100 \qquad 100 > 98$$

CLASSROOM ROUTINES: REVIEW AND PRACTICE

Display 78 + 32 and repeat the above steps. Once again, students think on their own and then with a partner. Discuss strategies as a class, highlighting the importance of looking, for each number, first at the number of tens by looking at the digit in the tens place and then at the number of ones by looking at the digit in the ones place.

Find the exact answer as a class, using equations to record, and then use the less-than and greater-than signs to compare that number to 100.

If time permits, students generate equations for one of Today's Numbers: 98 or 110. Alternatively, they can work on Today's Number at some other point in the day or for homework.

1 DISCUSSION

Strategies for *Capture 5*

MATH FOCUS POINT FOR DISCUSSION

○ Adding and subtracting a number of tens and/or ones to/from a 2-digit number

Gather students to play a round or two of *Capture 5* together. Distribute G31 and two chips to each pair. **PD**

Display the Game Presentation, or use a set of game materials with a game piece on 35 and a chip on 52.

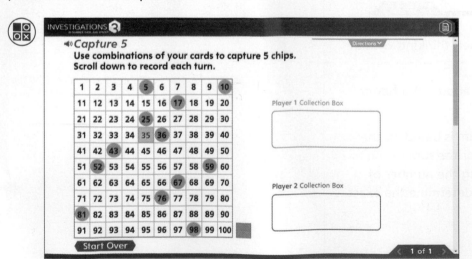

My game piece is on 35. Look at my Change Cards. Do you see a way to capture the chip that is on 52? Remember, you can use a combination of plus and minus cards. Talk to a partner. You can use your 100 chart to think about possible moves.

After a few minutes, ask a volunteer to share a combination of cards. Use an equation to record, while a different volunteer models the moves on the 100 chart.

PROFESSIONAL DEVELOPMENT

PD DIALOGUE BOX 3: Strategies for *Capture 5*

Did anyone find a *different* way? One that uses *different* Change Cards? MN1

Record equations for both moves. MN2

$$35 + 30 - 10 - 3 = 52 \qquad 35 + 20 - 3 = 52$$

You've been playing *Capture 5* for a few days now. What are some strategies you are finding useful when playing this game? How did you decide which cards to use for this round?

STUDENTS MIGHT SAY

"I try different cards to see where I can move my game piece. For this round, I started with the $+ 30$ card. That took me too far, so I used the $- 10$ card, and that got me in the same row as 52. Minus 3 landed me right on 52."

"I figure out how far I need to move to capture a chip. Then I look at my cards to see if I can make that amount. I knew it was 17 spaces from 35 to 52, so I looked for cards that equaled 17. I used 20 and $- 3$."

As students share strategies, check for understanding by asking other students to explain and model the moves. MPN

Do you agree with [Paige] that the distance between 35 and 52 is 17? Can someone show us on the 100 chart? . . . What about in our equation? Where do you see the 17?

Encourage students to try out one of these strategies and think about others as they play *Capture 5*.

2 MATH WORKSHOP

How Many More to 100? How Much More to $1.00?

 30

Students should begin with How Many More to 100? How Much More to $1.00? because Problem 1 will be discussed at the end of the session. Then they can chose from among the following activities.

---

2 A   How Many More to 100? How Much More to $1.00?

On *Student Activity Book* pages 307–310, students solve problems in which they combine two amounts of money or stickers and then determine the difference between that sum and $1.00 or 100 stickers. Make tools (e.g., coins, 100 grids, cubes) available, as needed. Continue to use **Assessment Checklist: MP4 and MP7 (A38)** in this activity.

ONGOING ASSESSMENT   Observing Students at Work

Students solve 2-step problems in which they combine two 2-digit numbers and then determine the difference between the sum and 100.

○ **How do students add two 2-digit numbers?** For problems about money, do they think in terms of coins? (e.g., thinking of $35 + 37$ as $25 + 10 + 25 + 10 + 2$) Do they combine tens with tens, ones with ones, and then add those totals? Do they add one number on to the other in parts? Do they adapt the problem to make it easier to solve (e.g., thinking "If I take 3 from 35, and give it to 37, I've got $32 + 40$")? Do any need to show the amounts in coins? How do they show their work? Do they use sketches of coins? Equations? A number line? **MP7**

○ **What strategies do students use to find the difference between a 2-digit number and 100?** For problems about money, do they use or think in terms of coins? Do any use or think about a 100 grid? Do they add up from (or subtract back to) the given number? Do they add (or subtract) amounts that get them to multiples of 10 (e.g., add 8 to 72 first to get to 80, an easy number to work with)? Do they use multiples of 10? Do any subtract the given amount from 100? How do they show their work? Do they use coins or a 100 grid? A number line? Equations? **MP7**

⦿ DIFFERENTIATION   Supporting the Range of Learners

> For another practice activity to be done outside of class, see *Problems about 100: Representing Strategies on the Number Line* at the end of this investigation.

INTERVENTION   **Suggest a Tool** Encourage students who have difficulty adding two 2-digit numbers to represent each quantity with coins or stickers or cubes. Work together to think about how to combine those quantities in ways that make sense (e.g., What if we put all the quarters [or strips of 10] together?). **MPN**

INTERVENTION   **Adapt the Learning Situation** Work in a small group with students who have difficulty determining the difference between a 2-digit number and 100. Encourage them to first show the given number on a 100 grid (T43). Model and discuss what is known (how many cents or stickers you have; the total number of cents or stickers) and what they are trying to find out (how many more cents or stickers are needed). **MWI**

ENGLISH LANGUAGE LEARNERS   **Partner Talk** To help students prepare for the class discussion, have them rehearse with a partner and explain how they solved Problem 1 on *Student Activity Book* page 307. Provide a sequence that students can use. *First, I _____. Next, I _____. Then, I _____.* Encourage partners to help each other complete the sequence, and help students as needed. Then provide time for students to rehearse reading their steps to partners.

---

2 B   *Make a Dollar*

For complete details on this activity, see Session 1.4.

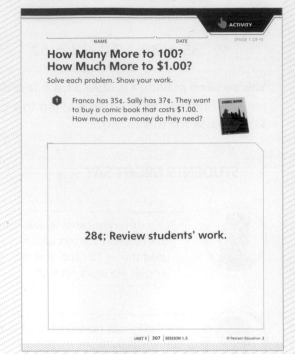

ACTIVITY

NAME   DATE   (PAGE 1 OF 10)

How Many More to 100?
How Much More to $1.00?

Solve each problem. Show your work.

1   Franco has 35¢. Sally has 37¢. They want to buy a comic book that costs $1.00. How much more money do they need?

28¢; Review students' work.

UNIT 5 | 307 | SESSION 1.5   © Pearson Education 2

MATH PRACTICE NOTE

MPN   **MP1 Make sense of problems and persevere in solving them;** and **MP5 Use appropriate tools strategically.** Using tools such as sticker representations or cubes to represent a problem is a first step toward making sense of the problem.

MATH WORDS AND IDEAS

MWI   Story Problems with One Addend Unknown

DIFFERENTIATION Supporting the Range of Learners

EXTENSION Adapt the Problem Students who easily find combinations of coins that equal $1.00 can make combinations of cards that equal $2.00. For example, a player could take three cards with 50¢, 70¢, and 80¢. A player's score at the end of the game equals the number of dollars they have collected.

> For a more comprehensive extension activity to be done outside of class, see *Make 2 or More Dollars* at the end of this investigation.

---

2 C   *Capture 5*

For complete details on this activity, see Sessions 1.2 and 1.3.

---

2 D   *Plus 9 or Minus 9 Bingo*

For complete details on this activity, see Sessions 1.1 and 1.3.

---

3 DISCUSSION

How Much More to $1.00?

MATH FOCUS POINT FOR DISCUSSION

○ Adding two 2-digit numbers and determining the difference between the sum and 100

Display the Teacher Presentation (or problem 1 on *Student Activity Book* page 307). Read the problem aloud.

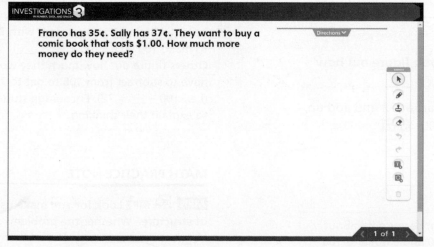

Franco has 35¢. Sally has 37¢. They want to buy a comic book that costs $1.00. How much more money do they need?

STUDENT ACTIVITY BOOK, P. 308

ACTIVITY

NAME _____ DATE _____ (PAGE 2 OF 4)

**How Many More to 100?
How Much More to $1.00?**

② a. Sally bought 38 cat stickers at Sticker Station. The next day she bought 27 more cat stickers. How many cat stickers does Sally have in all?

65 stickers; Review students' work.

b. How many more cat stickers does Sally need to have 100?

35 stickers; Review students' work.

UNIT 5 | 308 | SESSION 1.5   © Pearson Education 2

STUDENT ACTIVITY BOOK, P. 309

ACTIVITY

NAME _____ DATE _____ (PAGE 3 OF 4)

**How Many More to 100?
How Much More to $1.00?**

③ a. Jake has 32¢. Kira has 36¢. How much money do they have in all?

68¢; Review students' work.

b. Jake and Kira want to buy a comic book that costs $1.00. How much more money do they need?

32¢; Review students' work.

UNIT 5 | 309 | SESSION 1.5   © Pearson Education 2

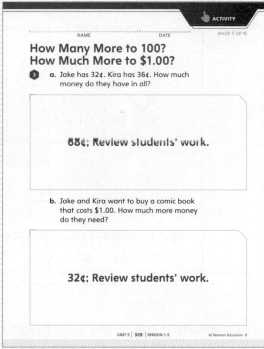

Focus first on making sense of the problem and on the fact that it's helpful to figure out how much money Franco and Sally have together. **MN1**

Discuss students' strategies for combining 35 and 37, modeling each and comparing them to each other.

❝ STUDENTS MIGHT SAY ❞

"I thought about money. 35 is a quarter and a dime, and 37 is a quarter, a dime, and 2 pennies. Two quarters are 50¢, two dimes gets me to 70¢; 71, 72."

"First I added the tens. 30 + 30 = 60. Then I did 5 + 7 = 12. Then I added 60 and 12. I know 60 + 10 is 70 and that 2 more would be 72."

"I started with 35 and then added on the 37. I used a number line. 35 + 10 = 45, 45 + 10 = 55, and 55 + 10 = 65. 65 + 5 is 70, and 2 more is 72. They have 72¢ together."

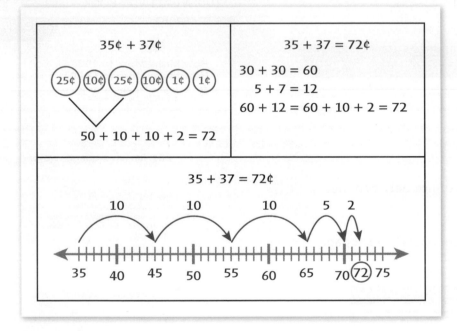

We agree that Franco and Sally have 72 cents. **How did you figure out how much money Franco and Sally need to have $1?** **MPN**

Most students use addition to solve this problem: they start at 72 and add up, keeping track of how much they have to add to get to 100. **MN2**

❝ STUDENTS MIGHT SAY ❞

"At first I wasn't sure how to solve this problem because it's about money, not stickers, but a sticker page has 100 and a dollar is 100 cents. So I showed the 72 cents they had and then counted the rest. 10, 20, and 8 . . . 28."

**How Many More to 100?
How Much More to $1.00?**

4 Franco bought 43 dog stickers at Sticker Station. The next day he bought 38 more dog stickers. How many more dog stickers does Franco need to have 100?

19 stickers; Review students' work.

UNIT 5 | 310 | SESSION 1.5   © Pearson Education 2

MATH NOTES

MN1 100 − 35 − 37 While most students combine 35 and 37 and then find the difference between the total and 100, a few may start with a dollar and subtract 35 first and then 37. Discuss this strategy at the end of the discussion if it arises.

MN2 Strategies for a Problem with One Addend Unknown While most students add to solve these problems (i.e., 72 + ___ = 100), some think "I can do 100 − 72. If I take away the 72¢ they have, I will find out what goes with 72 to make 100" (i.e., 100 − 72 = ___). Others figure out how much they would have to subtract from 100 to get to 72 (i.e., 100 − ___ = 72). Encourage students to explain their thinking.

MATH PRACTICE NOTE

MPN 🔍 MP7 Look for and make use of structure. Whether the problems are about stickers or money, the mathematical structures of the problems are the same, and students can use the methods they used to solve sticker problems to solve money problems.

" STUDENTS MIGHT SAY "

"I started at 72 on the number line and jumped by tens: 82, 92, and 8 more got me to 100. That's 28 in all."

"I added 8 to 72¢ to get to 80¢. I know 80¢ + 20¢ equals $1, so 20 + 8; they need 28¢ to get to a dollar."

As students share, ask the class where they can see the 28¢ needed to make a dollar in each representation. Model ways to record each student's strategy.

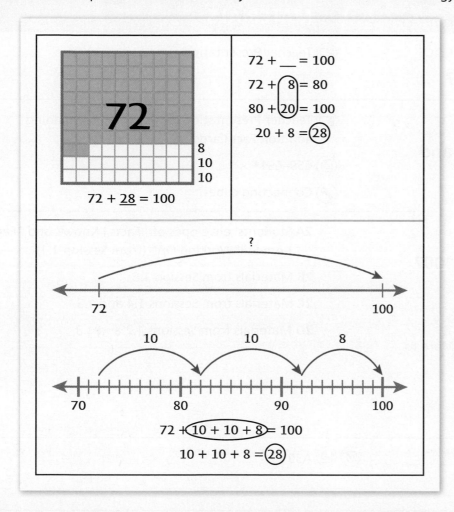

$72 + \_\_ = 100$

$72 + 8 = 80$

$80 + 20 = 100$

$20 + 8 = 28$

$72 + \underline{28} = 100$

$72 + (10 + 10 + 8) = 100$

$10 + 10 + 8 = 28$

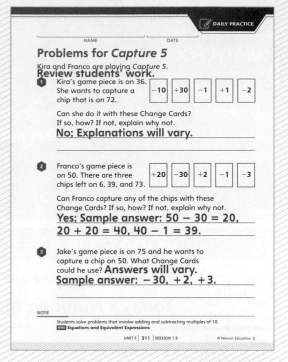

DAILY PRACTICE

NAME   DATE

Problems for *Capture 5*

Kira and Franco are playing *Capture 5.*
Review students' work.

1. Kira's game piece is on 36. She wants to capture a chip that is on 72.   [−10] [+30] [−1] [+1] [−2]

   Can she do it with these Change Cards? If so, how? If not, explain why not.
   No; Explanations will vary.

2. Franco's game piece is on 50. There are three chips left on 6, 39, and 73.   [+20] [−30] [+2] [−1] [−3]

   Can Franco capture any of the chips with these Change Cards? If so, how? If not, explain why not.
   Yes; Sample answer: 50 − 30 = 20, 20 + 20 = 40, 40 − 1 = 39.

3. Jake's game piece is on 75 and he wants to capture a chip on 50. What Change Cards could he use? **Answers will vary. Sample answer: − 30, +2, +3.**

NOTE
Students solve problems that involve adding and subtracting multiples of 10.
MW1 Equations and Equivalent Expressions

UNIT 5 | 311 | SESSION 1.5   © Pearson Education 2

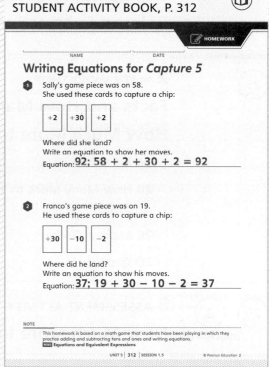

HOMEWORK

NAME   DATE

Writing Equations for *Capture 5*

1. Sally's game piece was on 58. She used these cards to capture a chip:

   [+2] [+30] [+2]

   Where did she land?
   Write an equation to show her moves.
   Equation: **92; 58 + 2 + 30 + 2 = 92**

2. Franco's game piece was on 19. He used these cards to capture a chip:

   [+30] [−10] [−2]

   Where did he land?
   Write an equation to show his moves.
   Equation: **37; 19 + 30 − 10 − 2 = 37**

NOTE
This homework is based on a math game that students have been playing in which they practice adding and subtracting tens and ones and writing equations.
MW1 Equations and Equivalent Expressions

UNIT 5 | 312 | SESSION 1.5   © Pearson Education 2

SESSION FOLLOW-UP: REVIEW AND PRACTICE

Daily Practice and Homework

✎ **DAILY PRACTICE** For reinforcement of this unit's content, students complete *Student Activity Book* page 311.

✎ **HOMEWORK** Students solve problems on *Student Activity Book* page 312, based on the game *Capture 5.*

How Much More to $1.00?

MATH FOCUS POINTS

o Solving 2-step problems

o Adding two 2-digit numbers and determining the difference between the sum and 100

o Finding combinations of coins that equal $1.00

o Adding and subtracting a number of tens and/or ones to/from a 2-digit number

o Developing fluency with addition and subtraction within 20

VOCABULARY

o addition facts

o Doubles Facts

o Make 10 Facts

TODAY'S PLAN

MATERIALS

(10) Class	**CLASSROOM ROUTINES: REVIEW AND PRACTICE** *Today's Number: More or Less?*	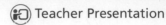 Teacher Presentation

1 ACTIVITY

The Remaining Addition Facts and Related Subtraction Facts

(15) Class

Teacher Presentation (or use the six remaining addition Fact Cards)

C59–C61*

Connecting cubes

2 MATH WORKSHOP

Facts and How Many More to 100?
How Much More to $1.00?

(25)

2A Fact Fluency

2B How Many More to 100? How Much More to $1.00?

2C *Make a Dollar*

2D *Capture 5*

2A Students' envelopes of "Facts I Know" and "Facts I Am Still Working On" (from Session 1.1)

2B Materials from Session 1.5

2C Materials from Sessions 1.4 and 1.5

2D Materials from Sessions 1.2 and 1.3

3 ASSESSMENT ACTIVITY

How Much More to $1.00?

(20) Individuals

A39*

SESSION FOLLOW-UP: REVIEW AND PRACTICE

Daily Practice

Student Activity Book, p. 313

* See *Materials to Prepare* in the Investigation 1 Planner.

| Common Core State Standards | **Classroom Routines:** 2.NBT.A.4, 2.NBT.B.5, 2.NBT.B.9, 2.MD.C.8
 Session: 2.OA.A.1, 2.OA.B.2, 2.NBT.B.5, 2.NBT.B.8, 2.MD.C.8 | **Daily Practice:** 2.MD.C.7 |

CLASSROOM ROUTINES: REVIEW AND PRACTICE

Today's Number: More or Less?

MATH FOCUS POINTS

○ Estimating the sum of two 2-digit numbers using known combinations, place value, and properties of operations

○ Using standard notation (<, >) to express the relationship between quantities

○ Generating equivalent expressions for a number

I'm going to display an addition problem. The sum is Today's Number. Today, before we figure out the exact answer, I want you to think about whether or not Today's Number is more or less than one dollar.

Review the equivalency of one dollar and 100 cents. Display the Teacher Presentation (or write 26¢ + 77¢ on the board).

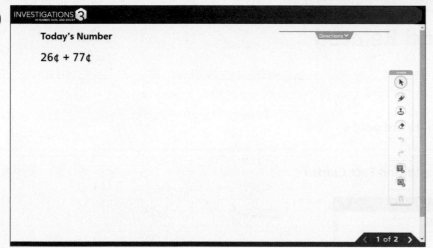

Students think about the problem individually, discuss their thinking with a partner, and then share strategies as a class.

What did you pay attention to when you were thinking about whether or not 26¢ + 77¢ was more or less than 100¢?

Listen for evidence that students' reasoning about the sum is based on what they know about money (e.g., "Four quarters make $1, and 26¢ is 1 quarter plus some more, and 77¢ is 3 quarters plus some more.") or place value (e.g., "There are 9 dimes and that's 90, but then there's enough pennies to make another dime." or "20 + 70 = 90, and 7 and 6 is more than 10.") Once students agree that the sum is greater than 100¢, determine the exact amount as a class. Use equations to record.

$$26¢ + 77¢ =$$
$$25¢ + 1¢ + 75¢ + 2¢ =$$
$$25¢ + 75¢ = 100¢$$
$$100¢ + 1¢ + 2¢ = 103¢$$

CLASSROOM ROUTINES: REVIEW AND PRACTICE

Finally, use symbols to compare Today's Number to 100¢:

$$103¢ > 100¢ \quad 100¢ < 103¢$$

Display 24¢ + 75¢ and repeat the above steps. Once again, students think on their own and then with a partner. Discuss students' strategies, which will likely include reasoning about quarters (e.g., "25¢ + 75¢ = 100¢ and 24¢ is smaller than a quarter"). Find the exact answer as a class, using equations to record, and then use notation to compare that number to 100¢.

If time permits, students generate equations for one of Today's Numbers: 103¢ or 99¢. Alternatively, they can work on Today's Number at some other point in the day or for homework.

1 ACTIVITY

The Remaining Addition Facts and Related Subtraction Facts

We are going to be looking at a new set of Fact Cards. There are only 6 addition facts in this set. **MWI1** **MWI2**

Display the Teacher Presentation (or use the 6 remaining addition Fact Cards.)

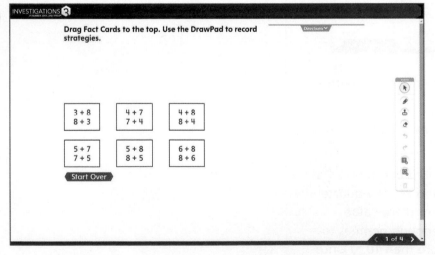

Some of you know some of these facts, and some of you have strategies for figuring them out quickly. Let's look at one. What would you tell someone who has a hard time with 6 + 8/8 + 6? **MPN**

MATH WORDS AND IDEAS

MWI1 Learning Addition Facts: Doubles Facts

MWI2 Learning Addition Facts: Make 10 Facts

MATH PRACTICE NOTE

MPN 🔍 **MP7 Look for and make use of structure.** When students use familiar facts to remember new facts, they are making use of structure. For example, to remember 8 + 6, they might think about ten: 8 + 2 = 10 and 4 more is 14. In this case, students are using the structure of tens as well as the decomposition of 6 into 2 + 4.

" STUDENTS MIGHT SAY "

"I try to make a 10. 6 + 4 is 10, and you can think of 8 as 4 and 4. 6 + 4 is 10 and 10 + 4 is 14."

"Doubles are easy for me. 6 + 6 is 12, and then there's still 2 more to add."

"If you break 6 into 2 + 4, you've got 8 + 2 + 4, and 10 + 4 is easy."

Build a tower of 6 cubes in one color, and a tower of 8 cubes in another color, and use them to model the strategies students share. **MPN**

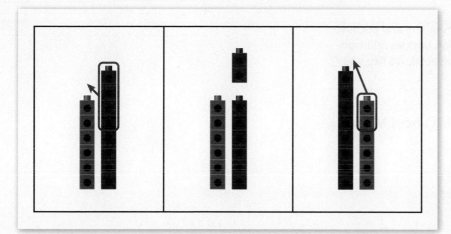

The Doubles Facts and Make 10 Facts are really useful, aren't they? That's why we worked on them early in the year, so they could help us with these harder facts.

There are some other facts in this set. They are subtraction facts, and they are related to the problems we just looked at. Let me show you an example. Here's a set of related facts.

6 + 8
8 + 6
Clue: _____

14 − 8
Clue: _____

14 − 6
Clue: _____

MATH PRACTICE NOTE

MPN **MP2 Reason abstractly and quantitatively.** Modeling strategies with cubes and other representations deepens students' understanding of the structures they and their classmates employ as they use familiar facts to help with harder facts.

These are 3 facts from the new cards that are related to each other. Talk with a partner about the answers to these problems, and how you think they are related. **MPN**

Call students back together, and ask what they notice about the three problems.

What did you and your partner think about how these cards were related?

Remind students that you already have a tower of 6 [blue] and 8 [red] cubes that they can use to explain their thinking, if they'd like.

" STUDENTS MIGHT SAY "

"If you know $6 + 8 = 14$, then $14 - 8$ would be 6 and $14 - 6$ would be 8. You can see it with the cubes. 14 is equal to one group of 8 and one group of 6. If you take away the 8, you're left with the 6. If you take away the 6, the 8 will be left."

"They're related because they have the same numbers and because subtraction and addition are related. Subtraction undoes addition. So if you add 8 to 6, you get 14. And if you subtract 8, it's like you undo it, and you're left with the 6."

Let's look at another one of the addition cards. Try to think about Making a 10 to help you remember this fact.

$$4 + 7$$
$$7 + 4$$

Clue: _____

" STUDENTS MIGHT SAY "

"$7 + 4$ is 1 more than $7 + 3$. $7 + 3 = 10$, so $7 + 4 = 11$."

"If you break 4 into $3 + 1$, you can do $7 + 3 = 10$, and 1 more is 11."

There are two subtraction cards in this set that are related to $4 + 7$ and $7 + 4$. Can you think of what problems might be on those cards? Talk to a partner.

Once students have had a chance to discuss this, display the two related subtraction cards, and again encourage students to try to articulate the relationship between the problems.

RESOURCE MASTERS, C59

Fact Cards: Set 6   (PAGE 1 OF 3)

NAME _____   DATE _____

$4 + 7$ $7 + 4$ Clue: _____	$3 + 8$ $8 + 3$ Clue: _____
$5 + 7$ $7 + 5$ Clue: _____	$4 + 8$ $8 + 4$ Clue: _____
$11 - 3$ Clue: _____	$5 + 8$ $8 + 5$ Clue: _____
$12 - 4$ Clue: _____	$6 + 8$ $8 + 6$ Clue: _____

C59   © Pearson Education 2

MATH PRACTICE NOTE

MPN **MP7 Look for and make use of structure.** Throughout the year, students have seen that some problems can be solved either by finding a missing addend or by subtracting, thus coming to recognize the relationship between addition and subtraction. The relationship between addition and subtraction comes into play again as students use addition facts to help with related subtraction facts.

Display the completed equations to support the conversation.

$$7 + 4 = \underline{11} \qquad 11 - 4 = \underline{7}$$
$$4 + 7 = \underline{11} \qquad 11 - 7 = \underline{4}$$

❝ STUDENTS MIGHT SAY ❞

"They're all about 11, 7, and 4."

"You get the big number when you put the two smaller numbers together. If you take one of the small numbers away from the big number, you get the other small number."

"7 + 4 = 11. So, if you have 11 and take away 4, the 7 is left. Or, you can take away the 7, and then the 4 is left."

Hand out a set of Fact Cards: Set 6 (C59–C61) to each student. Remind them *not* to write the answers on the cards and to label the back of each card with their initials.

Explain that going through the new set of cards will be a Math Workshop activity.

Before you figure out which facts you know and which you need to work on, work with a partner to see if you can find the related facts. See if you can explain to each other why they go together.

2 MATH WORKSHOP

Facts and How Many More to 100? How Much More to $1.00?

 25

Students choose among the following activities.

2 A Fact Fluency

Pairs look at the cards in Set 6 (C59–C61) and see if they can find groups of related facts and explain why they are related. Then, students determine which facts they know and which they are still working on.

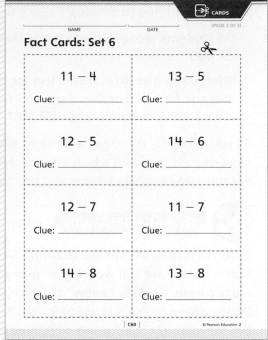

RESOURCE MASTERS, C60

Fact Cards: Set 6

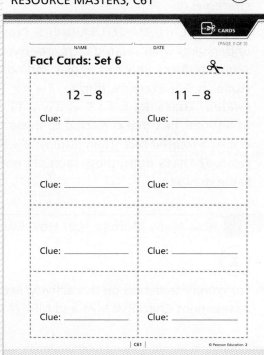

RESOURCE MASTERS, C61

Fact Cards: Set 6

ONGOING ASSESSMENT Observing Students at Work

Students continue to develop fluency with addition and subtraction within 20.

○ **Do students recognize which addition and subtraction facts are related?** 🔍 **MP7**

○ **What strategies do students use for problems they don't "just know"?** Do they use Make 10 or Doubles facts? Do they use addition facts they know to solve subtraction problems? 🔍 **MP7**

As you circulate, try to get a sense of which of the new problems are easy for most of your class and which are still challenging for most, in order to plan appropriate next experiences and practice.

 DIFFERENTIATION Supporting the Range of Learners

INTERVENTION Adapt the Learning Situation Work in a small group with students who are still working on many facts. Check first that students' sorts are accurate. Do they "know" the facts in their "Facts I Know" envelope? Do they have to use a strategy for the facts in their "Facts I Am Still Working On" envelope? Look for sets of related facts in the facts they're still working on, and do targeted work on those (e.g., connecting the Near Doubles to the Doubles), and work together to write clues that help students recreate such strategies.

ENGLISH LANGUAGE LEARNERS Provide Vocabulary Support Help students understand what *related facts* are. Two facts are *related* if they have the same numbers. Share examples and non-examples of *related facts* with students. For example, display: 3 + 9 = 12 and 12 − 9 = 3. Are these facts *related*? That's right, 3 + 9 = 12 and 12 − 9 = 3 are *related facts*. Can you think of another fact that is related to these two facts? That's right, 12 − 3 = 9 is also a *related fact*. Then display: 3 + 9 = 12 and 2 + 7 = 9. Are these facts *related*? That's right, these facts are *not related* because they do *not* have the same numbers.

---

2 B How Many More to 100? How Much More to $1.00?

For complete details on this activity, see Session 1.5. Continue to use **Assessment Checklist:** MP4 and MP7 (A38) in this activity.

---

2 C *Make a Dollar*

For complete details on this activity, see Sessions 1.4 and 1.5.

---

2 D *Capture 5*

For complete details on this activity, see Sessions 1.2 and 1.3.

ONLINE ASSESSMENT

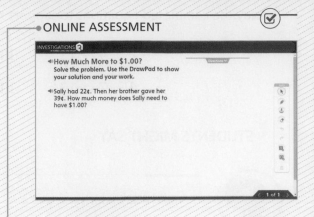

RESOURCE MASTERS, A39

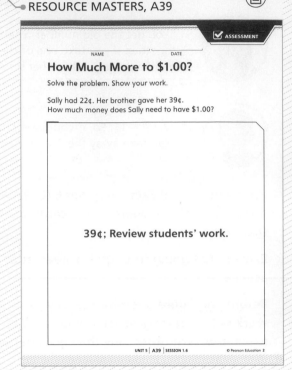

ASSESSMENT

NAME   DATE

How Much More to $1.00?

Solve the problem. Show your work.

Sally had 22¢. Her brother gave her 39¢. How much money does Sally need to have $1.00?

39¢; Review students' work.

UNIT 5 | A39 | SESSION 1.6   © Pearson Education 2

3 ASSESSMENT ACTIVITY

How Much More to $1.00?

Explain that students will work individually on a problem so that you can get a sense of how they have grown in their ability to solve such problems and show their work.

Display How Much More to $1.00? (A39 or the Online Assessment), and read it aloud. Explain that students should solve the problem and show their work and that you will reread the problem, as needed, as they work. **TN1** **TN2**

BENCHMARK	QUESTION
1: Solve a 2-step story problem that involves finding the difference between a 2-digit number and 100.	1

Depending on how students solve the problem, this task also provides information about Benchmark 5. Students are expected to add fluently within 100 by the end of this unit. Use students' work to gather information about the kinds of strategies students are using to add 2-digit numbers at this point in the unit.

ONGOING ASSESSMENT Observing Students at Work

Students solve a 2-step problem, and record their work. **PD**

○ **Can students make sense of the situation?** 🔍 **MP4**

○ **Can students solve the problem accurately?** What strategies do they use? Do they work numerically, breaking numbers apart, using facts and relationships they know? 🔍 **MP7**

○ **How do students record their strategies?** Do they use equations? Pictures? Words? A combination? Can you follow their thinking by looking at their written work? If asked to explain their thinking, does it match their oral explanation?

SESSION FOLLOW-UP: REVIEW AND PRACTICE

Daily Practice

 DAILY PRACTICE For ongoing review, students complete *Student Activity Book* page 313.

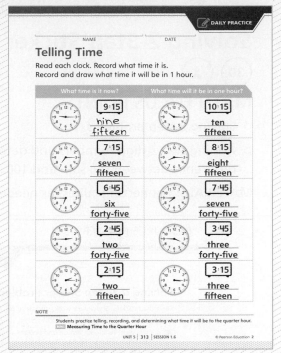

TEACHING NOTES

TN1 **Assessing Students' Use of the Number Line** This problem also provides an opportunity to see whether and how students are making use of the number line as a tool for representing, solving, and/or recording strategies for solving problems involving addition and subtraction.

TN2 **Assessing Students' Ability to Explain Their Strategy** This problem also provides an opportunity to observe students' growing ability to explain their strategies for solving addition and subtraction problems. Note whether students' strategies rely on place value and/or properties of operations (e.g., thinking $20 + 30 = 50$, and $50 + 11 = 61$ to add 22 and 39 or adding 40 and subtracting 1 to find the difference between 61 and 100).

PROFESSIONAL DEVELOPMENT

PD TEACHER NOTE 6: Assessment: How Much More to $1.00?

Solving 2-Step Sticker Problems

MATH FOCUS POINTS

○ Solving 2-step problems

○ Adding two 2-digit numbers and determining the difference between the sum and 100

MATERIALS: Connecting cubes (as needed), T43, T44, S61

RESOURCE MASTERS, S61

ACTIVITY

NAME   DATE

Solving a 2-Step Sticker Problem

Solve the problem. Show your work, and write an equation for each part of the problem.

1 **a.** Sally went to Sticker Station and bought 28 soccer stickers. The next day, she bought 26 more soccer stickers. How many soccer stickers does Sally have?

54 stickers; Review students' work.

b. How many more soccer stickers does Sally need to have 100 soccer stickers?

46 stickers; Review students' work.

UNIT 5 | S61 | INVESTIGATION 1   © Pearson Education 2

Display and read the following problem: Jake went to Sticker Station and bought 25 moon stickers and 17 sun stickers. How many stickers did he buy? Ask students to help you represent the problem with sticker notation and record an equation. Connect the information in the problem to both.

STUDENTS MIGHT SAY

 "We could add the strips first and then the singles."

 "We could start with the 25 stickers and then add the 10 and then the 7 from the 17."

Have students solve the problem using cubes or paper stickers if needed. Briefly discuss their strategies. As students share, model ways to notate them and relate each step using the cube model.

$$20 + 10 = 30 \qquad 25 + 10 = 35$$
$$5 + 7 = 12 \qquad 35 + 7 = 42$$
$$30 + 10 = 40$$
$$40 + 2 = 42$$

Where is the 20 from? The 10? What does 5 + 7 = 12 represent? How did [Gregory] add on the 12? Where do you see the 25 stickers? Where do you see the 17 stickers?

Jake put the 42 moon stickers he got on a sticker book page. What did the page in his sticker book look like? Distribute a copy of T43 to each student, and have them shade in 42. Display and shade in one grid. Draw a border around the part showing 42 and label it.

Jake's goal is to have 100 moon stickers. What part of the grid shows how many stickers he has? What part shows how many stickers he wants and how many he needs?

Connect each question to the grid, have students help you write an equation for the problem (42 + __ = 100), and, again, connect the parts of the equation to the grid.

Students solve the problem and discuss strategies. Connect each strategy to the grid. Encourage students to use combinations of 10 to think about how many stickers are needed to complete the row of 10 (i.e., 42 + 8 = 50). Distribute copies of Solving a 2-Step Sticker Problem (S61).

DIFFERENTIATION

ENGLISH LANGUAGE LEARNERS Partner Talk Before discussing as a class, have partners explain their strategies to each other. Encourage students to use models (e.g., cubes or the grid) to act out their strategies and show the connection to the equation. Provide a word list with the terms *tens, ones, strips,* and *singles,* which students can use to explain their thinking.

ADDITIONAL RESOURCES

Math Words and Ideas Story Problems with One Addend Unknown

Problems about 100: Representing Strategies on the Number Line

 (25) (👤)

MATH FOCUS POINTS

○ Solving 2-step problems

○ Adding two 2-digit numbers and determining the difference between the sum and 100

MATERIALS: paper (1 sheet per student), S62–S63

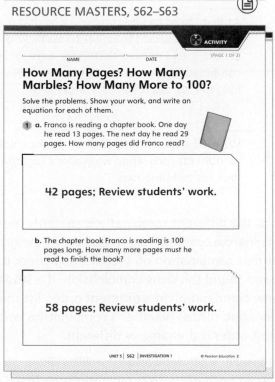

RESOURCE MASTERS, S62–S63

ACTIVITY
(PAGE 1 OF 2)

How Many Pages? How Many Marbles? How Many More to 100?

Solve the problems. Show your work, and write an equation for each of them.

1 a. Franco is reading a chapter book. One day he read 13 pages. The next day he read 29 pages. How many pages did Franco read?

42 pages; Review students' work.

b. The chapter book Franco is reading is 100 pages long. How many more pages must he read to finish the book?

58 pages; Review students' work.

UNIT 5 | S62 | INVESTIGATION 1   © Pearson Education 2

Display and read the following problem: Kira is reading a chapter book. On Monday she read 37 pages. On Tuesday she read 35 pages. How many pages did Kira read on Monday and Tuesday?

Ask students to help you write an equation. Distribute blank paper, and have students record the equation and then solve the problem. As students work, note the strategies they are using. Select one student who added tens and ones, and one student who added one number on in parts to share their strategies. Write equations to show the steps for each strategy.

Add Tens and Ones	Add One Number in Parts
37 + 35 =	37 + 35 =
30 + 30 = 60	37 + 30 = 67
7 + 5 = 12	67 + 5 = 72
60 + 12 = 72	

Then display the following problem: The chapter book Kira is reading is 100 pages long. How many more pages must she read to finish the book?

Ask students to help you write an equation and then solve the problem. Encourage students to show their work using equations.

When students are finished, bring them together to discuss their solutions. As students share, use the number line to represent each strategy. **How did you figure out how many more pages Kira needs to read to finish her book?**

❝ STUDENTS MIGHT SAY ❞

"I know that 72 + 8 is 80. 80 + 20 is 100. She needs to read 28 more pages in all."

"I sort of did the same but I counted up 72, 82, 92, that's 20. Then I know it's 8 more because 2 + 8 is 10."

Where do you see the number of pages Kira had left to read on these number lines? Where do you see the total number of pages? Why did I start on 72?

Distribute copies of How Many Pages? How Many Marbles? How Many More to 100? (S62–S63) to students. Encourage students to use a number line to show how they solved the problem.

DIFFERENTIATION

ENGLISH LANGUAGE LEARNERS Provide a Sequence If students are unable to explain their strategies verbally, encourage them to use the number line to communicate how they solved the problem. As they demonstrate each step, use simple language to describe it. Then pause so students can repeat after you or restate it in their own words using the sequence: *First, I _____. Next, I _____. Then, I _____.*

ADDITIONAL RESOURCES

Math Words and Ideas Story Problems with One Addend Unknown (MWI)

Make 2 or More Dollars

  25

MATH FOCUS POINTS

○ Recognizing and using coin equivalencies

○ Finding combinations of coins that equal $1.00.

MATERIALS: *Make a Dollar* Cards (1 deck per pair and 1 for demonstration), S64

RESOURCE MASTERS, S64

Students play *Make 2 or More Dollars*, a variation of *Make a Dollar* in which they work together to make combinations of *Make a Dollar* Cards that equal any whole dollar amount.

Display 8 *Make a Dollar* Cards, and model a round.

Look at our *Make a Dollar* Cards, and think about which of these 8 cards we could take. Do you see a combination of cards that equals a dollar? Two dollars? Three dollars?

 **STUDENTS MIGHT SAY**

"I see 4 cards that equal $2: 60¢ + 60¢ = 120¢, and 50¢ + 30¢ = 80¢. 80¢ + 120¢ = 200¢, which is $2."

"If you add the cards with 55¢, 45¢, and 60¢, 60¢, 50¢ and 30¢, you will have a combination that makes $3!"

Model how to record the moves students suggest on a copy of the *Make 2 or More Dollars* Recording Sheet (S64). Then replace the cards used, and play one more round together as a group.

Have pairs of students play *Make 2 or More Dollars*. Call students together at the end of the game to discuss the strategies they used as they played. **What strategies did you use to find combinations of cards worth $2 or more?**

 STUDENTS MIGHT SAY

"At first I tried to find combinations that made $1 that I could add together to make $2 or $3. But then I noticed that there were lots of combinations that made $2 like 50¢ + 70¢ + 80¢, so I started to look for those too."

"We used stick-on notes and wrote the total amount on each. Then we worked together to look for combinations."

Record all of the different combinations students found. As students share a combination, ask others in the group to look for that combination on their list and check it off if they too found the same combination. If a student has the same combination in a different order, list both combinations and discuss whether a combination written in a different order is the same or different.

We have 90 + 10 + 50 + 50 and 10 + 50 + 90 + 50 on our list. Should both of these combinations be listed or just one of them? Why or why not?

DIFFERENTIATION

ENGLISH LANGUAGE LEARNERS **Provide Sentence Stems**
Students may be able to find combinations of coins worth $2 or more, but they may need support to explain their strategies.

1. *First, I used _____ to make _____.*
2. *Next, I added _____ to make _____.*
3. *Then, I added _____ to make a total of _____.*

ADDITIONAL RESOURCES

Math Words and Ideas Coin Values and Equivalencies

INVESTIGATION 2

ADDING WITHIN 100 AND COUNTING TO 1,000

Main Math Ideas

o Understanding, representing, and solving problems involving addition and subtraction

o Understanding place value

o Using knowledge of place value to add and subtract

o Understanding and extending the counting sequence

Adding within 100 and Counting to 1,000

	SESSION 2.1	SESSION 2.2
	CLOSE TO 100 Students generate the two-addend combinations of 10 and the related combinations of 100 and think about the relationship between them. They use knowledge of place value and known combinations of sums of 100 (20 + 80, 25 + 75, 50 + 50, etc.) to find pairs of 2-digit numbers that add to 100 or close to 100.	**NUMBERS TO 1,000** Students are introduced to a 1,000 Book made of 200 charts and use it to play *Guess My Number*. Math Workshop continues, and discussion focuses on *Close to 100*.
Professional Development		**TEACHER NOTE 1** **DIALOGUE BOX 4**
Materials to View Ahead of Time	**TEACHER PRESENTATION:** 🎛 **Activity** Introducing *Close to 100* ⊙ **DIFFERENTIATION: ENGLISH LANGUAGE LEARNERS** See **Differentiation in This Unit** for session content to preview with students.	**TEACHER PRESENTATIONS:** 🎛 **Classroom Routine** *Quick Images: Stickers* 🎛 **Activity** Introducing the 1,000 Book 🎛 **Discussion** Strategies for *Close to 100* ⊙ **DIFFERENTIATION: ENGLISH LANGUAGE LEARNERS** See **Differentiation in This Unit** for session content to preview with students.
Materials to Gather	**Students' envelopes of "Facts I Know" and "Facts I Am Still Working On"** (from Session 1.6) **Connecting cubes or number line** 🔧 **Connecting cubes in towers of 10** (10 towers of 10 per pair) **Digit Cards, with Wild Cards removed** (1 deck per pair; from Unit 3)	**Wipe-off markers in light colors** (optional; 1 per student, if 1,000 Books are laminated) **Blank paper** (2 sheets per pair) **Materials for *Close to 100*** (from Session 2.1) **Materials for *Make a Dollar*** (from Sessions 1.4 and 1.5) **Digit Cards** (from Session 2.1; optional for display) 🔧 **Connecting cubes** (8 towers of 10 cubes in one color; 2 towers of 10 cubes in another color; optional; for display)
Materials to Prepare	**Chart: "Ways to Make 100"** Title a piece of chart paper "Ways to Make 100." 📄 **G36, *Close to 100* Recording Sheet** Make copies. (1 per student) 📄 **G37, *Close to 100* Directions** Make copies. 📄 **T43, 100 Grids** Make copies. (optional; for the Intervention)	**Envelope of stickers** (from Session 1.2) with at least 10 sheets of 100 made from T25 (optional) **1,000 Book** Copy T21 and T45–T48 on card stock if available, and laminate if possible. Staple together to make one book. (1 per student; 1 for display) 📄 **G38, *Guess My Number* Directions** Make copies.
Common Core State Standards	**Classroom Routines:** 2.OA.B.2 **Session:** 2.OA.B.2, 2.NBT.B.5 **Daily Practice:** 2.NBT.B.5	**Classroom Routines:** 2.NBT.A.1b, 2.NBT.A.2 **Session:** 2.NBT.A.2, 2.NBT.A.3, 2.NBT.A.4, 2.NBT.B.5, 2.NBT.B.9, 2.MD.C.8 **Daily Practice:** 2.NBT.B.5

	SESSION 2.3	SESSION 2.4
	STICKERS: HUNDREDS, TENS, AND ONES Students consider the composition of 3-digit numbers as hundreds, tens, and ones. Math Workshop continues with a new activity: using sticker notation and expanded form to represent a range of 3-digit numbers. Discussion focuses on the place value of 3-digit numbers.	**PLUS OR MINUS 10 OR 100** Students learn and play *Plus or Minus 10 or 100*. Math Workshop continues, and discussion focuses on strategies for playing *Close to 100*.
Professional Development	TEACHER NOTE 5	TEACHER NOTE 1 DIALOGUE BOX 4
Materials to View Ahead of Time	TEACHER PRESENTATIONS: **Activity** How Many Stickers: Hundreds, Tens, Ones? **Discussion** Equations for Three-Digit Numbers	TEACHER PRESENTATIONS: **Classroom Routine** *Today's Number: What Could It Be?* **Activity** Introducing *Plus or Minus 10 or 100* **Discussion** *Close to 100:* Strategies
Materials to Gather	**Connecting cubes** (4 bins) **Chart: "How Many Pockets?"** (from Unit 4) **Blank paper** (1 sheet per student) **Materials for *Guess My Number*** (from Session 2.2) **Materials for *Close to 100*** (from Session 2.1) **Materials for *Capture 5*** (from Sessions 1.2 and 1.3) **1,000 Books and counters that fit on those squares** (optional; for the Extension)	**Digit Cards** (optional, from Session 2.1) **Blank paper** (1 sheet per student) **1,000 Books** (1 per student) **Materials for *Guess My Number*** (from Session 2.2) **Materials for *Close to 100*** (from Session 2.1) **Materials for *Capture 5*** (from Sessions 1.2 and 2.3) **Connecting Cubes** (as needed)
Materials to Prepare	**Envelopes of stickers** (from Session 2.2; optional) **S65, How Many Stickers?** Make copies. (optional; as needed for the Intervention; 1 for display)	**G39, *Plus or Minus 10 or 100* Recording Sheet** Make copies. (1 per student per game) **G40, *Plus or Minus 10 or 100* Directions** Make copies. **+/−10 or 100 Number Cubes** (1 per pair) Label sides of number cubes "+10," "+10," "−10," "−10," "+100," "−100." **+/−10 Number Cubes** (optional; for the Intervention) Label 3 sides "+10" and 3 sides "−10." **+/−100 Number Cubes** (optional; for the Intervention) Label 3 sides "+100" and 3 sides "−100." **S65, How Many Stickers?** Make copies. (optional; for the Intervention)
Common Core State Standards	**Classroom Routines:** 2.OA.B.2, 2.NBT.B.5, 2.NBT.B.6 **Session:** 2.NBT.A.1, 2.NBT.A.1b, 2.NBT.A.3, 2.NBT.A.4, 2.NBT.B.5, 2.NBT.B.8 **Daily Practice:** 2.NBT.A.3, 2.NBT.A.4	**Classroom Routine:** 2.NBT.A.1, 2.NBT.A.3, 2.NBT.A.4, 2.NBT.B.5; **Session:** 2.NBT.A.1, 2.NBT.A.1b, 2.NBT.A.3, 2.NBT.A.4, 2.NBT.B.5, 2.NBT.B.8, 2.NBT.B.9 **Daily Practice:** 2.NBT.A.1, 2.NBT.A.3

Adding within 100 and Counting to 1,000

	SESSION 2.5	SESSION 2.6
	WHAT DO YOU KNOW ABOUT 345? Students discuss what they are learning about adding and subtracting 10 and 100 from numbers to 1,000. Math Workshop continues, and discussion focuses on the place value of 3-digit numbers.	**TEN HUNDREDS MAKE ONE THOUSAND** Students complete a brief assessment, and then Math Workshop continues. Discussion focuses on the relationship between 1, 10, 100, and 1,000.
Professional Development		
Materials to View Ahead of Time	**TEACHER PRESENTATIONS:** 🔲 **Classroom Routine** *Today's Number: What Could It Be?* 🔲 **Activity** Adding and Subtracting 10 or 100 🔲 **Discussion** What Do You Know about 345?	**TEACHER PRESENTATIONS:** 🔲 **Classroom Routine** *Today's Number: What Could It Be?* 🔲 **Discussion** Ten Hundreds Make One Thousand
Materials to Gather	**Digit Cards** (optional, from Unit 3) **Blank paper** (1 sheet per student) **1,000 Books** (1 per student) **Materials for *Plus or Minus 10 or 100*** (from Session 2.4) **Materials for *Guess My Number*** (from Session 2.2) **Materials for *Close to 100*** (from Session 2.1)	**Digit Cards** (optional, from Unit 3) **Blank paper** (1 sheet per student) **Materials for *Plus or Minus 10 or 100*** (from Sessions 2.4 and 2.5) **Materials for *Guess My Number*** (from Session 2.2) **Materials for *Close to 100*** (from Session 2.1) **Envelope of stickers** (from Session 2.2) **with at least 10 sheets of 100.**
Materials to Prepare	📄 **S66, Find the Number (Blank)** Make copies. (as needed; optional; for the Intervention; 1 for display) 📄 **S67–S68, Find the Number: Multiples of 10 and 100** Make copies. (optional; for the Extension) **+ / − multiples of 10 and 100 Number Cubes** (optional; for the Extension) Label number cubes with multiples of 10 and 100, such as "+ 20," "− 20," "+ 200," "− 200," etc.	☑ 📄 **A40, Quiz 1** Make copies. (1 per student) 📄 **S66, Find the Number (Blank)** Make copies. (optional; for the Extension)
Common Core State Standards	**Classroom Routines:** 2.NBT.A.1, 2.NBT.A.3, 2.NBT.A.4, 2.NBT.B.5 **Session:** 2.NBT.A.1, 2.NBT.A.3, 2.NBT.A.4, 2.NBT.B.5, 2.NBT.B.8 **Daily Practice:** 2.NBT.A.3, 2.NBT.B.8	**Classroom Routines:** 2.NBT.A.1, 2.NBT.A.3, 2.NBT.A.4, 2.NBT.B.5 **Session:** 2.NBT.A.1, 2.NBT.A.1a, 2.NBT.A.1b, 2.NBT.A.2, 2.NBT.A.3, 2.NBT.B.5, 2.NBT.B.8 **Daily Practice:** 2.NBT.A.1, 2.NBT.A.3, 2.NBT.A.4, 2.NBT.B.5

Close to 100

MATH FOCUS POINTS

o Relating the single-digit combinations of 10 (e.g., 8 + 2) to multiple of 10 combinations of 100 (e.g., 80 + 20)

o Using knowledge of place value to find pairs of 2-digit numbers that add to 100 or a number close to 100

o Finding the difference between a 2- or 3-digit number and 100

VOCABULARY

o Make-10 combinations

o combinations that make 100

TODAY'S PLAN

MATERIALS

  CLASSROOM ROUTINE: REVIEW AND PRACTICE
(10) Class
Fact Fluency

 Student Activity Book, p. 314

Students' envelopes of "Facts I Know" and "Facts I Am Still Working On" (from Session 1.6)

Connecting cubes or number line

---

(15) Class **1 ACTIVITY**
Combinations That Make 10 and 100

Chart: "Ways to Make 100"*

 Connecting cubes (10 towers of 10 per pair)

---

(15) Class **2 ACTIVITY**
Introducing *Close to 100*

 Close to 100 (or use one set of game materials (see Activity 3))

---

(30) Pairs **3 ACTIVITY**
Playing *Close to 100*

 G36–G37*

 T43* (optional; for the Intervention)

Digit Cards, with Wild Cards removed (1 deck per pair; from Unit 3)

Connecting cubes in towers of 10 (optional; for the Intervention)

SESSION FOLLOW-UP: REVIEW AND PRACTICE
Daily Practice and Homework

Student Activity Book, pp. 314 (from the Classroom Routine), 315

---

* See *Materials to Prepare* in the Investigation 2 Planner.

Common Core State Standards	Classroom Routines: 2.OA.B.2 Session: 2.OA.B.2, 2.NBT.B.5	Daily Practice: 2.NBT.B.5

CLASSROOM ROUTINE: REVIEW AND PRACTICE

Fact Fluency

MATH FOCUS POINTS

○ Relating unknown facts to known ones (e.g., $8 + 6 = 8 + 2 + 4$ or using $8 + 6 = 14$ to solve $14 - 8$)

○ Developing fluency with addition and subtraction within 20

Students review the cards in their "Facts I Am Still Working On" envelope. Ask them to choose six they are finding difficult to remember and record them on *Student Activity Book* page 314. **Let's think about how to write a clue to help with facts that you're finding challenging. Here's one I saw on several people's sheets. What could help someone remember this fact?**

$$13 - 8$$

Clue: _____

"I counted back, but it's not so quick. [Esteban] said what if you jump to 10 first. So I did $13 - 3$, and that's easy, it's 10. And then I figured out that I have to subtract 5 more, and that's easy too! $10 - 5 = 5$."

"$8 + 5$ is one I just know. If you know $8 + 5 = 13$, then you know $13 - 8 = 5$."

Model students' strategies with cubes or on the number line, and model ways to record them concisely on a Fact Card (e.g., $13 - 3 - 5$; $8 + 5 = 13$). Then set students to work writing clues for the facts they recorded on *Student Activity Book* page 314. Encourage partners to share strategies for finding and remembering the answers. Explain that students will be practicing these facts for homework tonight.

STUDENT ACTIVITY BOOK, P. 314

ACTIVITY

NAME _____ DATE _____

Practicing the Facts

Choose 6 facts that are hard for you to remember. Write them on the blank cards.

| 13 ⊟ 6 = 7 |
| Clue: 12 - 6 = 6 |

Use something you know to write a clue. Practice these with someone at home.

Answers will vary.

____ ☐ ____ = ____	____ ☐ ____ = ____
Clue: _____	Clue: _____
____ ☐ ____ = ____	____ ☐ ____ = ____
Clue: _____	Clue: _____
____ ☐ ____ = ____	____ ☐ ____ = ____
Clue: _____	Clue: _____

UNIT 5 | **314** | SESSION 2.1   © Pearson Education 2

1 ACTIVITY

Combinations That Make 10 and 100

Ask students to help you list the two-addend combinations of 10, in order, on the "Ways to Make 100" chart.

Ways to Make 100	
Ways to Make 10	Ways to Make 100
0 + 10	
1 + 9	
2 + 8	
3 + 7	
4 + 6	
5 + 5	
6 + 4	
7 + 3	
8 + 2	
9 + 1	
10 + 0	

Then, distribute 10 towers of 10 cubes to each pair.

How can you use these Make-10 combinations **to find** combinations that make 100**? For example, how does knowing that 1 + 9 = 10 help you figure out what to add to 10 to make 100? (Write 10 + __ = 100.) Work with your partner to show this with cubes.**

Ask a pair or two to demonstrate their thinking.

" STUDENTS MIGHT SAY "

"We had 100 cubes. We pulled one tower aside, and that's 10. That leaves 9 over here, and 9 tens are 90."

"We started with 10. Then we kept adding 10s: 20, 30, 40, 50, 60, 70, 80, 90, 100. So 10 (gesturing over the single tower) + 90 (gesturing over the 9 towers) = 100."

So we agree that 10 plus 90 equals 100. Work with your partner to find equations that relate to the other combinations that make 10.

Give students a few minutes to work on this. As students share combinations, ask them to model with cubes and explain how they know that they have 100. Record the combinations in order next to the Make-10 combinations.

Ways to Make 100	
Ways to Make 10	Ways to Make 100
0 + 10	0 + 100
1 + 9	10 + 90
2 + 8	20 + 80
3 + 7	30 + 70
4 + 6	40 + 60
5 + 5	50 + 50
6 + 4	60 + 40
7 + 3	70 + 30
8 + 2	80 + 20
9 + 1	90 + 10
10 + 0	100 + 0

What patterns do you notice on our chart?

Students will notice a variety of patterns. Many notice that the tens digits of the combinations that make 100 are the same as the ones digits of the combinations that make 10 (i.e., 1 plus 9 equals 10, and 10 plus 90 equals 100; 2 plus 8 equals 10, and 20 plus 80 equals 100; and so on). Focus the discussion on this observation, encouraging students to describe that pattern and why they think it happens. **MPN1** **MWI**

People are noticing something about the combination that makes 10 and the combination that makes 100 that's in the same row. Let's look at one row. What's the same about 8 + 2 = 10 and 80 + 20 = 100? What's different?

Listen for, highlight, and illustrate the idea that, in the combinations that make 100, the digits that represent groups of ten represent ones in the combinations that make 10. **MPN2**

❝ STUDENTS MIGHT SAY ❞

"8 plus 2 equals 10, so 8 tens plus 2 tens equal 10 tens, and 10 tens equal 100. Anytime you make 10 tens, you make 100."

"If you think about the cubes, you can sort of see it. 8 + 2 = 10 is 8 cubes plus 2 more cubes, and that makes 10 cubes. And then, it's sort of the same, but it's 8 *towers* of cubes plus 2 *towers* of cubes, and that makes 10 *towers*. 8 towers is 80, 2 towers is 20, and 10 towers is 100. 80 + 20 = 100."

MATH PRACTICE NOTES

MPN1 **MP8 Look for and express regularity in repeated reasoning.** Students may notice a pattern when moving from one row to the next (e.g., 10 + 90 and 20 + 80). This is related to an idea many students use in single-digit addition: if you take 1 from one of the addends and give it to the other addend, the sum remains the same. In this case, students think about moving one tower of 10. "If you take one from the 9 and give it to the 1, you get 2 + 8. Nothing changes. It's still 10. It's the same with the tens. If you take ten from the 90 and give it to the 10, you get 20 + 80. You are just moving around the groups of 10."

MPN2 🔍 **MP7 Look for and make use of structure.** Students recognize that those structures they have used when operating with ones also apply when they are operating with tens. Later they will discover that they also apply when operating with hundreds, thousands, ten thousands, etc. This is one aspect of the power of the base-10 place value system.

MATH WORDS AND IDEAS

MWI Ways to Make 100

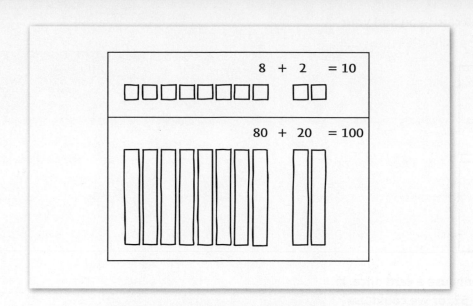

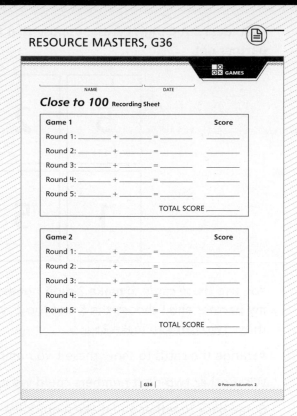

RESOURCE MASTERS, G36

2 ACTIVITY

Introducing *Close to 100*

We're going to learn a new game called *Close to 100*. The chart we just made may help you while you play.

Display the Game Presentation (or use a deck of Digit Cards with the Wild Cards removed and a Recording Sheet (G36)). Explain that this game is played cooperatively with a partner.

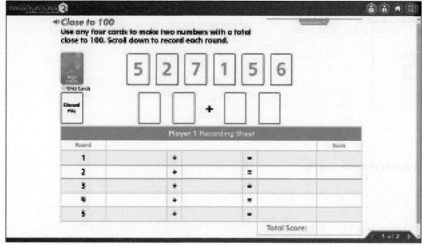

First, deal out 6 Digit Cards. Suppose that these are the 6 cards you and your partner get.

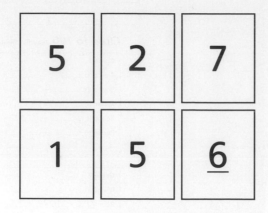

You use these cards to make 2-digit numbers. You can only use a card once. If my partner and I choose the 5 and the 2 we could make 52, or we could use those two cards to make 25.

Arrange the cards to show these two numbers. Then, put them back.

What other two-digit numbers could we make? Talk to a partner.

Come back together and make a quick list of some of the 2-digit numbers that can be made using the cards.

The goal of this game is to make two 2-digit numbers that add to as close to 100 as possible. Suppose I used 7 and 5 to make 75. How much more would I need to make 100?

Once the group agrees that 25 would combine with 75 to make 100, ask students if 25 can be made from the set of cards. Demonstrate how to organize the cards to show 75 and 25, and record an equation: 75 + 25 = 100.

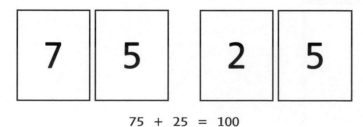

75 + 25 = 100

For the next round, we discard those cards and replace them with 4 new cards.

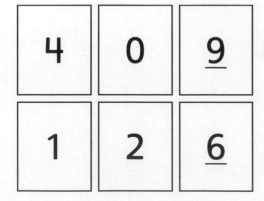

Ask partners to talk about a pair of numbers they can make that combine to 100.

See if you can make two 2-digit numbers that add to 100, or to a number really close to 100. Our chart "Ways to Make 100" might help.

After a few minutes, ask pairs to share their thinking and how they found their total. Use equations to record possible combinations, noting how different combinations can result in the same total.

$40 + 61 = 101$	$90 + 12 = 102$	$60 + 41 = 101$
$49 + 60 = 109$	$92 + 10 = 102$	$69 + 24 = 93$

Students may suggest a two-digit plus a single-digit number (e.g., $96 + 4$). Explain that, because you have to use four cards on each turn, a player must have a zero to play this combination (e.g., $96 + 04$). Add this combination to the list of possibilities.

You found a lot of combinations that got us really close to 100. That means it's probably a good strategy to try lots of different combinations when you play.

End the introduction by showing students how to record and score a round.

When you and your partner find a combination of numbers that totals 100 or close to 100, you both record that combination on the Recording Sheet.

Demonstrate how to record on G36, *Close to 100* Recording Sheet using one or several of the generated equations.

When you play *Close to 100*, your score for each round is the difference between your number and 100, or how far your answer is from 100. What would be the score for this combination? In other words, how far from 100 is this sum?

$40 + 61 = 101$	Score: 1
$49 + 60 = 109$	Score: 9
$96 + 04 = 100$	Score: 0

In this game, your goal is to get the *lowest* score. A low score means you were close to 100. So, if you were thinking about all of these equations, the one that equals 100 is the best choice.

Game 1				Score
Round 1: __9 6__ + __0 4__ = __100__				__0__

Play another round or two, as needed, until students understand how to play.

Highlight the following rules as you play:

○ After each round, discard the 4 cards used, and replace them with new cards. (You always start a new round with 6 cards.)

○ You must use exactly 4 cards. For example, students cannot use 93 + 7 unless they have a 0 and can make 93 + 07.

○ After five rounds, students total their score.

---

3 ACTIVITY

Playing *Close to 100*

Pairs play *Close to 100*, working together to make two 2-digit numbers that sum as close as possible to 100. Each pair needs a deck of Digit Cards with the Wild Cards removed. Both students record each round on G36. The directions are available on G37.

ONGOING ASSESSMENT Observing Students at Work

Students make two 2-digit numbers that sum as close as possible to 100.

○ **How do students play?** Do they try combinations randomly? Do they use known combinations of 100 (e.g., 50 + 50 or 30 + 70) and adjust as needed? Do they make one number and then think about how much more they need to get to 100? Do they think about what the number in the tens place of each number will sum to? 🔍 **MP7**

Students add 2-digit numbers as they play *Close to 100*.

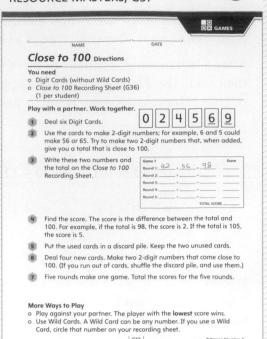

Circulate as students play, clarifying the rules of the game and helping students take turns and record rounds. Particularly in this first opportunity to play, most students are focused on learning how to play the game; strategic play comes later.

 DIFFERENTIATION Supporting the Range of Learners

INTERVENTION **Adapt the Learning Situation** Play in a small group with students you know will need more support. Make a 2-digit number that you know can be paired with another to get close to 100. Ask what number the student could make to add to yours to get to 100, and then ask if they can make that number with their set of cards. If they cannot, ask if they can make a number that is close. Provide a set of 100 cubes, as in Activity 1, that students can use to model the situation. They can also use a 100 Grid on T43, shading in the first number and determining the difference between it and 100.

INTERVENTION **Scaffold a Solution** Some students find it confusing to work with Digit Cards, where the number (e.g., 52) is made up of two separate cards (a 5 and a 2). These students might benefit from first making several 2-digit numbers with the cards, identifying each number, recording it on paper and, for some, building it with cubes. Providing a template similar to the recording sheet (e.g., _____ _____ + _____ _____) in which students can place the cards and then view them as 2-digit numbers may also help.

ENGLISH LANGUAGE LEARNERS **Model Thinking Aloud** Play a few rounds of the game with students to model how to play and use the vocabulary. Point to the cards. **I got [2, 5, 1, 7, 3, 8]. If I make [83], which number can I use in the *tens* place in my other number so the sum is as close to 100 as possible?** Continue the process for the *ones* place.

SESSION FOLLOW-UP: REVIEW AND PRACTICE

Daily Practice and Homework

✎ **DAILY PRACTICE** For reinforcement of this unit's content, students complete *Student Activity Book* page 315.

✎ **HOMEWORK** Students practice the facts they recorded on *Student Activity Book* page 314 with someone at home.

STUDENT ACTIVITY BOOK, P. 315

DAILY PRACTICE

NAME _____ DATE _____

Today's Number: 100
Today's Number is 100.

$$40 + 60 = 100$$
$$40 + 30 + 30 = 100$$
$$105 - 5 = 100$$

1 Show different ways to make Today's Number. Use addition and subtraction.

Answers will vary.

2 Write the number word for 100.
one hundred

NOTE
Students write equations that equal Today's Number. There are many possible solutions.
Equations and Equivalent Expressions

UNIT 5 | 315 | SESSION 2.1   © Pearson Education 2

SESSION 2.2

Numbers to 1,000

MATH FOCUS POINTS

- Reasoning about the magnitude of and relationship between 2- and 3-digit numbers
- Using standard notation ($>$, $<$) to express the relationship between two quantities
- Using knowledge of place value to find pairs of 2-digit numbers that add to 100 or a number close to 100
- Using known pairs of 2-digit numbers that add to 100 to find related pairs that add to 100 or a number close to 100 (for example: $80 + 20 = 100$, so $79 + 21 = 100$)
- Finding combinations of coins that equal $1.00

VOCABULARY

- 1-digit number
- 2-digit number
- 3-digit number

TODAY'S PLAN	MATERIALS
(10) **Class** **CLASSROOM ROUTINES: REVIEW AND PRACTICE** ***Quick Images: Stickers***	Teacher Presentation (or envelope of stickers with at least 10 sheets of 100 made from T25*)
(20) **Class** **1 ACTIVITY** **Introducing the 1,000 Book**	Teacher Presentation (or use T21) 1,000 Book* Wipe-off markers in light colors (optional; 1 per student)
(25) **2 MATH WORKSHOP** **Combinations of 100 and a Dollar** **2A** *Guess My Number* **2B** *Close to 100* **2C** *Make a Dollar*	**2A** 1,000 Book (1 per student) Blank paper (2 sheets per pair) G38* **2B** Materials from Session 2.1 **2C** Materials from Sessions 1.4 and 1.5
(15) **Class** **3 DISCUSSION** **Strategies for *Close to 100***	Teacher Presentation (or use Digit Cards and 8 towers of 10 cubes in one color and 2 towers of 10 in another color)
SESSION FOLLOW-UP: REVIEW AND PRACTICE **Daily Practice**	Student Activity Book, p. 316

* See *Materials to Prepare* in the Investigation 2 Planner.

Common Core State Standards	Classroom Routines: 2.NBT.A.1b, 2.NBT.A.2 Session: 2.NBT.A.2, 2.NBT.A.3, 2.NBT.A.4, 2.NBT.B.5, 2.NBT.B.9, 2.MD.C.8	Daily Practice: 2.NBT.B.5

CLASSROOM ROUTINES: REVIEW AND PRACTICE

Quick Images: Stickers

MATH FOCUS POINTS

○ Determining the quantity represented by a given number of hundreds

○ Using an equation to represent a 3-digit multiple of 100 as the sum of hundreds (e.g., 300 = 100 + 100 + 100)

Display the Teacher Presentation (or use an envelope of stickers, with at least 10 sheets of 100, from Investigation 1).

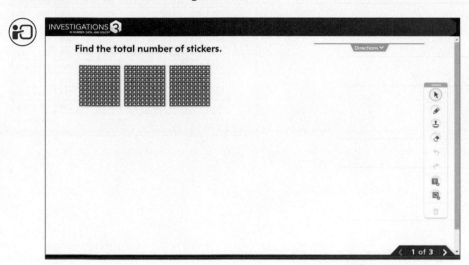

Display three sheets of 100 stickers. Follow the basic *Quick Images* routine. **TN**

As students share their thinking, encourage them to count by 100 to verify the amount and to use place-value language to describe it (e.g., "There are 3 groups of 100 in 300."). Ask them to suggest equations to represent the amount (e.g., 100 + 100 + 100 = 300, 300 = 100 + 200, etc.).

Add two more sheets of 100 stickers, and repeat as a *Quick Image*. Then discuss how students determined that there were 500 stickers. As you did for 300, count by 100s, describe the amount in terms of groups of 100, and record equations.

Repeat again, adding a row of five sheets of 100 under the five just discussed. As you discuss how students know that there are 1,000 stickers, ask several volunteers to model counting by 100s to 1,000 and practice doing this together as a class. Then have students describe the amount in terms of groups of 100, and record equations.

TEACHING NOTE

TN *Quick Images* Routine

○ Briefly show the image.

○ Students think about what they saw.

○ Show the image again, briefly.

○ Students revise their thinking.

○ With the image showing, volunteers share how many stickers they saw, how they were arranged, and how they remembered.

Introducing the 1,000 Book

Distribute a 1,000 Book (made from T21 and T45–T48) to each student. Briefly discuss what students notice, before focusing their attention on the first page (T21).

 STUDENTS MIGHT SAY "

"It's like the one we used before, but the pages have more numbers."

"Yes, the first page goes to 200 instead of 100."

"It goes to 1,000!"

We are going to use the whole book, but let's start by looking at the first page. Display the Teacher Presentation (or use a 1–200 Chart (T21)). **This page has 1-digit numbers, 2-digit numbers, and 3-digit numbers.** MWI

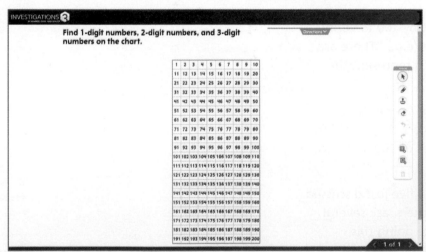

Find all the numbers that have only one digit. What is the smallest 1-digit number on your chart? (1) **What's the biggest?** (9) **Now find the numbers that have 2 digits. What is the smallest 2-digit number?** (10) **The biggest?** (99) **Find the 3-digit numbers. What is the smallest 3-digit number?** (100) **The biggest?** (200)

⊕ TEACHING AIDS

NAME   DATE

201–400 Chart

201	202	203	204	205	206	207	208	209	210
211	212	213	214	215	216	217	218	219	220
221	222	223	224	225	226	227	228	229	230
231	232	233	234	235	236	237	238	239	240
241	242	243	244	245	246	247	248	249	250
251	252	253	254	255	256	257	258	259	260
261	262	263	264	265	266	267	268	269	270
271	272	273	274	275	276	277	278	279	280
281	282	283	284	285	286	287	288	289	290
291	292	293	294	295	296	297	298	299	300
301	302	303	304	305	306	307	308	309	310
311	312	313	314	315	316	317	318	319	320
321	322	323	324	325	326	327	328	329	330
331	332	333	334	335	336	337	338	339	340
341	342	343	344	345	346	347	348	349	350
351	352	353	354	355	356	357	358	359	360
361	362	363	364	365	366	367	368	369	370
371	372	373	374	375	376	377	378	379	380
381	382	383	384	385	386	387	388	389	390
391	392	393	394	395	396	397	398	399	400

| T45 | © Pearson Education 2

MATH WORDS AND IDEAS

MWI Representing Place Value: Hundreds, Tens, and Ones

Next, have students locate specific numbers on the chart. If their books are laminated, they can lightly shade the squares in question with wipe-off markers. TN1

Find the number 100 on your chart. What number comes after 100? (101) **Now find the number 110 on your chart. What number comes after 110?** (111) **Now find 200. What number comes after 200?** (201) **How would I write that number?** Point out that they can check by turning the page.

Once they are oriented to the 1–200 chart, remind students of the basic rules of *Guess My Number*. TN2

Let's play a round of *Guess My Number*. I'm going to choose a number on this page and keep it a secret. Secretly write the number on scrap paper. Your job is to ask questions that help you figure out my number in as few guesses as possible.

Here are my first two clues. My number is greater than 1. My number is less than 200. What do we know?

My number is:
> 1
< 200

" STUDENTS MIGHT SAY "

"Not much!"

"All we know is your number isn't 1 and it isn't 200."

"It's between 1 and 200."

I will take guesses about my number. Before you ask, think about which number to choose that will give you the most information about my secret number.

Then take guesses from one student at a time. After each guess, respond with a new clue and record that information, using < and > notation where appropriate.

My number is:
> 1
< 200
> 100
a counting by 10s number

RESOURCE MASTERS, T46

⊕ **TEACHING AIDS**

NAME   DATE

401–600 Chart

401	402	403	404	405	406	407	408	409	410
411	412	413	414	415	416	417	418	419	420
421	422	423	424	425	426	427	428	429	430
431	432	433	434	435	436	437	438	439	440
441	442	443	444	445	446	447	448	449	450
451	452	453	454	455	456	457	458	459	460
461	462	463	464	465	466	467	468	469	470
471	472	473	474	475	476	477	478	479	480
481	482	483	484	485	486	487	488	489	490
491	492	493	494	495	496	497	498	499	500
501	502	503	504	505	506	507	508	509	510
511	512	513	514	515	516	517	518	519	520
521	522	523	524	525	526	527	528	529	530
531	532	533	534	535	536	537	538	539	540
541	542	543	544	545	546	547	548	549	550
551	552	553	554	555	556	557	558	559	560
561	562	563	564	565	566	567	568	569	570
571	572	573	574	575	576	577	578	579	580
581	582	583	584	585	586	587	588	589	590
591	592	593	594	595	596	597	598	599	600

T46   © Pearson Education 2

TEACHING NOTES

TN1 **1,000 Books** If students' 1,000 Books are laminated, they can use wipe-off markers to mark certain numbers or patterns in their work throughout this investigation and beyond. For example, they can keep track of the impact of guesses in a game of *Guess My Number* or look at the pattern in the numbers said when counting by 5s or 10s in Sessions 3.3–3.8. The books need to be "bound" in a way that each individual page can lie flat, so it could be used, for example, as a gameboard when students play *Capture 5* on the 1–200 chart as an extension in Session 2.3.

TN2 **Guess My Number** Students played *Guess My Number* as a class in Unit 1 and Unit 3, and pairs played in their 500 books in Unit 3. In this session, they play with numbers to 200 and, in subsequent sessions, play with numbers to 1,000.

What do we know so far? Talk with a partner about what you know.

If students have laminated 1,000 Books, they can mark up their 1–200 chart to show what numbers are still possible. If not, demonstrate this on the displayed 1–200 chart, asking different students to mark the numbers that each clue eliminates.

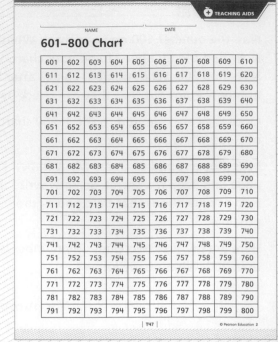

Summarize what is known, and then continue recording clues until someone guesses your number.

Explain that pairs will play *Guess My Number* during Math Workshop. They should play first on the 1–200 chart; then they can choose what page of their 1,000 Book to play on.

You and your partner should take turns choosing a secret number and guessing the number. As you play, find a way to record the information you collect about the number. You might want to use words or numbers, the greater than/less than notation, or a combination of these. The most important thing is to keep track of the information you learn about the secret number.

RESOURCE MASTERS, T47

TEACHING AIDS

NAME | DATE

601–800 Chart

601	602	603	604	605	606	607	608	609	610
611	612	613	614	615	616	617	618	619	620
621	622	623	624	625	626	627	628	629	630
631	632	633	634	635	636	637	638	639	640
641	642	643	644	645	646	647	648	649	650
651	652	653	654	655	656	657	658	659	660
661	662	663	664	665	666	667	668	669	670
671	672	673	674	675	676	677	678	679	680
681	682	683	684	685	686	687	688	689	690
691	692	693	694	695	696	697	698	699	700
701	702	703	704	705	706	707	708	709	710
711	712	713	714	715	716	717	718	719	720
721	722	723	724	725	726	727	728	729	730
731	732	733	734	735	736	737	738	739	740
741	742	743	744	745	746	747	748	749	750
751	752	753	754	755	756	757	758	759	760
761	762	763	764	765	766	767	768	769	770
771	772	773	774	775	776	777	778	779	780
781	782	783	784	785	786	787	788	789	790
791	792	793	794	795	796	797	798	799	800

| T47 | © Pearson Education 2

RESOURCE MASTERS, T48

TEACHING AIDS

NAME | DATE

801–1,000 Chart

801	802	803	804	805	806	807	808	809	810
811	812	813	814	815	816	817	818	819	820
821	822	823	824	825	826	827	828	829	830
831	832	833	834	835	836	837	838	839	840
841	842	843	844	845	846	847	848	849	850
851	852	853	854	855	856	857	858	859	860
861	862	863	864	865	866	867	868	869	870
871	872	873	874	875	876	877	878	879	880
881	882	883	884	885	886	887	888	889	890
891	892	893	894	895	896	897	898	899	900
901	902	903	904	905	906	907	908	909	910
911	912	913	914	915	916	917	918	919	920
921	922	923	924	925	926	927	928	929	930
931	932	933	934	935	936	937	938	939	940
941	942	943	944	945	946	947	948	949	950
951	952	953	954	955	956	957	958	959	960
961	962	963	964	965	966	967	968	969	970
971	972	973	974	975	976	977	978	979	980
981	982	983	984	985	986	987	988	989	990
991	992	993	994	995	996	997	998	999	1,000

| T48 | © Pearson Education 2

2 MATH WORKSHOP

Combinations of 100 and a Dollar

 25

Students choose among the following three activities.

---

2 A   *Guess My Number*

Pairs play *Guess My Number*. Player 1 picks and writes a secret number on scrap paper. Player 2 makes guesses and records on blank paper what they know about the number, given feedback from Player 1. Then players switch roles. Pairs should start with a game on the 1–200 chart; then they can choose which page in their 1,000 Book to play on. The directions are available on G38. **MPN** **TN**

ONGOING ASSESSMENT   Observing Students at Work

Students think about the order and magnitude of numbers to 1,000.

○ **Do students keep track of the information they gather after each guess?** Can they keep track of how the range of possible numbers changes after each guess?

○ **How do students notate the information they are gathering?** Are they able to use notation accurately and with understanding? Do they have other effective ways of notating clues and keeping track of information?

○ **Do students play strategically, choosing numbers midway in the range so as to eliminate the most possibilities?**

 DIFFERENTIATION   Supporting the Range of Learners

INTERVENTION **Scaffold a Solution** Encourage students who have difficulty keeping track of information to stop after each guess and review what they know thus far. Some students will mark the upper and lower range of numbers on their 1–200 chart, while others may benefit from recording the possible range of numbers after each guess. For example, model for students how to record information gathered from each guess (e.g., Guess 1: 1 to 200; Guess 2: 55 to 200; Guess 3: 55 to 120).

ENGLISH LANGUAGE LEARNERS **Provide Vocabulary Support** Help students understand the meanings of *greater than, less than,* and *between.* If you made a vocabulary word chart of the terms (with definitions, sketches, and labels), remind students to refer to the chart as needed. Encourage students to use the terms when giving clues to their partners. For example, if a student says, "It has more than 125," rephrase the information by saying, "Yes, your number is *greater than* 125."

 RESOURCE MASTERS, G38

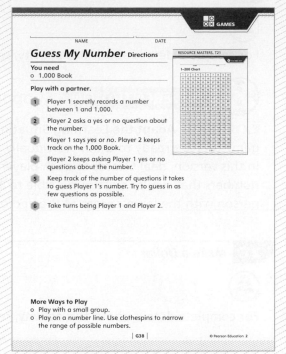

MATH PRACTICE NOTE

MPN **MP7 Look for and make use of structure.** Whatever strategies students employed playing on the 1–200 chart can be employed on any page of their 1,000 Book. However, this may be something students have yet to discover as they work with unfamiliar numbers.

TEACHING NOTE

TN **Recording Clues** Students are likely to use a variety of methods for recording *Guess My Number* clues. Some will use words, numbers, and/or < and > notation, while others may block off chunks of numbers on their 1–200 chart. Encourage students to use a method that is clear to them so that they can accurately keep track of and understand the information they collect throughout the game.

2 B *Close to 100*

For complete details about this activity, see Session 2.1.

 DIFFERENTIATION Supporting the Range of Learners

EXTENSION **Adapt the Learning Situation** Pair students who understand the game and are ready to think individually about combinations that make 100. In this version, deal 6 cards to each player. Both students make two 2-digit numbers that sum as close as possible to 100 and record their round. The person with the lowest score at the end of five rounds wins. **TN**

2 C *Make a Dollar*

For complete details about this activity, see Sessions 1.4 and 1.5.

3 DISCUSSION

Strategies for *Close to 100*

 (15)

MATH FOCUS POINTS FOR DISCUSSION

○ Using knowledge of place value to find pairs of 2-digit numbers that add to 100 or a number close to 100

○ Using known pairs of 2-digit numbers that add to 100 to find related pairs that add to 100 or a number close to 100 (for example, $80 + 20 = 100$, so $79 + 21 = 100$)

Gather students to discuss *Close to 100*. Display the Teacher Presentation (or 8 towers of 10 cubes in one color and 2 towers of 10 in another color). **PD**

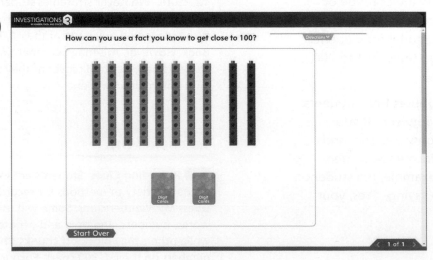

TEACHING NOTE

TN **Encouraging Cooperation** Even though this version is "competitive," stress the importance of taking turns and helping each other find the combination closest to 100. Some teachers suggest that students wait until a player's turn has come up to deal out the new cards for that turn. This helps both players focus on the cards of the player whose turn is in progress and fosters more cooperation and discussion during the game.

PROFESSIONAL DEVELOPMENT

PD **DIALOGUE BOX 4:** Playing *Close to 100*

I know that 80 + 20 = 100. I wanted to use that fact in a round of *Close to 100*, but I didn't have the right cards. What I did have was a 7 and a 9, and 79 is close to 80.

Display a 7 and a 9.

If I had 79, what number would I need to get to 100? Talk to a partner, and see if my cubes and the fact I know 80 + 20 = 100 can help you think about it. **PD**

As pairs talk, listen for students who are thinking about moving one of the 80 cubes to join the 20. Ask a pair that used this strategy to share, or share it yourself.

 STUDENTS MIGHT SAY

"Well this is 80, right? And your card says 79. So if you take one cube off the 80, you have 79. You have to put it over here now so that you'll still have 100 cubes. So we think 79 + 21 is 100."

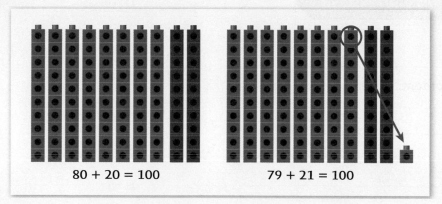

| 80 + 20 = 100 | 79 + 21 = 100 |

Ask volunteers to restate and model this strategy and to explain why it works. Then, double-check the answer using other strategies. **MPN1** **MPN2**

 STUDENTS MIGHT SAY

"I thought of a page in a sticker book. If you have 79, you need one more to get to 80. And then there are 2 empty rows. So I agree that it's 21."

"I looked at the 100 chart. 79 to 89 is 10. 89 to 99 is 10. And 1 more is 100. So it took 21 jumps."

"I did it like [Tia] but I looked at our number line. One jump got me to 80, and then I just know that it's 20 to 100. So it's 21."

PROFESSIONAL DEVELOPMENT

PD TEACHER NOTE 1: Algebra Connections in This Unit

MATH PRACTICE NOTES

MPN1 **MP8 Look for and express regularity in repeated reasoning.** Although students are familiar with strategies such as this—increasing one addend by 1 and decreasing the other by 1 results in the same sum—they now think about using them in a new context with greater numbers.

MPN2 **MP3 Construct viable arguments and critique the reasoning of others.** Students explain and listen to their classmates' explanations of why it is always true that if one addend increases by some amount and the other addend decreases by the same amount, the sum is unchanged. See **Teacher Note 1**, Algebra Connections in This Unit, for further discussion of students' mathematical arguments.

Here's another question. We figured out that I'd need a 21 to go with 79. What if I didn't have a 2 and a 1? What other numbers might you look for?

 STUDENTS MIGHT SAY

"22. It's not 21 but it's close, so your answer should be close to 100."

"I was thinking the same thing, but one smaller. Do you have 2 and 0? You could make 20."

Record equations using the numbers students suggest, noting what the score would be for each.

SESSION FOLLOW-UP: REVIEW AND PRACTICE

Daily Practice

📝 **DAILY PRACTICE** For reinforcement of this unit's content, students complete *Student Activity Book* page 316.

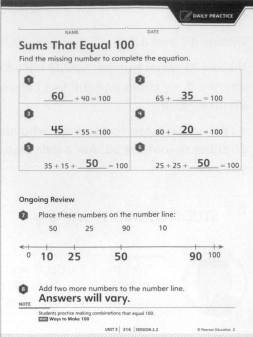

STUDENT ACTIVITY BOOK, P. 316

DAILY PRACTICE

NAME   DATE

Sums That Equal 100

Find the missing number to complete the equation.

① ___**60**___ + 40 = 100

② 65 + ___**35**___ = 100

③ ___**45**___ + 55 = 100

④ 80 + ___**20**___ = 100

⑤ 35 + 15 + ___**50**___ = 100

⑥ 25 + 25 + ___**50**___ = 100

Ongoing Review

⑦ Place these numbers on the number line:
50   25   90   10

0   **10**   **25**   **50**   **90**   100

⑧ Add two more numbers to the number line.
NOTE **Answers will vary.**

Students practice making combinations that equal 100.
Ways to Make 100

UNIT 5 | 316 | SESSION 2.2   © Pearson Education 2

SESSION 2.3

Stickers: Hundreds, Tens, and Ones

MATH FOCUS POINTS

- Using a place-value model to represent 3-digit numbers as hundreds, tens, and ones
- Comparing 3-digit numbers by comparing like places (i.e., hundreds with hundreds, tens with tens, ones with ones)
- Reading and writing 3-digit numbers
- Representing 3-digit numbers in expanded form

VOCABULARY

- hundreds
- hundreds place
- tens place
- tens
- greater than
- less than

TODAY'S PLAN

	MATERIALS

  CLASSROOM ROUTINE: REVIEW AND PRACTICE
10 Class

How Many Pockets?: Adding Four Groups

 1 ACTIVITY
15 Class

How Many Stickers: Hundreds, Tens,
 Ones?
Pairs

30 **2 MATH WORKSHOP**

3-Digit Numbers

   2A How Many Stickers?

   2B *Guess My Number*

   2C *Close to 100*

   2D *Capture 5*

 3 DISCUSSION
15 Class

Equations for 3-Digit Numbers

SESSION FOLLOW-UP: REVIEW AND PRACTICE

Daily Practice

- *Student Activity Book*, p. 317
- Connecting cubes (4 bins)
- Chart: "How Many Pockets?" (from Unit 4)

- Teacher Presentation (or envelopes of stickers, from Session 2.2)
- *Student Activity Book*, p. 318
- Blank paper (1 sheet per student)

- **2A** *Student Activity Book*, pp. 318–319
- S65* (optional; for the Intervention)
- **2B** Materials from Session 2.2
- **2C** Materials from Session 2.1
- **2D** Materials from Sessions 1.2 and 1.3
- 1,000 Book and counters that fit on those squares (optional; for the Extension)

- Teacher Presentation (or use S65)

- *Student Activity Book*, p. 320

* See *Materials to Prepare* in the Investigation 2 Planner.

Common Core State Standards	**Classroom Routines:** 2.OA.B.2, 2.NBT.B.5, 2.NBT.B.6 **Session:** 2.NBT.A.1, 2.NBT.A.1b, 2.NBT.A.3, 2.NBT.A.4, 2.NBT.B.5, 2.NBT.B.8	**Daily Practice:** 2.NBT.A.3, 2.NBT.A.4

CLASSROOM ROUTINE: REVIEW AND PRACTICE

How Many Pockets?: Adding Four Groups

MATH FOCUS POINTS

○ Collecting, counting, representing, and comparing data

○ Adding four 2-digit numbers

Organize students into four groups, and give each a bin of cubes. Students take as many cubes as they have pockets and then figure out how many pockets in their group. Encourage them to think about facts they know as they combine their pockets.

Ask each group to share their total and give you their cubes, in towers of 10 and a tower of leftovers. Record the four totals, and display the cube towers beneath them.

Students work to determine the total number of pockets the class is wearing. They record their work on *Student Activity Book*, page 317. Encourage students to use what they know about adding tens and ones to determine the total number of pockets.

When students are finished, discuss a few strategies for combining the 4 quantities. Model each with the cubes and record equations. If students do not suggest finding the total of two groups and then adding the two subtotals, suggest it as a strategy. Confirm the total by counting the cube towers by 10s and then 1s, and record the data on the Pocket Data chart.

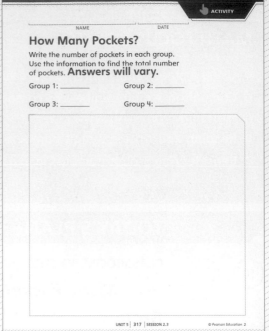

How Many Pockets?

Write the number of pockets in each group.
Use the information to find the total number
of pockets. **Answers will vary.**

Group 1: _____   Group 2: _____

Group 3: _____   Group 4: _____

---

1 ACTIVITY

How Many Stickers: Hundreds, Tens, Ones?

Display the Teacher Presentation (or use 62 stickers: 6 strips, 2 singles).

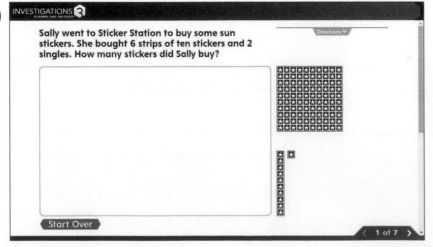

Sally went to Sticker Station to buy some sun stickers. She bought 6 strips of ten stickers and 2 singles. How many stickers did Sally buy? How would you write that number in words? How could we record this using an equation?

Record "sixty-two" and $60 + 2 = 62$. Discuss the connection between the two representations and the image of the stickers. Next, pose a problem that involves a sheet of 100 stickers.

Sally also bought some moon stickers. She bought 1 sheet of 100 stickers, 2 strips of 10 stickers, and 4 singles.

Ask a student volunteer to display Sally's moon stickers.

Talk with a partner about how we could write an equation that would represent the number of moon stickers Sally bought.

Then, ask a volunteer to share his or her equation while another explains what each number represents in the sticker representation.

Record the following, reminding students about sticker notation. **MWI** **MN** **TN**

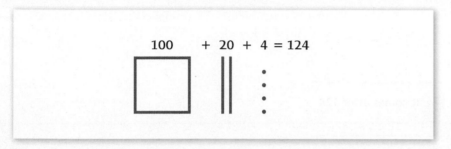

[Nadia] said that Sally bought 124 stickers. She bought one sheet of 100. I'm going to use a square to represent this. (Draw a square under the 100.) **She bought two strips of 10, or 20. I'm going to draw two lines to show these.** (Draw 2 lines under the 20.) **And she bought 4 singles, so I'm going to draw 4 small dots.** (Draw 4 dots under the 4.)

Write the number words for 124 under the representation, and ask students to think about the connection between the words, the number, and the sticker notation. **PD** **MPN**

This is how 124 is written in words. Which part of the sticker notation shows one hundred? And which part of the number shows one hundred?

Ask a volunteer to point out each part, and then ask students about the words, notation, and digits in the tens place and the ones place.

Pose another problem about 146. This time use only sticker notation.

This is what Jake bought when he went to Sticker Station.

Talk with a partner about how many stickers Jake bought. Then, on a piece of paper, show the stickers using sticker notation, and write an equation that represents these stickers.

Walk around to get a sense of how students are working with these ideas and to see if they can use the notation to write an equation.

This square shows that Jake bought one sheet of 100 stickers. How should I show that with a number? What about these 4 lines? How many strips of 10 did Jake buy? How many stickers is that? What about these 6 dots?

MATH WORDS AND IDEAS

MWI Representing Place Value: Hundreds, Tens, and Ones

MATH NOTE

MN **Expanded Form** Expanded form is a way to show how much each digit in a multi-digit number represents. The value of the number is the sum of each digit multiplied by the value of its place. In this example, 124 has 1 hundred, 2 tens, and 4 ones. This can be recorded as $100 + 20 + 4 = 124$. Sticker problems are one of the many opportunities in Grade 2 to record numbers in expanded form. Expanded form is sometimes referred to as expanded notation.

TEACHING NOTE

TN **Place-Value Representation** Students used sticker notation in Unit 3 and earlier in this unit. Sticker notation is a quick way of representing 2- and 3-digit numbers and is useful for representing the hundreds, tens, and ones structure of numbers. This structure is not as easily seen on the 100 or 1,000 charts or the number line.

PROFESSIONAL DEVELOPMENT

PD TEACHER NOTE 5: Place Value in Second Grade

MATH PRACTICE NOTE

MPN **MP2 Reason abstractly and quantitatively.** Students make meaning for words and symbols by connecting number words, numerical symbols, representations such as sticker notation, and contexts such as Sticker Station.

As students share, record the following equation and the number word under the sticker notation, and connect both to the sticker notation.

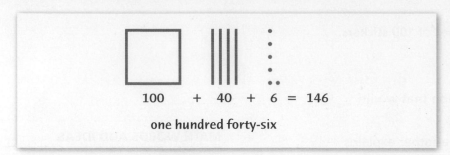

100   +   40   +   6   =   146

one hundred forty-six

So, Jake bought 146 stickers, and Sally bought 124 stickers. Who bought more stickers? How do you know?

❝ STUDENTS MIGHT SAY ❞

"Jake bought more because 146 is more than 124. It comes after 124 on the 200 chart. It's bigger."

"146 stickers are more than 124 stickers. You can tell because they both have a sheet of 100, but Jake has 4 strips of ten and Sally only has 2 strips of ten. The singles don't really matter."

Find ways to illustrate students' ideas. For example, point out the number on a 1–200 chart or highlight the parts of each number using stickers or sticker notation.

[Leigh] said that you can compare the numbers by comparing each part of the number. First, you look at the hundreds or the number in the hundreds place. Since both numbers have 1 hundred, you look at the tens place next. Four tens is more than two tens. So, 146 is greater than 124. **MWI** **MPN**

Record 146 > 124.

We can also look at which number is less than the other. 124 is less than 146.

Record 124 < 146.

Suppose Sally bought another sheet of 100 stickers and added them to the 124. How many stickers would Sally have now? (224) What equation could represent this amount?

Record the following equation, and ask a student volunteer to use sticker notation below the equation.

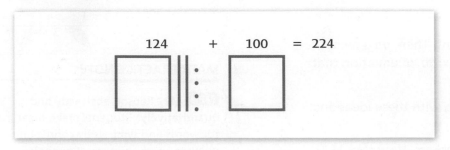

124   +   100   =   224

MATH WORDS AND IDEAS

MWI Comparing 3-Digit Numbers

MATH PRACTICE NOTE

MPN MP8 **Look for and express repeated reasoning.** As students recognize that each time they compare two numbers they use the same strategy, they can formulate a generalization.

What part of 124 changed when you added another 100? Right, the number in the hundreds place changed from a 1 to a 2 because now Sally has 2 sheets, or 2 groups of 100, plus 24 stickers. She has 224 stickers. **MPN**

Now who has more stickers, Sally or Jake? How can we show this information using the greater than or less than sign?

$$224 > 146 \qquad 146 < 224$$

Explain that students will be doing a similar activity during Math Workshop. Display *Student Activity Book* page 318, and do the first number, 135, together so that students understand what information they need to include for each number.

2 MATH WORKSHOP

3-Digit Numbers

30

Students choose among the following activities.

2 A How Many Stickers?

Students use sticker notation to represent the 3-digit numbers on *Student Activity Book* pages 318–319. For each, they record the number of sheets, strips, and singles; they record the number of hundreds, tens, and ones; and write an equation in expanded form.

ONGOING ASSESSMENT Observing Students at Work

Students use place-value notation and expanded form to represent 3-digit numbers.

○ **Do students correctly read each number?** Are they able to use sticker notation to represent the number of hundreds, tens, and ones in each number?

○ **Do students accurately record an equation that represents the notation and the value of each number?**

STUDENT ACTIVITY BOOK, P. 318

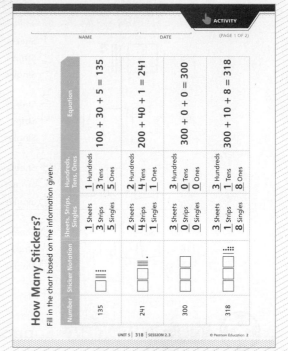

STUDENT ACTIVITY BOOK, P. 319

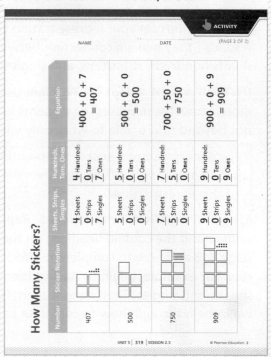

MATH PRACTICE NOTE

MPN MP7 **Look for and make use of structure.** Just as students have recognized that when 10 is added to a number, the tens digit increases by 1, now they see that when 100 is added to a number, the hundreds digit increases by 1.

Number	Sticker Notation	Sheets, Strips, Singles	Hundreds, Tens, Ones	Equation
135	□ ||| ⋮	1 Sheets 3 Strips 5 Singles	1 Hundreds 3 Tens 5 Ones	$100+30$ $+5=135$
241	□□ |||| .	2 Sheets 4 Strips 1 Singles	2 Hundreds 4 Tens 1 Ones	$200+40$ $+1=241$
300	□□ □	3 Sheets 0 Strips 0 Singles	3 Hundreds 0 Tens 0 Ones	$300+0$ $+0=300$
318	□□□	⋮⋮	3 Sheets 1 Strips 8 Singles	3 Hundreds 1 Tens 8 Ones	$300+10$ $+8=318$

RESOURCE MASTERS, S65

 DIFFERENTIATION Supporting the Range of Learners

INTERVENTION Suggest a Tool Talk with students who are having difficulty to identify what they are and are not understanding. Are they able to read the number in the first column? Use sticker notation to represent it? If not, can they interpret your representation of the number using sticker notation? If so, can they make a connection between the picture and the number of sheets/hundreds, strips/tens, and singles/ones?

INTERVENTION Adapt the Problem Use S65, How Many Stickers?, to provide more accessible numbers for students who can read numbers in the 100s but not beyond or are able to work only with tens and ones.

> For a more comprehensive intervention activity to be done outside of class, see *Representing 3-Digit Numbers with Stickers and Equations* at the end of this investigation.

ENGLISH LANGUAGE LEARNERS Repeat and Clarify Help students understand the column headings on the chart on *Student Activity Book* page 318 and how to complete it. Work with students to complete the second row. For example, begin by having them build the number 241 using stickers, sheets, and singles. Then have students use their models for reference as you walk them through how to complete each cell in that row.

 2 B   *Guess My Number*

For complete details about this activity, see Session 2.2.

DIFFERENTIATION Supporting the Range of Learners

INTERVENTION Vary the Problem Students who are ready for more challenge can play on other pages of their 1,000 Book. The first clue should be, "My number is on the [201–400] chart."

2 C *Close to 100*

For complete details about this activity, see Sessions 2.1 and 2.2.

2 D *Capture 5*

For complete details about this activity, see Sessions 1.2 and 1.3.

 DIFFERENTIATION Supporting the Range of Learners

EXTENSION Vary the Problem Students who are ready for more challenge can play the same game, but on the first page of their 1,000 Book (the 1–200 chart). In this version, the chips will be much more spread out and may need to be smaller to fit in the squares, and students will be adding and subtracting within 200.

3 DISCUSSION

Equations for 3-Digit Numbers

MATH FOCUS POINTS FOR DISCUSSION

○ Using a place-value model to represent and compare 3-digit numbers as hundreds, tens, and ones

○ Representing 3-digit numbers using expanded form

Display the Teacher Presentation (or use S65), and gather students to discuss what a row of the How Many Stickers? chart would look like for a few numbers they didn't investigate. This provides an opportunity to see whether and how students are generalizing about the composition of 3-digit numbers as hundreds, tens, and ones.

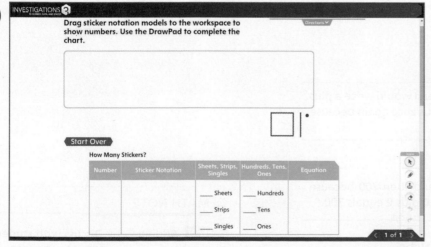

Sketch a sheet of 100, a strip of 10, and a single sticker in the second cell of the first row.

Take a minute to think. How many stickers do I have? How would I write that number?

After thinking on their own, ask students to turn and talk to a partner about how many stickers there are and how they figured it out.

" STUDENTS MIGHT SAY "

"Well there's 100, then 10 more is 110, and 1 more is 111."

"The 10 and the 1 make 11, and $100 + 11 = 111$."

"There's one of each! There's one sheet, one strip, and one single. Which means there's one hundred, one ten, and one one. $100 + 10 + 1 = 111$"

Ask a volunteer to help you fill in the rest of the row.

Here's another problem. I bought 700 stickers.

Write 700 in the first cell of the second row, and ask a volunteer to sketch your stickers.

Now, we need to fill in the information about the number of sheets, strips, and singles and hundreds, tens, and ones. What should I write?

After recording, display the following:

<u>7</u>	Sheets	<u>7</u>	Hundreds
<u>0</u>	Strips	<u>0</u>	Tens
<u>0</u>	Singles	<u>0</u>	Ones

What equation would you write to show that you had seven hundreds and zero tens and zero ones?

" STUDENTS MIGHT SAY "

"Well I would write 700 for the seven sheets. Then I would write a plus sign and then a zero or maybe plus zero and plus zero again because you don't have any strips or singles."

"And you would have to write an equal sign and then 700 because you have 700 stickers. So, it would be 700 plus 0 plus 0 equals 700."

Record student suggestions in the rightmost cell. Some may be unsure about how to represent zero tens and zero ones. Explain that $700 + 0 + 0 = 700$ is a way to show that there are no strips or singles in the collection of stickers. **MN**

> **MATH NOTE**
>
> **MN Adding Zero** Discuss with students that the equation $700 + 0 + 0 = 700$ can also be written as $700 = 700$ and that $700 + 0 + 5 = 705$ can be written as $700 + 5 = 705$.

Suppose I added 5 single stickers to this group. How many stickers would I have now? What would they look like in sticker notation?

Again, work together to complete a row on S65, and display the relevant information about the composition of those numbers in a second way:

7	Sheets	7	Hundreds
0	Strips	0	Tens
5	Singles	5	Ones

When I had 700 stickers we wrote 700 + 0 + 0 = 700. What part of that equation would change to show this new amount? Would the 700 change? Why or why not? Would the number of tens change? Would the number of ones change?

$$700 + 0 + 0 = 700$$

$$700 + 0 + 5 = 705$$

Repeat the same steps with 710 stickers.

7	Sheets	7	Hundreds
1	Strips	1	Tens
0	Singles	0	Ones

$$700 + 0 + 0 = 700$$

$$700 + 0 + 5 = 705$$

$$700 + 10 + 0 = 710$$

Daily Practice

DAILY PRACTICE For reinforcement of this unit's content, students complete *Student Activity Book* page 320.

1

Number of stickers
143

Number of stickers
134

How do you know which is greater? _____
because there one more ten in this one

2

Number of stickers
209

Number of stickers
215

How do you know which is greater? _____
there is no ten in this one but there is one in this one

3

Number of stickers
321

Number of stickers
286

How do you know which is greater? _____
because it had one more hunderds then this one

STUDENT ACTIVITY BOOK, P. 320

DAILY PRACTICE

NAME _____ DATE _____

Comparing Stickers

Look at the sets of stickers. Circle the set that has more, and tell how you know.

1
Number of stickers
143

Number of stickers
134

How do you know which is greater? **Answers will vary.**

2
Number of stickers
209

Number of stickers
215

How do you know which is greater? **Answers will vary.**

3
Number of stickers
321

Number of stickers
286

How do you know which is greater? **Answers will vary.**

NOTE

Students identify the greater number by comparing the number of hundreds, tens, and ones.
Representing Place Value: Hundreds, Tens, and Ones

UNIT 5 | 320 | SESSION 2.3   © Pearson Education 2

Plus or Minus 10 or 100

MATH FOCUS POINTS

- Reading and writing 3-digit numbers
- Adding 10 or 100 to and subtracting 10 or 100 from a given number, and describing what part of the number changes
- Using knowledge of place value to find pairs of 2-digit numbers that add to 100 or a number close to 100
- Using known pairs of 2-digit numbers that add to 100 to find related pairs that add to 100 or a number close to 100 (for example: $80 + 20 = 100$, so $79 + 21 = 100$)

VOCABULARY

- hundreds place

TODAY'S PLAN	MATERIALS

10
Class

CLASSROOM ROUTINES: REVIEW AND PRACTICE

Today's Number: What Could It Be?

 Teacher Presentation (or use Digit Cards 5, 6, 7)

Blank paper (1 sheet per student)

15
Class

1 ACTIVITY

Introducing *Plus or Minus 10 or 100*

 Plus or Minus 10 or 100 (or use one set of game materials (see Activity 2A))

1,000 Books (1 per student)

30

2 MATH WORKSHOP

Working with 3-Digit Numbers

2A *Plus or Minus 10 or 100*

2B How Many Stickers?

2C *Guess My Number*

2D *Close to 100*

2E *Capture 5*

2A G39–G40*

1,000 Books (1 per student)

$+/-10$ or 100 Number Cubes (1 per pair)*

$+/-10$ Number Cubes* (optional; for the Intervention)

$+/-100$ Number Cubes* (optional; for the Intervention)

2B *Student Activity Book*, pp. 321–322

S65* (optional; for the Intervention)

2C Materials from Session 2.2

2D Materials from Session 2.1

2E Materials from Sessions 1.2 and 2.3

15
Class

3 DISCUSSION

***Close to 100:* Strategies**

 Close to 100 (or use one set of *Close to 100* game materials)

Connecting cubes (as needed)

SESSION FOLLOW-UP: REVIEW AND PRACTICE

Daily Practice and Homework

Student Activity Book, pp. 323–324

---

* See *Materials to Prepare* in the Investigation 2 Planner.

Common Core State Standards	**Classroom Routines:** 2.NBT.A.1, 2.NBT.A.3, 2.NBT.A.4, 2.NBT.B.5 **Session:** 2.NBT.A.1, 2.NBT.A.1b, 2.NBT.A.3, 2.NBT.A.4, 2.NBT.B.5, 2.NBT.B.8, 2.NBT.B.9	**Daily Practice:** 2.NBT.A.1, 2.NBT.A.3

CLASSROOM ROUTINES: REVIEW AND PRACTICE

Today's Number: What Could It Be?

MATH FOCUS POINTS

○ Reasoning about the place value of 3-digit numbers

○ Expressing a 3-digit number in expanded form

○ Generating equivalent expressions for a number

Display the Teacher Presentation (or use Digit Cards showing 5, 6, and 7).

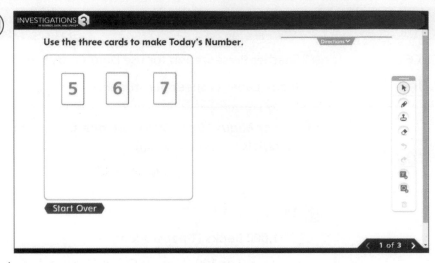

We are going to use these three cards to make Today's Number. Talk to a partner. What numbers could we make?

Generate and ask volunteers to record the 6 possibilities.

567   765   675   756   576   657

Today's Number has the largest digit in the hundreds place.

Ask what your number could be and how they know.

765   756

What question could you ask me to determine which of these two numbers is Today's Number?

Record students' questions, which might include asking about the number of tens or ones, the digit in the tens or ones place, and whether it's the larger/ smaller number. Respond to each, making sure to use greater than/less than notation to compare the two numbers.

[Juanita] asked if it's the bigger number. Which one is the bigger number? How do you know? Can you help me use greater than and less than notation to show that information?

765 > 756   756 < 765

Explain that 765 is Today's Number. Write the number in words, connecting each word to the part of the number it represents.

CLASSROOM ROUTINES: REVIEW AND PRACTICE

I'd like you to include, as one of your ways to make 765, an equation that shows 765 as the sum of hundreds, tens, and ones.

Students generate ways to make 765. After they've had time to work, share a few solutions. Be sure to discuss $700 + 60 + 5 = 765$ (or $765 = 700 + 60 + 5$). **MPN**

Introducing *Plus or Minus 10 or 100*

Today we're going to learn a new game called *Plus or Minus 10 or 100*. The first thing you do is choose a Start Number from your 1,000 Book. For this game, our Start Number will be 234. Find 234 in your 1,000 Book.

After students have located 234 in their 1,000 Books, ask a volunteer to tell you how to write the number and use sticker notation to represent it.

234

Display the Game Presentation (or use G39 and $+/-$ 10 or 100 Number Cubes).

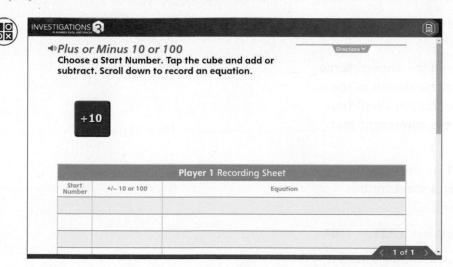

In this game, partners take turns rolling a cube labeled with $+10$, -10, $+100$, or -100. The cube will tell you what to add to or subtract from your Start Number.

What if we rolled a $+100$. What is $234 + 100$?

Record the problem, and ask students how they determined the sum.

GAMES

| NAME | | DATE |

Plus or Minus 10 or 100 Recording Sheet

Start Number	+/− 10 or 100	Equation

| G39 | © Pearson Education 2

MATH PRACTICE NOTE

MPN **MP6 Attend to precision.** Varying the format of equations reminds students that the equals sign indicates that the expressions on either side are equivalent.

❝ STUDENTS MIGHT SAY ❞

"I know that 100 + 200 is 300. Then 34 more would be 334."

"It's like adding a sheet of stickers. Now there are 3 hundreds, 3 tens, and 4 ones. 334."

Add a sheet of stickers to the representation, and record the sum in the equation.

We started with 234, and now we're at 334. How are those numbers similar? How are they different? Why do you think so?

❝ STUDENTS MIGHT SAY ❞

"We added a group of 100, but we didn't add any more tens or ones, so just the number of hundreds changed."

"If we had added a 10, the 34 would have changed to 44, but since we added a group of 100, the 34 stayed the same. Only the number that shows how many hundreds changed."

Model how to fill out the recording sheet (G39). Explain that 334 is the new Start Number and demonstrate another round.

Suppose on the next turn, I rolled a − 10. Our next problem to solve is 334 − 10.

Record the problem, and ask students how they determined the answer. Some students use their 201–400 chart or refer to the sticker representation to solve the problem. Others use what they know about 34 − 10 or reason about how a number changes when you subtract 10. Make sure there is agreement that 334 − 10 = 324. **MWI**

Cross out a strip of 10 in the sticker representation of 334, and record the answer in the equation. Model how to fill out the recording sheet for this round.

Now 324 is our Start Number. What if we rolled a − 100. What is 324 − 100?

Once again record the problem, and ask students to share how they solved it.

MATH WORDS AND IDEAS

MWI Adding and Subtracting 10 or 100

" STUDENTS MIGHT SAY "

"You can see it on the picture. If you take one sheet away, there are 200 left plus the 24, which together makes 224."

"It's like adding 100 but the opposite. Instead of going from 300 to 400 it goes from 300 to 200 because you are taking away 100."

Model crossing out a sheet of stickers from the sticker representation of 324 and record the answer at the end of the equation.

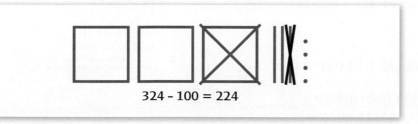

324 – 100 = 224

Ask students to again consider what is the same and what is different about the starting number and the ending number for this round and why they think so.

Model filling in this round on the Recording Sheet. Explain that sometimes adding or subtracting 10 or 100 will result in a number that is not in their 1,000 Book (e.g., 0, or 1,001). In this case, they should roll again. Tell students that the game ends when each partner's recording sheet is full.

2 MATH WORKSHOP

Working with 3-Digit Numbers

(30)

Students choose from the activities below. Explain that How Many Stickers? 2 is very similar to the activity they worked on and discussed in the previous session. In this version, the information provided in a row varies and is not necessarily the total number of stickers. All students should play a round of *Close to 100*, as the discussion at the end of the Session will focus on strategies for playing that game.

2 A *Plus or Minus 10 or 100*

Pairs play *Plus or Minus 10 or 100*. Each pair needs a +/– 10 or 100 Number Cube, and each student needs a Recording Sheet (G39) and their 1,000 Book, for reference. Students select a start number and take turns rolling the cube. They each record the resulting equation. The directions are available on G40. **TN**

TEACHING NOTE

TN **Selecting a Start Number and Numbers Less Than Zero** Depending on the Start Number and the series of rolls, it is possible that the total will go below zero. Explain to students that if that happens, they should roll again until they get a number above zero. Selecting a Start Number that is greater than 100 can help avoid this to some degree.

ONGOING ASSESSMENT Observing Students at Work

Students add or subtract 10 or 100 to or from numbers to 1,000 and use an equation to record.

○ **How do students add or subtract 10 to or from the given number?** Do they add or subtract mentally? Do they use their 1,000 Books? Do they recognize which digit changes when 10 is added to or subtracted from a number? **TN**

○ **How do students add or subtract 100 to or from the given number?** Do they add or subtract mentally? Do they use their 1,000 Books? Do they know that the hundreds digit increases or decreases by one when 100 is added to or subtracted from a number? Do they recognize that the tens and ones digits do not change?

○ **Can students accurately record an equation that represents the addition or subtraction situation?**

 DIFFERENTIATION Supporting the Range of Learners

INTERVENTION Adapt the Problem Some students benefit from using a modified number cube. Consider making a cube with only +/−10 or only +/−100. This will allow students to focus on adding and subtracting only one amount at a time so that they can gain more practice with noticing what happens to numbers when 10 (or 100) is added or subtracted.

ENGLISH LANGUAGE LEARNERS Repeat and Clarify Observe students as they begin to play the game to confirm that they understand the directions (G40) and how to complete the recording sheet (G39). If students need additional support, play a few rounds with them and model how to record. Provide prompts and ask questions, as needed, to support students. **What did you pick as your start number? You write that here. What did you get when you rolled the cube? You record that in this column. Can you write an equation that shows the problem you need to solve? What is the sum [difference]? Where will you write that?**

---

2 B How Many Stickers?

Students complete the rows on *Student Activity Book* pages 321–322. For complete details about this activity, see Session 2.3. In addition, consider:

ONGOING ASSESSMENT Observing Students at Work

○ **Can students complete a row given the total number?** The sticker notation? The number of sheets, strips, and singles? The number of hundreds, tens, and ones? An equation in expanded form?

○ **Are students writing 3-digit numbers accurately?** Can they record an equation in expanded form (e.g., $300 + 40 + 2 = 342$)?

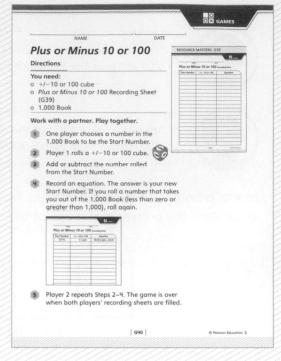

RESOURCE MASTERS, G40

TEACHING NOTE

TN Adding and Subtracting 10 Students had experience adding and subtracting 10 to/from numbers to 500 in Unit 3. This game extends that work to 1,000. Note whether students understand that the strategies they use for numbers to 500 also apply to numbers to 1,000.

DIFFERENTIATION Supporting the Range of Learners

> For another practice activity to be done outside of class, see *How Many Stickers? How Many Hundreds, Tens, and Ones?* at the end of this investigation.

INTERVENTION **Adapt the Problem** Some students benefit from more practice with problems where the given information is the total number of stickers. Use S65 to give them a set of problems appropriate for them. Work together to represent the number with sticker notation, record the number of sheets/strips/singles, hundreds/tens/ones, and write an equation in expanded form.

EXTENSION **Adapt the Problem** Students can choose a number from *Student Activity Book* page 322 and find additional ways to make that number using sheets, strips, and singles.

> For a more comprehensive extension activity to be done outside of class, see *Sticker Combinations* at the end of this investigation.

2 C   *Guess My Number*

For complete details about this activity, see Session 2.2.

DIFFERENTIATION Supporting the Range of Learners

EXTENSION **Extend Thinking** Students can play a version where determining which page of the 1,000 Book the number is on becomes part of the challenge. So, the secret number can be any number in their 1,000 Book.

2 D   *Close to 100*

For complete details about this activity, see Sessions 2.1 and 2.2.

2 E   *Capture 5*

For complete details about this activity, see Sessions 1.2 and 2.3.

STUDENT ACTIVITY BOOK, P. 321

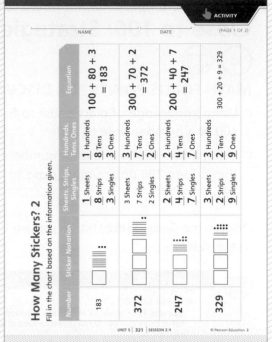

STUDENT ACTIVITY BOOK, P. 322

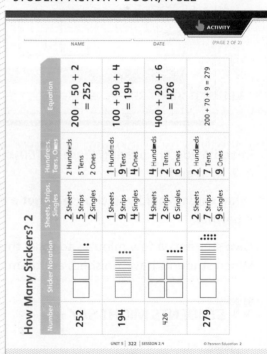

3 DISCUSSION

Close to 100: Strategies

MATH FOCUS POINTS FOR DISCUSSION

○ Using knowledge of place value to find pairs of 2-digit numbers that add to 100 or a number close to 100

○ Using known pairs of 2-digit numbers that add to 100 to find related pairs that add to 100 or a number close to 100 (for example: $80 + 20 = 100$, so $79 + 21 = 100$)

Display the Game Presentation (or use a deck of Digit Cards and a Recording Sheet, G36).

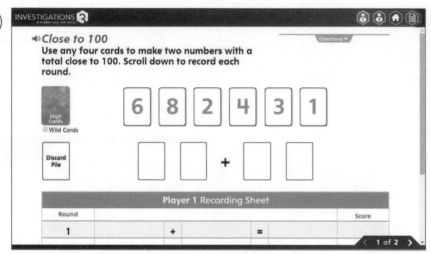

Imagine you are playing *Close to 100* and you draw the following 6 cards: 6, 8, 2, 4, 3, and 1.

What cards would you choose to get a combination closest to 100? Talk with a partner.

Give students a few minutes to solve this problem and discuss their thinking. When students have finished, ask them to share their strategies. **TN** **PD**

❝❝ STUDENTS MIGHT SAY ❞❞

"I just pick two cards and make a number. Then I think, how far is it from 100? If I don't have the tens number to make that number, I try again. So say 43. I would need . . . 57. There's no 5. So I'd try another number, like 68. For that you need 32, and we have that. $68 + 32 = 100$"

TEACHING NOTE

TN **Strategies for *Close to 100*** Expect a range of strategies. Some students make two 2-digit numbers, add them, and figure out how far they are from 100. Others make a 2-digit number and then look to make a number close to its complement of 100. Still others use a known fact and adjust those numbers to find a combination close to 100 or look first for digits to use in the tens place. If some of these do not come up, consider introducing and modeling them yourself.

PROFESSIONAL DEVELOPMENT

PD DIALOGUE BOX 4: Playing *Close to 100*

Interesting. [Simon] makes a 2-digit number, and then what does [he] do? (Figures out what [he'd] need to make 100.) Then [he] looks to see if [he] can make a number near that number. Why do you think sometimes [he] says, "Try again"?   **MPN1**

STUDENTS MIGHT SAY

"I know why! That was how I played for a while but I never started over. And sometimes I got scores that were like twenty something!"

Who has a different strategy for playing *Close to 100?*

STUDENTS MIGHT SAY

"I saw 6 and 4, so I started with 60 + 40, which is 100. Then, there aren't any zeros, so I looked for the lowest numbers I could find. I made 61 + 42 = 103."

[Melissa] used the known combination of [60 + 40 = 100] and then made numbers close to that. Did anyone else have a similar strategy?   **MPN2**

STUDENTS MIGHT SAY

"I started with 60 + 40 = 100 too, but then I decided to change the numbers a little. I knew if I gave one from the 40 to the 60, I would have 39 + 61, but there isn't a 9. So I gave another one from the 39 to the 60, which would be 38 + 62, and we have all those numbers."

So [Jacy] used a combination [she] knew and then adjusted the numbers. Let's see if we can show [Jacy]'s strategy with cubes.   **PD**

Display 6 towers of 10 cubes in one color and 4 towers of 10 in another color to represent the known fact 60 + 40 = 100. Ask volunteers to restate and model this strategy and to explain why it works.   **MPN3**

STUDENT ACTIVITY BOOK, P. 323

> DAILY PRACTICE

NAME _____ DATE _____

How Many Stickers?

1. Find how many stickers are shown.
   Write an equation to show each group.

Sticker Notation	Equation
‖‖‖ ⋮	70 + 3 = 73
☐ ‖ ⋮	100 + 30 + 5 = 135
☐☐☐ ‖‖ ⋮	300 + 40 + 8 = 348
☐☐☐☐☐ ⋮	500 + 0 + 6 = 506

2. Use sticker notation.

Show 246 stickers.	Show 413 stickers.
☐☐ ‖‖ ⋮	☐☐ ☐☐ ⋮

NOTE

Students work with place value as they determine a total amount based on the number of hundreds, tens, and ones and as they represent an amount using place-value notation.
Representing Place Value: Hundreds, Tens, and Ones

UNIT 5 | 323 | SESSION 2.4   © Pearson Education 2

MATH PRACTICE NOTES

MPN1 MP3 Construct viable arguments and critique the reasoning of others. As students offer their strategies, classmates listen to make sense of the strategies.

MPN2 MP3 Construct viable arguments and critique the reasoning of others. For students to consider if they had a similar strategy, they must first understand their classmate's strategy and then compare it to their own.

MPN3 MP3 Construct viable arguments and critique the reasoning of others. Demonstrating a strategy with cubes to explain why it works is a step toward proving a general claim. See **Teacher Note 1**, Algebra Connections in This Unit, for further discussion of students' mathematical arguments.

PROFESSIONAL DEVELOPMENT

PD TEACHER NOTE 1: Algebra Connections in This Unit

What other strategies did you use? Did anyone find a different combination of cards that also equals 100? MN

STUDENTS MIGHT SAY

"I choose the tens numbers first. At first I looked for numbers that made 10, but all my answers were over 100. So I started looking for 9s instead. So for these cards I saw 8 and 1, so 80 + 10 = 90, and then I saw a 4 and a 6, and that makes 10, and 90 and 10 makes 100. So I made 84 + 16 and that makes 100."

$$8 + 1 = 9 \longrightarrow \begin{array}{c} 80 \\ 4 \end{array} + \begin{array}{c} 10 \\ 6 \end{array} = \begin{array}{c} 90 \\ 10 \end{array} \longrightarrow 90 + 10 = 100$$

$$84 + 16 = 100$$

SESSION FOLLOW-UP: REVIEW AND PRACTICE

Daily Practice and Homework

DAILY PRACTICE For reinforcement of this unit's content, students complete *Student Activity Book* page 323.

HOMEWORK Students imagine playing two rounds of *Close to 100* on *Student Activity Book* page 324.

STUDENT ACTIVITY BOOK, P. 324

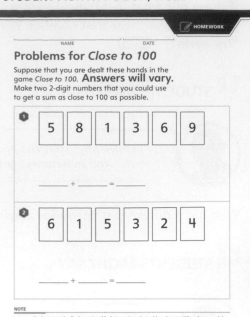

MATH NOTE

MN **Are They the Same?** Students commonly find different ways to use the same set of cards to make 100, for example, using 8, 6, 1, and 4 to make 86 + 14 and 84 + 16 and then wonder whether those are "different." On the one hand, they use the same four cards, have the same tens digits and ones digits, and sum to 100. Because the two 2-digit numbers are different, consider these answers different. However, students may be noticing something more general here: that the ones digits (or the tens digits) can be switched and the total remains the same.

What Do You Know about 345?

MATH FOCUS POINTS

○ Reading and writing 3-digit numbers

○ Adding 10 or 100 to and subtracting 10 or 100 from a given number and describing what part of the number changes

○ Using knowledge of place value to find pairs of 2-digit numbers that add to 100 or a number close to 100

○ Identifying the value that each digit in a 3-digit number represents

TODAY'S PLAN	MATERIALS
(10) Class CLASSROOM ROUTINES: REVIEW AND PRACTICE ***Today's Number: What Could It Be?***	Teacher Presentation (or use Digit Cards 2, 3, 9) Blank paper (1 sheet per student)
(15) Class **1** ACTIVITY **Adding and Subtracting 10 or 100**	Teacher Presentation (or use S66*) 1,000 Books (1 per student)

(30) **2** MATH WORKSHOP
Working with 3-Digit Numbers
  2A Find the Number
  2B *Plus or Minus 10 or 100*
  2C *Guess My Number*
  2D *Close to 100*
	2A *Student Activity Book,* pp. 325–326
	  S66* (optional; for the Intervention)
	  S67–S68* (optional; for the Extension)
	2B Materials from Session 2.4
	  + / − multiples of 10 and 100 Number Cubes*
	  (as needed, for the Extension)
	2C Materials from Session 2.2
	2D Materials from Session 2.1

(15) Class **3** DISCUSSION **What Do You Know about 345?**	Teacher Presentation (or use the board)
SESSION FOLLOW-UP: REVIEW AND PRACTICE **Daily Practice**	*Student Activity Book,* pp. 327–328

* See *Materials to Prepare* in the Investigation 2 Planner.

Common Core State Standards	**Classroom Routines:** 2.NBT.A.1, 2.NBT.A.3, 2.NBT.A.4, 2.NBT.B.5 **Session:** 2.NBT.A.1, 2.NBT.A.3, 2.NBT.A.4, 2.NBT.B.5, 2.NBT.B.8	**Daily Practice:** 2.NBT.A.3, 2.NBT.B.8

CLASSROOM ROUTINES: REVIEW AND PRACTICE

Today's Number: What Could It Be?

MATH FOCUS POINTS

○ Reasoning about the place value of 3-digit numbers

○ Expressing a 3-digit number in expanded form

○ Generating equivalent expressions for a number

Display the Teacher Presentation (or use Digit Cards showing 2, 3, and 9).

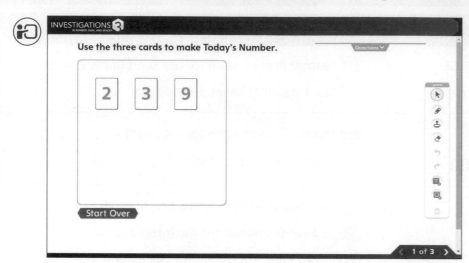

We are going to use these three cards to make Today's Number. Talk to a partner. What numbers could we make?

Generate and ask volunteers to record the 6 possibilities.

239   293   392   329   932   923

Today's Number is the number that has the most hundreds.

Ask what your number could be and how they know.

932   923

What question could you ask me to determine which of these two numbers is Today's Number?

Record students' questions, which might include asking about the number of tens or ones and whether it's the larger/smaller number. Respond to each, making sure that using greater than/less than notation to compare the two numbers comes up.

[Gregory] asked if it's the bigger number. Which one is the bigger number? How do you know? Can you help me use greater than and less than notation to show that information?

932 > 923   923 < 932

Explain that 932 is Today's Number. Write the number in words, connecting each word to the part of the number it represents.

I'd like you to include, as one of your ways to make 932, an equation that shows 932 as the sum of hundreds, tens, and ones.

Students generate ways to make 932. After they've had time to work, share a few solutions. Be sure to discuss $900 + 30 + 2 = 932$ (or $932 = 900 + 30 + 2$).

1 ACTIVITY

Adding and Subtracting 10 or 100

Imagine you are playing *Plus or Minus 10 or 100* and your Start Number is 756. Find 756 in your 1,000 Book.

Ask volunteers how to write this number and how to record it using sticker notation.

756
seven hundred fifty-six

What number would you get if you rolled a + 10? (766) What number would you get if you rolled a − 10? (746)

Ask students how to write the numbers and where you'd find them in their 1,000 Book. Record them in a column, discussing what part of the numbers change and why. **MPN**

746

756

766

❝❝ STUDENTS MIGHT SAY ❞❞

"The 5 in 756 stands for 5 tens. When you add a ten, you end up with 6 tens or 60. If you subtract 10, you end up with 4 tens or 40. The 7 and the 6 don't change because they represent the hundreds and the 6 ones, and you didn't add any hundreds or ones."

"Thinking about stickers helps me. When you add 10, you're adding 1 strip. When you subtract 10, you're taking a strip away. You don't do anything to the sheets of 100 or the 6 singles. Only the number of strips or tens changes."

"On the 601–800 chart, these numbers are in the same column. 756 is 10 more than 746, and 766 is 10 more than 756. You're just adding and subtracting 10, so only the number of tens changes."

MATH PRACTICE NOTE

MPN **MP2 Reason abstractly and quantitatively.** When students have a variety of representations and contexts to represent 3-digit numbers, they can call upon these to reason about what happens to the digits of a number when adding or subtracting 10 or 100.

Next ask students how to write the number 627, and how to show it with sticker notation.

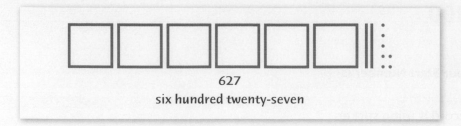

627

six hundred twenty-seven

What number is 100 more than 627? . . . Can you find this number in your 1,000 Book? What number is 100 less than 627? (Note that students will need to turn the page in their 1,000 Book when subtracting 100 from 627.)

Ask students how to write those numbers, and record them in a column. Discuss what part of the numbers change and why.

527

627

727

❝ STUDENTS MIGHT SAY ❞

"The number of hundreds is changing. When you add 100 to 600, the number of hundreds changes from 6 to 7. When you subtract 100, the number of hundreds goes from 6 to 5."

"If we had added a 10 to 27, it would have changed to 37, but since we're adding 100 and subtracting 100, the 27 stays the same. Just the digit that shows the hundreds changed."

"It's like [Holly] said before. If you did these problems with stickers, you're only using the sheets. You don't do anything with the strips and singles."

Repeat with 882, this time introducing the format students will see on *Student Activity Book* pages 325–326. Display the Teacher Presentation (or use S66).

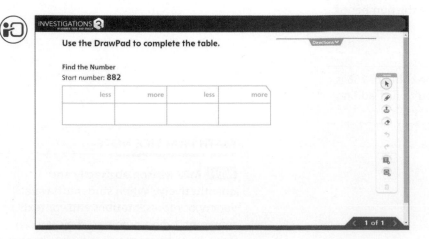

Ask students to help you fill in the numbers that are 10 more and less and 100 more and less than 882. Explain that this will be a Math Workshop activity today.

STUDENT ACTIVITY BOOK, P. 325

ACTIVITY

NAME _____ DATE _____ (PAGE 1 OF 2)

Find the Number

Write each number.

1 Start number: 189

10 less	10 more	100 less	100 more
179	199	89	289

2 Start number: 339

10 less	10 more	100 less	100 more
329	349	239	439

3 Start number: 571

10 less	10 more	100 less	100 more
561	581	471	671

4 Start number: 690

10 less	10 more	100 less	100 more
680	700	590	790

5 Start number: 801

10 less	10 more	100 less	100 more
791	811	701	901

UNIT 5 | 325 | SESSION 2.5   © Pearson Education 2

STUDENT ACTIVITY BOOK, P. 326

ACTIVITY

NAME _____ DATE _____ (PAGE 2 OF 2)

Find the Number

Write each number.

6 Start number: 273

10 less	10 more	100 less	100 more
263	283	173	373

7 Start number: 482

10 less	10 more	100 less	100 more
472	492	382	582

8 Start number: 796

10 less	10 more	100 less	100 more
786	806	696	896

9 Start number: 857

10 less	10 more	100 less	100 more
847	867	757	957

10 Start number: 694

10 less	10 more	100 less	100 more
684	704	594	794

UNIT 5 | 326 | SESSION 2.5   © Pearson Education 2

2 MATH WORKSHOP

Working with 3-Digit Numbers

 30

All students should begin Math Workshop with Find the Number. Then they can choose from the 3 remaining activities.

2 A Find the Number

Students complete *Student Activity Book* pages 325–326. Given a Start Number, they find it in their 1,000 Book and then figure out and record the numbers that are 10 and 100 more and less than that number. Encourage students to confirm their work with a partner. **MPN**

ONGOING ASSESSMENT Observing Students at Work

Students locate numbers in their 1,000 Books and then figure out and record the numbers that are 10 and 100 more and less than that number.

- ○ **Are students able to locate each number in the 1,000 Book?** Do they seem to have an approximate sense of where the number is located, or do they have to page through and scan each chart to find the number?

- ○ **How do students figure out 10 more/less and 100 more/less than a number?** Do they just know? Do they use what they know about which part of the number increases/decreases? Do they have to count forward or back to figure it out? 🔍 **MP7**

- ○ **Can students explain how they figured out 10 more/less or 100 more/less?** 🔍 **MP7**

- ○ **Can students accurately write 3-digit numbers?**

 DIFFERENTIATION Supporting the Range of Learners

INTERVENTION Adapt the Problem If students are having difficulty, check to see if they are able to read the start numbers. If not, determine what the greatest number is that they are able to recognize and use S66 to adjust their set of starting numbers so that they are only working with a limited set of numbers. These students may need to focus primarily on 10 more/10 less initially. Note whether, for those problems, students calculate mentally, move one row up/down in their 1,000 Book, or count forward/back 10 spaces on the chart.

EXTENSION Adapt the Problem For students who work fluently with this activity, use S67–S68, which asks them to add and subtract different multiples of 10 and 100 to/from the same start numbers.

ENGLISH LANGUAGE LEARNERS Provide Sentence Stems Some students may need support to verbalize their responses when asked: *What number is [10 more/10 less/100 more/100 less]?* Provide a sentence stem that students can use as needed. For example: *I know that [228] is [10 less] than [238] because _____.*

RESOURCE MASTERS, S66

ACTIVITY

NAME _____ DATE _____

Find the Number (Blank)

1 Start number: _____

_____less	_____more	_____less	_____more

2 Start number: _____

_____less	_____more	_____less	_____more

3 Start number:

_____less	_____more	_____less	_____more

4 Start number:

_____less	_____more	_____less	_____more

5 Start number:

_____less	_____more	_____less	_____more

UNIT 5 | S66 | SESSION 2.5   © Pearson Education 2

MATH PRACTICE NOTE

MPN 🔍 **MP7 Look for and make use of structure.** Students are working on the idea that when a number increases (or decreases) by 10 or 100, the tens or hundreds digit increases (or decreases) by 1. They use a variety of representations and contexts to reason about the structure of place value.

2 B   *Plus or Minus 10 or 100*

For complete details about this activity, see Session 2.4.

 DIFFERENTIATION Supporting the Range of Learners

EXTENSION   **Adapt the Problem** The game can be made more challenging by providing cubes with multiples of 10 and 100.

2 C   *Guess My Number*

For complete details about this activity, see Session 2.2.

2 D   *Close to 100*

For complete details about this activity, see Sessions 2.1 and 2.2.

3 DISCUSSION

What Do You Know about 345?

MATH FOCUS POINT FOR DISCUSSION

○ Identifying the value that each digit in a 3-digit number represents

Gather students for a discussion about the place value of 3-digit numbers. Use this as an opportunity to consolidate the work students have been doing: identifying and representing numbers in/with stickers, writing the numbers, writing equations in expanded form, and thinking about the number of sheets/hundreds, strips/tens, and singles/ones in 3-digit numbers and how that relates to how the numbers are written.

We have been doing a lot of work with 3-digit numbers. You have used sticker notation to represent large amounts of stickers, and you have also written equations using hundreds, tens, and ones to show how these groups of stickers combine to equal a specific amount. MWI

RESOURCE MASTERS, S67

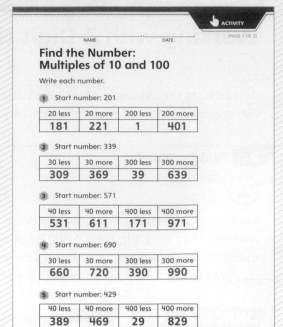

ACTIVITY (PAGE 1 OF 2)

NAME   DATE

Find the Number: Multiples of 10 and 100

Write each number.

1   Start number: 201

20 less	20 more	200 less	200 more
181	221	1	401

2   Start number: 339

30 less	30 more	300 less	300 more
309	369	39	639

3   Start number: 571

40 less	40 more	400 less	400 more
531	611	171	971

4   Start number: 690

30 less	30 more	300 less	300 more
660	720	390	990

5   Start number: 429

40 less	40 more	400 less	400 more
389	469	29	829

UNIT 5 | S67 | SESSION 2.5   © Pearson Education 2

RESOURCE MASTERS, S68

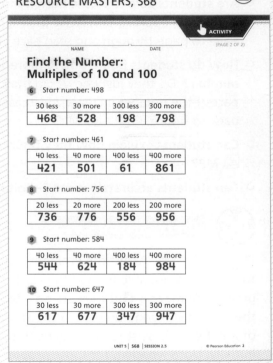

ACTIVITY (PAGE 2 OF 2)

NAME   DATE

Find the Number: Multiples of 10 and 100

6   Start number: 498

30 less	30 more	300 less	300 more
468	528	198	798

7   Start number: 461

40 less	40 more	400 less	400 more
421	501	61	861

8   Start number: 756

20 less	20 more	200 less	200 more
736	776	556	956

9   Start number: 584

40 less	40 more	400 less	400 more
544	624	184	984

10   Start number: 647

30 less	30 more	300 less	300 more
617	677	347	947

UNIT 5 | S68 | SESSION 2.5   © Pearson Education 2

MATH WORDS AND IDEAS

MWI Representing Place Value: Hundreds, Tens, and Ones

Display the Teacher Presentation (or use the board).

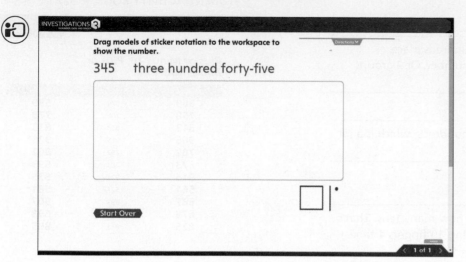

Let's look together at the number 345. How would I write that number?

Display the number 345, and write the number in words below it.

How would I show that number with stickers?

Ask students to direct you in drawing 345 in sticker notation.

How would I write an equation that shows that number as the sum of sheets, strips, and singles? As the sum of hundreds, tens, and ones?

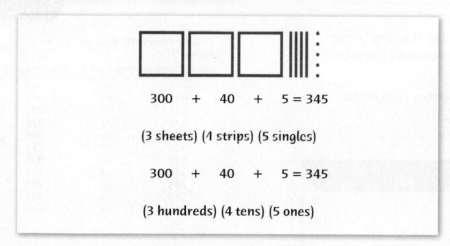

I'm wondering, when you look at all of this information, what you can say about the way we write 3-digit numbers? What would you tell first graders, or [Ms. Lopez] if [she] came in here, about what you know about 3-digit numbers?

STUDENTS MIGHT SAY

"I would tell them that the 3 in 345 is in the hundreds place. And that means there are 3 hundreds in the number. Or 3 groups of 100."

"Yeah it looks like it's just a 3, but really it's 3 *hundreds*, which is a lot more than 3."

"It's kind of the same with the 4—it tells you how many tens. That's not 4 (holding up 4 fingers); it's 4 tens (flashing 10 fingers 4 times). That's why they call it the tens place."

"The 5 is really just 5. It's the leftovers—the singles."

"The equations up there show all that. 300 + 40 + 5 shows that you can break a number into hundreds, tens, and ones."

As students share, ask others to point out where you can see the idea being shared in what's been recorded. Encourage volunteers to rephrase another student's idea or to build on that idea.

Repeat for another number or two, including a number with a zero in the tens or ones place.

SESSION FOLLOW-UP: REVIEW AND PRACTICE

Daily Practice

 DAILY PRACTICE For reinforcement of this unit's content, students complete *Student Activity Book* pages 327–328.

STUDENT ACTIVITY BOOK, P. 327

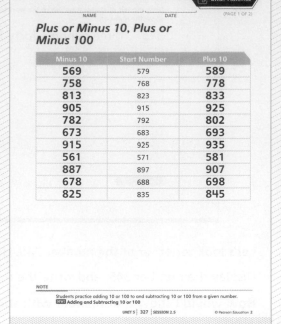

DAILY PRACTICE (PAGE 1 OF 2)

NAME _____ DATE _____

Plus or Minus 10, Plus or Minus 100

Minus 10	Start Number	Plus 10
569	579	589
758	768	778
813	823	833
905	915	925
782	792	802
673	683	693
915	925	935
561	571	581
887	897	907
678	688	698
825	835	845

NOTE
Students practice adding 10 or 100 to and subtracting 10 or 100 from a given number.
Adding and Subtracting 10 or 100

UNIT 5 | 327 | SESSION 2.5   © Pearson Education 2

STUDENT ACTIVITY BOOK, P. 328

DAILY PRACTICE (PAGE 2 OF 2)

NAME _____ DATE _____

Plus or Minus 10, Plus or Minus 100

Minus 100	Start Number	Plus 100
747	847	947
442	542	642
531	631	731
678	778	878
796	896	996
457	557	657
738	838	938
518	618	718
705	805	905
557	657	757
489	589	689

Ongoing Review

Which combination does **not** make 100?

Ⓐ 65 + 35   ● 25 + 70   Ⓒ 88 + 12   Ⓓ 77 + 23

UNIT 5 | 328 | SESSION 2.5   © Pearson Education 2

Ten Hundreds Make One Thousand

MATH FOCUS POINTS

- Reading and writing 3-digit numbers
- Identifying the value that each digit in a 3-digit number represents
- Adding 10 or 100 to and subtracting 10 or 100 from a given number, and describing what part of the number changes
- Using knowledge of place value to find pairs of 2-digit numbers that add to 100 or a number close to 100
- Working with the relationship between 1, 10, 100, and 1,000

VOCABULARY

- one thousand

TODAY'S PLAN	MATERIALS

 (10) Class   **CLASSROOM ROUTINES: REVIEW AND PRACTICE** | Teacher Presentation (or use Digit Cards 1, 4, 8)

Today's Number: What Could It Be? | Blank paper (1 sheet per student)

---

 (10) Individuals   **1 ASSESSMENT ACTIVITY** | A40*

Quiz 1 |

---

(30)   **2 MATH WORKSHOP** | 2A *Student Activity Book* pp. 329–330

Working with 3-Digit Numbers | S66* (optional, for the Extension)

   2A *Find the Number* | 2B Materials from Sessions 2.4 and 2.5

   2B *Plus or Minus 10 or 100* | 2C Materials from Session 2.2

   2C *Guess My Number* | 2D Materials from Session 2.1

   2D *Close to 100* |

---

  (20) Class   **3 DISCUSSION** | Teacher Presentation (or use one sheet of stickers)

Ten Hundreds Make One Thousand | Envelope of stickers (from Session 2.2) with at least 10 sheets of 100

SESSION FOLLOW-UP: REVIEW AND PRACTICE | *Student Activity Book*, pp. 331–334

Daily Practice and Homework |

---

* See *Materials to Prepare in the Investigation 2* Planner.

| Common Core State Standards | **Classroom Routines:** 2.NBT.A.1, 2.NBT.A.3, 2.NBT.A.4, 2.NBT.B.5
 Session: 2.NBT.A.1, 2.NBT.A.1a, 2.NBT.A.1b, 2.NBT.A.2, 2.NBT.A.3, 2.NBT.B.5, 2.NBT.B.8 | **Daily Practice:** 2.NBT.A.1, 2.NBT.A.3, 2.NBT.A.4, 2.NBT.B.5 |

CLASSROOM ROUTINES: REVIEW AND PRACTICE

Today's Number: What Could It Be?

MATH FOCUS POINTS

○ Reasoning about the place value of 3-digit numbers

○ Expressing a 3-digit number in expanded form

○ Generating equivalent expressions for a number

Display the Teacher Presentation or (use Digit Cards showing 1, 4, and 8).

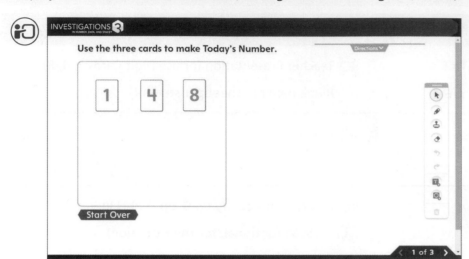

We are going to use these three cards to make Today's Number. Talk to a partner. What numbers could we make?

Generate and ask volunteers to record the 6 possibilities.

148   184   418   481   814   841

Today's Number is the number that has the most tens.

Ask what your number could be and how they know.

184   481

What question could you ask me to determine which of these two numbers is Today's Number?

Record students' questions, which might include asking about the number of hundreds or ones and whether it's the larger/smaller number. Respond to each, making sure that using greater than/less than notation to compare the two numbers comes up.

[Monisha] asked if it's the bigger number. Which one is the bigger number? How do you know? Can you help me use greater than and less than notation to show that information?

184 < 481   481 > 184

Explain that 481 is Today's Number. Write the number in words, connecting each word to the part of the number it represents.

I'd like you to include, as one of your ways to make 481, an equation that shows 481 as the sum of hundreds, tens, and ones.

Students generate ways to make 481. After they've had time to work, share a few solutions. Be sure to discuss $400 + 80 + 1 = 481$ (or $481 = 400 + 80 + 1$).

1 ASSESSMENT ACTIVITY

Quiz 1

Students complete Questions 1–4 on Quiz 1 (A40).

Review the format with students. Explain that students will solve the problems on their own, so you can get a sense of how they are growing in their math thinking.

Use this information, along with other information you have collected during this unit, when assessing a student's progress towards these Benchmarks.

BENCHMARKS	QUESTIONS
2: Understand that three-digit numbers represent amounts of hundreds, tens, and ones.	1, 3–4
3: Read, write, count, and compare numbers to 1,000.	1–4
4: Add/subtract 10 or 100 to/from numbers within 1,000.	2

2 MATH WORKSHOP

Working with 3-Digit Numbers

Students choose from the following four activities.

2 A Find the Number

For complete details on this activity, see Session 2.5. Additional problems are available on *Student Activity Book* pages 329–330.

 DIFFERENTIATION Supporting the Range of Learners

EXTENSION Adapt the Problem For students who work fluently with this activity, use S66 to give them different start numbers and different numbers to add/subtract. For example, these students can find 50 more/less and 120 more/less and then describe how the numbers change.

RESOURCE MASTERS, A40

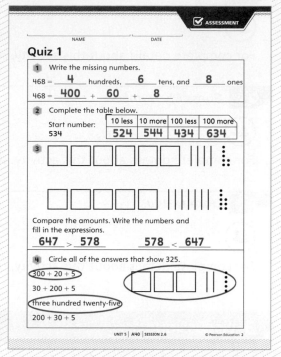

STUDENT ACTIVITY BOOK, P. 329

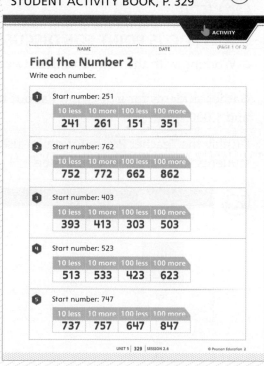

2 B   *Plus or Minus 10 or 100*

For complete details about this activity, see Sessions 2.4 and 2.5.

2 C   *Guess My Number*

For complete details about this activity, see Session 2.2.

2 D   *Close to 100*

For complete details about this activity, see Sessions 2.1 and 2.2.

---

3 DISCUSSION

Ten Hundreds Make One Thousand

MATH FOCUS POINT FOR DISCUSSION

○ Working with the relationship between 1, 10, 100, and 1,000

Gather students for a discussion about the relationship between 1, 10, 100, and 1,000. **MPN**

Display the Teacher Presentation (or use one sheet of stickers), and ask students to describe what they see.

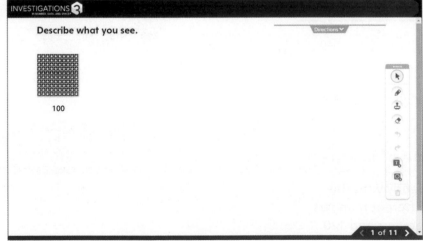

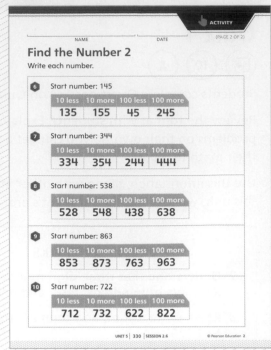

ACTIVITY

(PAGE 2 OF 2)

NAME _____ DATE _____

Find the Number 2
Write each number.

6   Start number: 145

10 less	10 more	100 less	100 more
135	155	45	245

7   Start number: 344

10 less	10 more	100 less	100 more
334	354	244	444

8   Start number: 538

10 less	10 more	100 less	100 more
528	548	438	638

9   Start number: 863

10 less	10 more	100 less	100 more
853	873	763	963

10   Start number: 722

10 less	10 more	100 less	100 more
712	732	622	822

UNIT 5 | 330 | SESSION 2.6   © Pearson Education 2

MATH PRACTICE NOTE

MPN 🔍 **MP7 Look for and make use of structure.** In this discussion, students explore a key feature of place value: that 10 ones make ten, 10 tens make one hundred, and 10 hundreds make one thousand. In later years, they will come to see that the value of each place is ten times greater than the value of the place to its right.

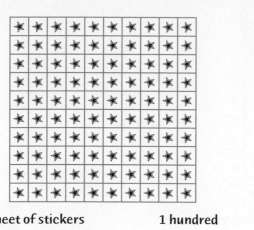

1 sheet of stickers   1 hundred

10 strips of 10 stickers   10 tens

100 stickers   100 ones

Add another sheet of 100 to the right of the first.

How could we describe two sheets of stickers? We can see that there are two sheets, or two hundreds. And the words tell us that there are 200 singles or ones. How many groups of ten are there?

2 sheets of stickers   2 hundred

20 strips of 10 stickers   20 tens

Continue adding sheets, one at a time, and counting the new set by hundreds each time, until you have a row of 5. In a separate space, track the growing number of hundreds and stickers using equations.

$$100$$
$$100 + 100 = 200$$
$$100 + 100 + 100 = 300$$
$$100 + 100 + 100 + 100 = 400$$
$$100 + 100 + 100 + 100 + 100 = 500$$

Continue, adding 5 more sheets, one by one below the first row, and recording the corresponding equation. Make sure the total number lines up so that students can see the growing pattern of numbers.

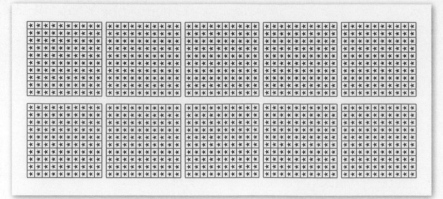

Now we have one thousand stickers. Take a minute. What's something you could say about this image of 1,000 stickers? Talk to a partner.

STUDENTS MIGHT SAY

"There are 1,000 stickers there. You could think of every square as one single sticker."

"There are 10 sheets of 100."

"And 10 tens make 100, and 20 tens are 200, so we could figure out how many tens are in 1,000. It would be a lot."

If we counted the stickers by 1s, what number would we land on? How many ones are in 1,000?

Record this information.

What if we count each group of 10 on each of the 100 grids by 10s? What number do you think we'll land on? Let's try it.

Count by 10s together as a class, to 1,000, pointing to each group of 10 on the hundred squares as you count.

We counted by 10s, and we got to 1,000. I wonder how many 10s we counted? And I wonder how many numbers we said?

If no one mentions counting each square by 10s, suggest it yourself.

[Monisha] said there are 10 tens in each group of 100. So 10 tens for the first hundred and 20 tens for the second hundred.

Continue counting each grid by 10s until you reach 100 tens.

There are 100 tens in 1,000.

How many hundreds make 1,000?

Count each grid square by 100s, and record this information.

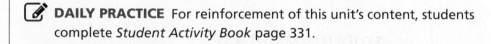

One Thousand
There are 1,000 ones   in 1,000.
There are   100 tens   in 1,000.
There are   10 hundreds   in 1,000.

End the discussion by connecting 10 hundreds in 1,000 back to the equation and the representation.

SESSION FOLLOW-UP: REVIEW AND PRACTICE

Daily Practice and Homework

DAILY PRACTICE For reinforcement of this unit's content, students complete *Student Activity Book* page 331.

HOMEWORK Students show numbers using sticker notation, equations, and numerals on *Student Activity Book* page 332.

FAMILY LETTER Send home *Student Activity Book* pages 333–334.

STUDENT ACTIVITY BOOK, P. 331

DAILY PRACTICE

NAME   DATE

Today's Number: Guess the Number

| 1 | 7 | 9 |

1 Write all of the possible numbers you can create with the three numbers above.
179, 197, 719, 791, 917, 971

2 Today's Number is less than 750.
Which numbers could it be? **179, 197, and 719**

3 Today's Number also has more 1s than 10s.
Which numbers could it be? **179 and 719**

4 Today's Number solves this equation:
21 + _____ = 200.
What is today's number? **179**

5 Write the number word for Today's Number.
one hundred seventy-nine

NOTE Students use clues to figure out Today's Number.
Representing Place Value: Hundreds, Tens, and Ones

UNIT 5 | 331 | SESSION 2.6   © Pearson Education 2

STUDENT ACTIVITY BOOK, P. 332

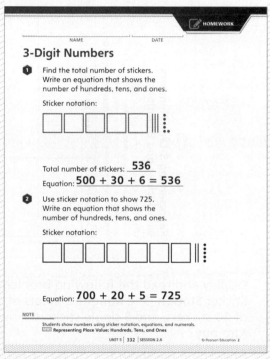

HOMEWORK

NAME   DATE

3-Digit Numbers

1 Find the total number of stickers. Write an equation that shows the number of hundreds, tens, and ones.

Sticker notation:

Total number of stickers: **536**
Equation: **500 + 30 + 6 = 536**

2 Use sticker notation to show 725. Write an equation that shows the number of hundreds, tens, and ones.

Sticker notation:

Equation: **700 + 20 + 5 = 725**

NOTE Students show numbers using sticker notation, equations, and numerals.
Representing Place Value: Hundreds, Tens, and Ones

UNIT 5 | 332 | SESSION 2.6   © Pearson Education 2

Representing 3-Digit Numbers with Stickers and Equations

(30) (👤)

MATH FOCUS POINTS

○ Reading and writing 3-digit numbers

○ Using a place-value model to represent 3-digit numbers as hundreds, tens, and ones

○ Representing 3-digit numbers in expanded form

MATERIALS: 1 set of paper stickers (made from T44), 1,000 Books (1 per student), S69

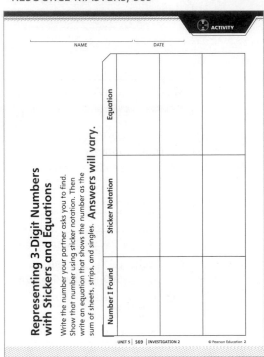

RESOURCE MASTERS, S69

Display and read the following problem: Kira went to Sticker Station. She bought 2 sheets of 100 stickers, 3 strips of 10 stickers, and 5 single stickers. How many stickers did Kira buy?

How could we show the stickers Kira bought? How many sheets of 100 stickers did she buy? How many strips? How many singles?

Ask a student to show the amount using a set of paper stickers. Then have all students record the sheets, strips, and singles given in the problem, using sticker notation.

How many stickers did Kira buy? How do you know?

Once students are in agreement about the total number of stickers Kira bought (235), have them write this number underneath their sticker representations.

How many stickers were on all of the sheets she bought? (200) How many stickers were on all of the strips she

bought? (30) How many singles were there? (5) **Write an equation under your sticker notation that shows 235 as the sum of sheets, strips, and singles. (200 + 30 + 5 = 235)**

Talk with students about the numbers in the hundreds, tens, and ones places. Help them connect those numbers to the numbers in their equation and to the sticker notation.

Can you find the number 235 in your 1,000 Book? On what page would you find it? How do you know?

Pose additional problems for students using the numbers 241 and 306, following the same steps as for 235.

Can you find the number 241 in your 1,000 Book? The number 306? How did you find these numbers? What did you look for?

 STUDENTS MIGHT SAY

 "I knew that 241 is greater than 235, but not by too much. I saw 240 at the end of the row near 235. So I had to go to the beginning of the next row.

"306 is bigger than both 235 and 241. I was going to turn the page when I realized that the 300 numbers were on that page too. So I looked for 300. Then I saw 306 in the next row."

Now you will work with a partner, taking turns choosing a number on the 201–400 chart. Once you find the number, show it in stickers and write an equation.

Distribute copies of Representing 3-Digit Numbers with Stickers and Equations (S69).

DIFFERENTIATION

ENGLISH LANGUAGE LEARNERS **Provide Vocabulary Support** Review the meanings of the terms *hundreds, tens,* and *ones* with students. As the terms are encountered, remind students of their meanings, and provide visuals to support students' comprehension. Look for opportunities to model the correct use of the terms, and encourage students to use them in their explanations.

ADDITIONAL RESOURCES

Math Words and Ideas Representing Place Value: Hundreds, Tens, and Ones

How Many Stickers? How Many Hundreds, Tens, and Ones?

MATH FOCUS POINTS

○ Reading and writing 3-digit numbers

○ Representing 3-digit numbers in expanded form

MATERIALS: 1 set of paper stickers (made from T44), blank paper (1 sheet per student), S70

RESOURCE MASTERS, S70

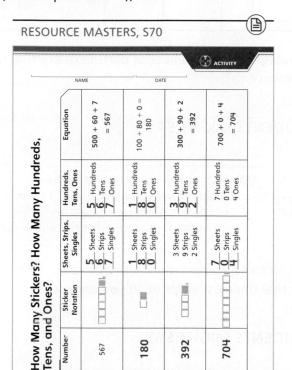

Display the following problem: Jake bought stickers at Sticker Station. He bought 4 sheets of 100, 5 strips of 10, and 8 singles. How many stickers did Jake buy?

Ask students to show the stickers Jake bought using sticker notation and to check their work with a partner.

How many stickers did Jake buy altogether? How do you know? Discuss these questions, and have students record the number 458 under their sticker representations. **How many hundreds are in the number 458? How many tens? How many ones?**

Some of you noticed that the number of sheets is the same as the number in the hundreds place, the number of strips is the same as the number in the tens place, and the number of singles is the same as the number in the ones place. Why do you think that is? Do you think that would be true for other numbers as well?

STUDENTS MIGHT SAY

"The number of hundreds will always be the same as the number of sheets. I know because there are always 100 stickers in a sheet. The same is true for strips and tens. There are always 10 stickers in a strip, and a single is equal to 1 sticker. It doesn't matter which number you use. That's how many you have of them."

What equation could we write to show the total number of sheets of 100, strips of 10, and single stickers Jake got? $(400 + 50 + 8 = 458)$

Once students are in agreement, have them record the equation under their sticker representation. Then display the following: 3 hundreds 6 tens 2 ones.

Kira went to Sticker Station and bought some stickers. How many sheets of stickers did she buy? How many strips of 10? How many single stickers? Share your thinking with a partner. Then work together to draw the amount of stickers Kira bought using sticker notation.

When students are finished, discuss their work together as a class. Then have students determine the total number of stickers (362) and the equation that represents this total $(300 + 60 + 2 = 362)$.

Distribute copies of How Many Stickers? How Many Hundreds, Tens, and Ones? (S70) for students to work on in pairs. Students should solve the problems together but record their work separately.

DIFFERENTIATION

ENGLISH LANGUAGE LEARNERS Partner Talk As partners work together to solve the problems on S70, observe them to confirm that they understand the vocabulary and are using it correctly. Ask questions to help facilitate their discussions. For example: **What number is in the [hundreds/tens/ones] place? How do you know? How will you show the value of the digit in the [tens] place? Why? How many [ones] are in the number [567]?** Also, have students use the expanded form of the numbers to practice reading the numbers aloud.

ADDITIONAL RESOURCES

Math Words and Ideas Representing Place Value: Hundreds, Tens, and Ones

Sticker Combinations

MATH FOCUS POINTS

○ Using a place-value model to represent 3-digit numbers as hundreds, tens, and ones

○ Representing 3-digit numbers in expanded form

MATERIALS: Cubes (137 per pair as needed), S71, S72

RESOURCE MASTERS, S71–S72

NAME _____ DATE _____

Combinations of 137

Find at least 4 ways to make 137 stickers using sheets of 100, strips of 10, and singles.

Answers will vary.

Equation	Singles	Strips	Sheets

UNIT 5 | S71 | INVESTIGATION 2 | © Pearson Education 2

Display 137 stickers using sticker notation. Ask students how many stickers are represented.

Imagine you are going to Sticker Station to buy 137 stickers. Work with a partner to find as many ways as you can to make 137 stickers.

Students work in pairs to record their work on S71. Students should model their ideas with cubes and then record each combination using sticker notation. When students have finished, call the group together to discuss their solutions.

What combinations of 137 did you find? Which combinations did you find that used a sheet of 100? Do we have all the combinations that used a sheet of 100? How do you know?

Which combinations did you find that used the most strips of 10?

As students share, record their combinations.

Sheets of 100	Strips of 10	Singles
	‖	• • • • • • • • • • • •
		27 •

What strategies did you and your partner use to find the combinations?

❝ STUDENTS MIGHT SAY ❞

"My partner and I tried to find all the combinations we could make with 1 sheet of 100 stickers. Then we worked on finding combinations that used only strips and singles."

Did anyone find a combination with more than 13 strips of 10? Is that the most strips of 10 you can use?

❝ STUDENTS MIGHT SAY ❞

"There are 10 strips of 10 in 100, and 3 strips of 10 makes 30. That's 13 strips altogether. You can't have more than 13 strips because 14 strips would be 140, which is too many."

Distribute copies of S72 for students to work on in pairs.

DIFFERENTIATION

ENGLISH LANGUAGE LEARNERS Provide Sentence Stems
Students may need support in order to verbalize their reasoning for how they can make 156 in different ways on S72. Provide sentence stems that students can use to answer questions. For example: *I can use _____ hundreds, _____ tens, and _____ ones to make _____. Could you use only tens and ones? How? I can use _____ tens and _____ ones to make _____.*

ADDITIONAL RESOURCES

Math Words and Ideas Representing Place Value: Hundreds, Tens, and Ones

INVESTIGATION 3

FLUENCY WITHIN 100

Main Math Ideas

○ Understanding, representing, and solving problems involving addition and subtraction

○ Using knowledge of place value to add and subtract

○ Extending the counting sequence

Fluency within 100

SESSION 3.1	SESSION 3.2
STRATEGIES FOR ADDITION Students solve addition problems and record their work. Class discussion focuses on strategies for adding 2-digit numbers.	**COMPARISON PROBLEMS WITH THE BIGGER AMOUNT UNKNOWN** Students are introduced to comparison problems with a bigger amount unknown. They solve these and other story problems and record their work. Discussion focuses on solution strategies.

	SESSION 3.1	SESSION 3.2
Professional Development	**TEACHER NOTES 6–8** **DIALOGUE BOXES 4–5**	**TEACHER NOTE 4**
Materials to View Ahead of Time	**TEACHER PRESENTATION:** ▸ **Classroom Routine** *What Time Is It? What Time Will It Be?: Quarter Hours*	**TEACHER PRESENTATIONS:** ▸ **Activity** Introducing Comparison Problems with a Bigger Unknown ▸ **Discussion** Discussing Strategies for Comparison Problems with a Bigger Unknown
Materials to Gather	**Demonstration clock** (optional) 🔧 **Student clocks** (1 per student) **Blank paper** (1 sheet per student) ☑ 📄 **A38, Assessment Checklist: MP4 and MP7** (from Session 1.3) 🔧 **Connecting cubes** (in towers of 10)	**1,000 Books** (from Investigation 2; as needed) **Blank paper** (1 sheet per student) ☑ 📄 **A38, Assessment Checklist: MP4 and MP7** (from Session 1.3) **Class number line**
Materials to Prepare	**Chart: "Adding Tens and Ones"** Title a piece of chart paper "Adding Tens and Ones." **Chart: "Adding One Number On in Parts"** Title a piece of chart paper "Adding One Number On in Parts."	

	SESSION 3.1	SESSION 3.2
Common Core State Standards	**Classroom Routines:** 2.MD.C.7 **Session:** 2.OA.A.1, 2.NBT.B.5, 2.NBT.B.6, 2.NBT.B.9, 2.MD.B.6 **Daily Practice:** 2.MD.C.7	**Classroom Routines:** 2.NBT.A.1, 2.NBT.A.2, 2.NBT.A.3, 2.NBT.B.5 **Session:** 2.OA.A.1, 2.NBT.B.5, 2.NBT.B.6, 2.NBT.B.9, 2.MD.B.6 **Daily Practice:** 2.NBT.A.2

| Present | Videos | Tools | Games | Assessment | MWI | Portfolio | eText | PDF |

	SESSION 3.3	SESSION 3.4
	CAPTURE 5 IN THE 1,000 BOOK Students solve comparison story problems with the bigger amount unknown, play *Close to 100*, or play *Capture 5* on any chart in their 1,000 Books. The session ends with a short discussion about skip counting by 5s and 10s.	**ADDING TENS AND ONES** Students discuss the strategy of adding tens and ones and practice using this strategy to solve problems. During Math Workshop, in addition to story problems, students can choose to play *Close to 100* or *Capture 5* on any chart in the 1,000 Book.
Professional Development	**DIALOGUE BOX 6**	
Materials to View Ahead of Time	**TEACHER PRESENTATION:** 📱 **Discussion** Skip Counting by 5s and 10s	**TEACHER PRESENTATION:** 📱 **Discussion** Adding Tens and Ones
Materials to Gather	**Students' envelopes of "Facts I Know" and "Facts I Am Still Working On"** (from Session 1.6) **Change Cards** (1 deck per pair; from Session 1.2) 📄 **G33, *Capture 5* Game Directions** (from Session 1.2) **1,000 Books** (from Investigation 2) **Translucent colored chips that fit on the squares of 1,000 Books** (12 per pair) **Game pieces that fit on the squares of 1,000 Books** (1 per pair) ☑📄 **A38, Assessment Checklist: MP4 and MP7** (from Session 1.3) **Materials for *Close to 100*** (from Session 2.1) **Wild Cards from Digit Cards** (from Unit 3; optional; for the Extension)	**1,000 Books** (from Investigation 2; as needed) **Blank paper** (1 sheet per student) **Chart: "Adding Tens and Ones"** (from Session 3.1) 🔧 **Connecting cubes** (in towers of 10) ☑📄 **A38, Assessment Checklist: MP4 and MP7** (from Session 1.3) **Materials for *Capture 5* in the 1,000 Book** (from Session 3.3) **Materials for *Close to 100*** (from Session 3.3)
Materials to Prepare	📄 **G32, *Capture 5* Recording Sheet** Make copies. (at least 1 per student, plus extras as needed) 📄 **G36, *Close to 100* Recording Sheet** Make copies. (1 per student, plus extras as needed)	📄 **S73, Solving Problems by Adding Tens and Ones** Make copies. (optional; for the Extension)
Common Core State Standards	**Classroom Routines:** 2.OA.B.2 **Session:** 2.OA.A.1, 2.OA.B.2, 2.NBT.A.2, 2.NBT.B.5, 2.NBT.B.6, 2.NBT.B.8 **Daily Practice:** 2.NBT.B.5	**Classroom Routines:** 2.NBT.A.2 **Session:** 2.OA.A.1, 2.NBT.B.5, 2.NBT.B.9 **Daily Practice:** 2.OA.A.1, 2.NBT.B.5

Fluency within 100

	SESSION 3.5	SESSION 3.6
	ADDING ONE NUMBER ON IN PARTS Students discuss the strategy of keeping one number whole and adding the other on in parts and practice using this strategy to solve problems. Math Workshop continues. Counting by 5s Strips are added to Math Workshop.	**ENOUGH FOR THE GRADE?** Students revisit and extend a familiar context, Enough for the Class?, as they solve 1- and 2-step story problems that ask instead whether there are Enough for the Grade? These problems are added to Math Workshop, and discussion focuses on what went wrong on sample Counting Strips.
Professional Development		
Materials to View Ahead of Time	**TEACHER PRESENTATIONS:** 📲 **Classroom Routine** *Today's Number: More or Less?* 📲 **Discussion** Adding On in Parts	**TEACHER PRESENTATIONS:** 📲 **Activity** Introducing Enough for the Grade? 📲 **Discussion** What Went Wrong?
Materials to Gather	**Blank paper** (1 sheet per student) **Chart: "Adding One Number On in Parts"** (from Session 3.1) 🔧 **Connecting cubes** (as needed) **Number lines** (as needed) **Tape** (as needed) **Materials for Solving Story Problems** (from Sessions 3.2, 3.3, and 3.4) **Materials for *Capture 5* in the 1,000 Book** (from Session 3.3) **Materials for *Close to 100*** (from Session 3.3)	**1,000 Books** (from Investigation 2; as needed) ☑ 📄 **A38, Assessment Checklist: MP4 and MP7** (from Session 1.3) **Materials for Counting Strips: 5s and 10s** (from Session 3.5) **Additional strips of adding machine tape** (as needed) **Materials for *Capture 5* in the 1,000 Book** (from Session 3.3) **Materials for *Close to 100*** (from Session 3.3)
Materials to Prepare	**Counting strips** Cut adding machine tape into strips about 2 feet long. (3–4 per student) 📄 **S74, Solving Problems by Adding On in Parts** Make copies. (optional; for the Extension)	📄 **S75, Enough for the Grade?: Bean Bags** Make copies. (optional; for the Extension) 📄 **S76, Enough for the Grade?: Cupcakes** Make copies. (optional; for the Extension) **Erroneous skip counting strips** Prepare several sections of skip counting strips, showing typical errors.
Common Core State Standards	**Classroom Routines:** 2.NBT.A.4, 2.NBT.B.5, 2.NBT.B.9 **Session:** 2.OA.A.1, 2.NBT.A.2, 2.NBT.A.3, 2.NBT.B.5, 2.NBT.B.8, 2.NBT.B.9, 2.MD.B.6 **Daily Practice:** 2.NBT.A.2	**Classroom Routines:** 2.NBT.A.1b, 2.NBT.A.2, 2.NBT.A.3, 2.NBT.B.5 **Session:** 2.OA.A.1, 2.NBT.A.1, 2.NBT.A.1b, 2.NBT.A.2, 2.NBT.A.3, 2.NBT.B.5, 2.NBT.B.8, 2.NBT.B.9, 2.MD.B.6 **Daily Practice:** 2.NBT.B.6

Present   Videos   Tools   Games   Assessment   MWI   Portfolio   eText   PDF

SESSION 3.7	SESSION 3.8
FLUENCY WITH ADDITION Students discuss efficient ways to notate their addition strategies. Math Workshop continues, and the session ends with a short assessment.	**ADDING WITHIN 100, COUNTING WITHIN 1,000** As an assessment, students solve two story problems: a comparison problem with a bigger unknown and an add to problem with result unknown. They also solve an addition problem presented only with numbers and notation and complete four skip counting strips.

	SESSION 3.7	SESSION 3.8
Professional Development	**TEACHER NOTE 5**	**TEACHER NOTE 9**
Materials to View Ahead of Time	**TEACHER PRESENTATION:** **Discussion** Are There Enough Bean Bags for the Grade?	**TEACHER PRESENTATION:** **Classroom Routine** *Today's Number: More or Less?*
Materials to Gather	**Connecting cubes** (4 bins) **Chart: "How Many Pockets?"** (from Session 2.3) **A38, Assessment Checklist: MP4 and MP7** (from Session 1.3) **Materials for Counting Strips: 5s and 10s** (from Session 3.5) **Additional strips of adding machine tape** (as needed) **Materials for *Capture 5* in the 1,000 Book** (from Session 3.3) **Materials for *Close to 100*** (from Session 3.3)	**Blank paper** (1 sheet per student)
Materials to Prepare	**S77, Enough for the Grade?: Pencils** Make copies. (optional; for the Extension) **S78, Enough for the Grade?: Ice Pops** Make copies. (optional; for the Extension) **A41–A42, Quiz 2** Make copies.	**A43–A44, How Many Points?** Make copies or use the Online Assessment. **A45, Skip Counting Strips** Make copies or use the Online Assessment.
Common Core State Standards	Classroom Routines: 2.OA.B.2, 2.NBT.B.5, 2.NBT.B.6 Session: 2.OA.A.1, 2.NBT.A.1, 2.NBT.A.2, 2.NBT.A.3, 2.NBT.B.5, 2.NBT.B.6, 2.NBT.B.8, 2.NBT.B.9 Daily Practice: 2.OA.B.2	Classroom Routines: 2.NBT.A.4, 2.NBT.B.5, 2.NBT.B.9 Session: 2.OA.A.1, 2.NBT.A.2, 2.NBT.B.5 Daily Practice: 2.NBT.A.1b, 2.NBT.A.3, 2.NBT.A.4, 2.NBT.B.5

Strategies for Addition

MATH FOCUS POINTS

o Visualizing, representing, and solving add to story problems with the result unknown

o Developing efficient strategies for adding 2-digit numbers

o Developing efficient methods for notating addition strategies

VOCABULARY

o adding one number in parts

o adding tens and ones

	TODAY'S PLAN	MATERIALS
Class (10)	**CLASSROOM ROUTINES: REVIEW AND PRACTICE** *What Time Is It? What Time Will It Be?:* *Quarter Hours*	Teacher Presentation (or use the demonstration clock) Student clocks Blank paper (1 sheet per student)
Individuals Class (20)	**1** ACTIVITY **An Addition Problem**	Student Activity Book, p. 335 Student Activity Book, p. 336 (optional; for the Extension) A38 (from Session 1.3) Connecting cubes (optional; for the Intervention)
Class (20)	**2** DISCUSSION **Strategies for Addition**	Student Activity Book, p. 335 Chart: "Adding Tens and Ones"* Chart: "Adding One Number On in Parts"* Connecting cubes (in towers of 10)
Individuals Class (20)	**3** ACTIVITY **More Addition Problems**	Student Activity Book, pp. 335–338 A38 (from Activity 1)
	SESSION FOLLOW-UP: REVIEW AND PRACTICE **Daily Practice and Homework**	Student Activity Book, pp. 339–342

* See *Materials to Prepare* in the Investigation 3 Planner.

Common Core State Standards	**Classroom Routines:** 2.MD.C.7 **Session:** 2.OA.A.1, 2.NBT.B.5, 2.NBT.B.6, 2.NBT.B.9, 2.MD.B.6	**Daily Practice:** 2.MD.C.7

What Time Is It?: What Time Will It Be?: Quarter Hours

MATH FOCUS POINTS

○ Naming, notating, and telling time to the hour, half hour, and quarter hour using analog and digital formats

○ Determining what time it will be when given start and elapsed times that are multiples of 15 minutes

Ask students to set their clocks to 2:00 and to record the time in digital format. Display the Teacher Presentation (or set the demonstration clock to 2:00), and ask **"In 15 minutes what time will it be?"**

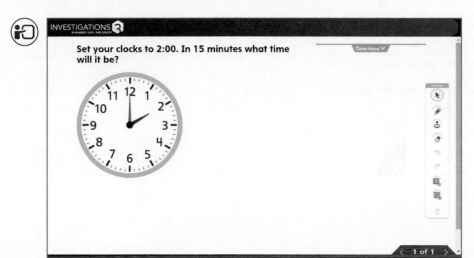

Pairs set their clocks, record the new time, and discuss how they knew. Emphasize counting by 5s as a way of determining 15 minutes. Record the new time (2:15), and ask **"In 15 minutes what time will it be?"** Students set their clocks, record the time (2:30), and discuss how they knew with their partner. Repeat with start times of 4:45 and 7:00. **MWI**

---

1 ACTIVITY

An Addition Problem

Explain to students that for the rest of this unit, they will find and practice ways to add 2-digit numbers that are both efficient and accurate. **PD** **MPN1**

Read aloud Problem 1 on *Student Activity Book* page 335.

Kira had 48 balloons. Jake gave her 33 more balloons. How many balloons does Kira have now?

Ask several students to retell the story and predict whether there will be more or fewer balloons at the end of the story. Students then work individually on *Student Activity Book* page 335 to write an equation that represents the problem and to solve the problem, being sure to show their work. **MPN2**

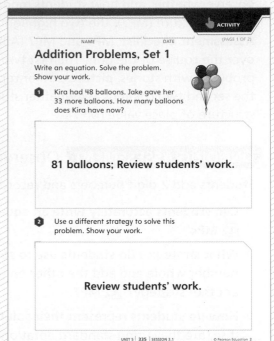

ACTIVITY

NAME   DATE   (PAGE 1 OF 2)

Addition Problems, Set 1

Write an equation. Solve the problem. Show your work.

1 Kira had 48 balloons. Jake gave her 33 more balloons. How many balloons does Kira have now?

81 balloons; Review students' work.

2 Use a different strategy to solve this problem. Show your work.

Review students' work.

UNIT 5 | **335** | SESSION 3.1   © Pearson Education 2

MATH WORDS AND IDEAS

MWI Telling Time to the Quarter Hour

PROFESSIONAL DEVELOPMENT

PD TEACHER NOTE 7: Students' Addition Strategies

MATH PRACTICE NOTES

MPN1 🔍 **MP7 Look for and make use of structure.** Efficient strategies make use of the base 10 structure of numbers.

MPN2 🔍 **MP4 Model with mathematics.** Representing a context with an equation is one aspect of mathematical modeling.

The addition and subtraction problems in this unit provide an opportunity to observe whether and how students model with mathematics (MP4) and make use of structure (MP7), the two highlighted math practices in this unit. Use **Assessment Checklist:** MP4 and MP7 (A38) to keep track of your observations over the course of the unit. The first two columns ask how students represent problems with stories, pictures, other representations, and equations (MP4); the second two columns ask whether students use strategies that rely on the structure of place value (MP7).

ONGOING ASSESSMENT Observing Students at Work

Students add 2-digit numbers and record their work.

○ **Can students accurately write an equation that represents the problem?** 📭 **MP4**

○ **What strategies do students use to solve the problem?** Do they keep one number whole and add the other on in parts? Add tens and ones? Use another strategy? 📭 **MP7**

○ **How do students represent their solution strategy?** Do they use equations? If so, are they using standard notation accurately? A number line? Sticker notation? A combination? Can you tell how they solved the problem?

Make note of students who are adding one number in parts and also those who are adding by place to call on in the discussion that follows.

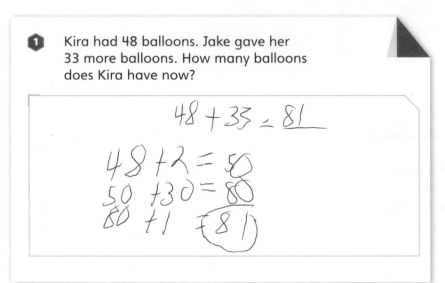

1 Kira had 48 balloons. Jake gave her 33 more balloons. How many balloons does Kira have now?

$$48 + 33 = 81$$
$$48 + 2 = 50$$
$$50 + 30 = 80$$
$$80 + 1 = (81)$$

1 Kira had 48 balloons. Jake gave her 33 more balloons. How many balloons does Kira have now?

$$48$$
$$+33$$
$$\overline{}$$
$$70 + 11 = 81$$

DIFFERENTIATION Supporting the Range of Learners

For another practice activity to be done outside of class, see *Adding On in Parts* at the end of this investigation.

INTERVENTION Adapt the Learning Situation Meet in a small group with students who need extra support. Talk through the problem, asking students to describe both quantities in tens and ones. Model representing the quantities with sticker notation. Suggest that students add by place to solve the problem: adding the tens, adding the ones, and then adding the results. Model the problem with cubes if needed, making explicit how more than 10 ones can make another ten.

For a more comprehensive intervention activity to be done outside of class, see *Adding Tens and Ones* at the end of this investigation.

EXTENSION Extend Thinking Ask students who solve this problem efficiently and accurately and who adequately show their work in a concise way if they can also solve the same problem using a different strategy. For example, if they added by place can they also solve the problem by keeping one number whole and adding the other on in parts? Have them find a different way to solve the same problem. They can also begin work on *Student Activity Book* page 336.

ENGLISH LANGUAGE LEARNERS Provide Opportunities for Practice To help students prepare for the class discussion, have them explain their strategies for solving the problem to partners. Provide a sequence that students can use. *First, I _____. Next, I _____. Then, I _____.* If students point to information or explain by using one or two words, then restate the information using simple sentences and have students repeat after you. Alternatively, write students' explanations, and have them practice reading or retelling their explanations to partners.

2 DISCUSSION

Strategies for Addition

MATH FOCUS POINTS FOR DISCUSSION

○ Developing efficient strategies for adding 2-digit numbers

○ Developing efficient methods for notating addition strategies

When all students have solved the problem on *Student Activity Book* page 335, call them together to discuss their strategies. The goal of this conversation is to discuss two strategies in particular: keeping one number whole and adding the other on in parts and adding tens and ones. Students will be practicing these two strategies throughout this investigation. MN1 PD1

Begin by asking students about the equations they wrote to show what the problem was asking. Notate the problem using horizontal and vertical notation. PD2 MN2

STUDENT ACTIVITY BOOK, P. 336

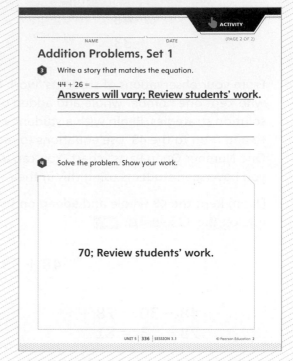

ACTIVITY

NAME   DATE   (PAGE 2 OF 2)

Addition Problems, Set 1

3 Write a story that matches the equation.

$44 + 26 =$ _____

Answers will vary; Review students' work.

4 Solve the problem. Show your work.

70; Review students' work.

UNIT 5 | 336 | SESSION 3.1   © Pearson Education 2

MATH NOTES

MN1 **Order Does Not Matter** All of the strategies in this discussion involve breaking apart one or both addends and combining the parts in a different order. These ideas are discussed in Unit 3. See **Teacher Note 6:** Does Order Matter? and **Dialogue Box 4:** Does Order Matter?, both in Unit 3.

MN2 **Vertical or Horizontal?** Throughout this investigation, use both vertical and horizontal notation, emphasizing that both methods mean the same thing and that the way a problem is written does not dictate how students must solve it.

PROFESSIONAL DEVELOPMENT

PD1 DIALOGUE BOX 5: Addition Strategies

PD2 TEACHER NOTE 8: Notating Addition Strategies

$$48 + 33 = \qquad\qquad 33 + 48 =$$

$$\begin{array}{r} 48 \\ +\ 33 \\ \hline \end{array} \qquad\qquad \begin{array}{r} 33 \\ +\ 48 \\ \hline \end{array}$$

From your observations of students' work in the first activity, call on students who kept one number whole and added on the other in parts to share their solution strategies. Begin with a student who broke the 33 into tens and ones to add it on to the 48. Use equations to record the strategy on the "Adding One Number On in Parts" chart. You can also model it with vertical notation if you have seen students using this in their work. MN1

[Juan] kept the 48 whole and added on the 33. [He] used tens and ones to add on the 33 in parts. MWI

$$48 + 33 =$$

$$48 + 30 = 78$$
$$78 + \ 3 = 81$$

$$\begin{array}{r} 48 \\ +\ 30 \\ \hline 48 + 30 = \quad 78 \\ +\ \ 3 \\ \hline 81 \end{array}$$

Ask another student who used a number line to notate their strategy to share their work or demonstrate. Highlight that the 33 was added in two groups, specifically that the 30 was added on in one step, rather than adding on 3 groups of 10.

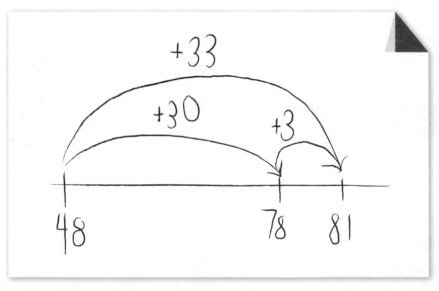

[Carla's Work]

Developing an efficient strategy for adding two numbers means that you are adding the biggest groups possible. So when [Carla] added the 30 on in one step rather than adding a group of 10 and another group of 10 and another group of 10, [she] was being efficient. [She] added the 30 in one step rather than 3 steps. MN2

As you discuss this strategy, focus the discussion on how students choose to add on the 33 (or the 48 if they kept the 33 whole) and how you can "see" the 33 in the strategy.

STUDENT ACTIVITY BOOK, P. 337

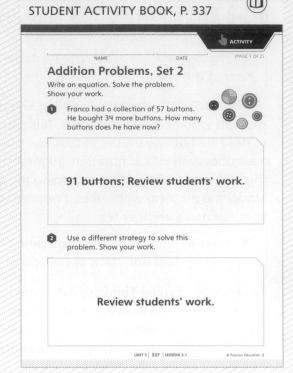

Addition Problems, Set 2

Write an equation. Solve the problem. Show your work.

❶ Franco had a collection of 57 buttons. He bought 34 more buttons. How many buttons does he have now?

91 buttons; Review students' work.

❷ Use a different strategy to solve this problem. Show your work.

Review students' work.

UNIT 5 | 337 | SESSION 3.1   © Pearson Education 2

MATH NOTES

MN1 **Understanding Vertical Notation** Some students use vertical notation to record. As you model their strategies, add notation that shows what was added (e.g., $48 + 30$) to help students make sense of both the strategy and the notation. Emphasize that you are doing this for demonstration purposes. Students who use vertical notation do not need to do this when they record.

MN2 **Efficiency** Some students break the 30 into 3 tens and add $48 + 10 + 10 + 10 + 3$. Help them compare this strategy with $48 + 30 + 3$. Because fluently adding within 100 is a Benchmark for the end of this unit, students should be working toward increasingly efficient strategies. Thus, students who can easily add tens should try adding multiples of 10. Students who are counting by ones should try adding groups of 10 and would benefit from targeted support.

MATH WORDS AND IDEAS

MWI Strategies for Adding 2-Digit Numbers: Adding One Number On in Parts

Where is the 33 in [Juan]'s equations? Where can we see the 33 in [Carla]'s number line?

Some students feel more comfortable adding on to a number that is a multiple of 10. These students solve this problem by adding 48 + 2 + 30 + 1. If there are students who used this strategy, discuss and record it or ask them to share their work, again focusing on how students added the 33 and how they can *see* the 33 in the number line representation.

[Leo] kept the 48 whole, too, but [he] added on the 33 differently. [Leo], why did you start by adding 2?

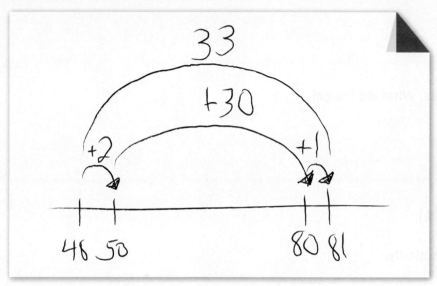

[Leo's Work]

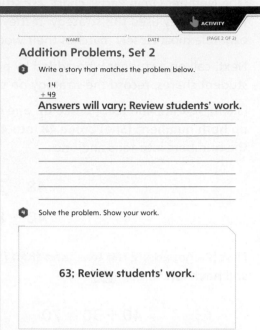

STUDENT ACTIVITY BOOK, P. 338

ACTIVITY

NAME   DATE   (PAGE 2 OF 2)

Addition Problems, Set 2

3   Write a story that matches the problem below.

$$\begin{array}{r} 14 \\ +\ 49 \\ \hline \end{array}$$

<u>Answers will vary; Review students' work.</u>

4   Solve the problem. Show your work.

63; Review students' work.

UNIT 5 | **338** | SESSION 3.1   © Pearson Education 2

If students used a number line to represent their strategy, demonstrate how equations can be used to notate what was represented on the number line.

$$48 + 33 = \underline{\quad}$$

$$48 + \ \ 2 = 50$$

$$50 + 30 = 80$$

$$80 + \ \ 1 = 81$$

[Leo] solved the problem in 3 steps. After [he] added 2 to get to 50 how much of the 33 was left? Think about how you could add that amount to the 50.

STUDENTS MIGHT SAY

"I can just see it in my head. I know 50 plus 30 is 80 and then 1 more is 81! 50 plus 31 is 81!"

"I would think 5 plus 3 is 8 and so I know 50 plus 30 is 80 and like [Anita] said, 1 more is 81. So you could solve the problem in two steps."

When you have several variations of this strategy recorded on the "Adding One Number On in Parts" chart, ask students to look at their work and decide whether they used this strategy. If they did, ask them to consider which example most closely matches their work.

Next, call on a student who added by place to solve the problem. As the student shares, record the strategy on the "Adding Tens and Ones" chart.

[Juan], [Carla], and [Leo] broke up one of the numbers, the 33. [Paige] broke up both numbers. [She] broke 48 into 40 + 8 and 33 into 30 + 3. [She] broke the numbers into tens and ones.

$$48 + 33 = ?$$

$$40 + 8 + 30 + 3 = ?$$

First [Paige] added the tens, and then [she] added the ones. What did [Paige] still have left to do? MWI

$$40 + 30 = 70$$

$$8 + 3 = 11$$

$$70 + 11 = 81 \text{ (or, } 70 + 10 + 1 = 81\text{)}$$

Also discuss how the same information can be recorded vertically.

$$
\begin{array}{r}
48 \\
+\,33 \\
\hline
70 \quad (40 + 30) \\
+\,11 \quad (8 + 3) \\
\hline
81 \quad (70 + 10 + 1)
\end{array}
$$

Ask another student to use sticker notation to model the strategy for the class, or ask the class to help you do so. Be sure to demonstrate how the 11 singles can be represented as one additional group of ten and one single.

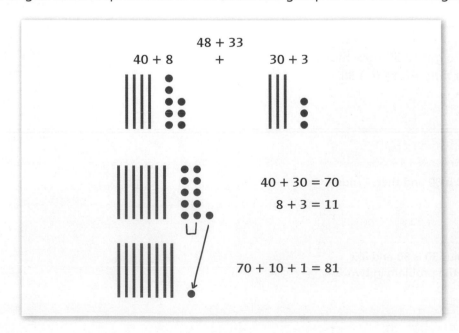

MATH WORDS AND IDEAS

MWI Strategies for Adding 2-Digit Numbers: Adding Tens and Ones

If you have students who used another version of adding tens and ones, ask one of them to share. MN1 MN2

After you have recorded one or two strategies on your "Adding Tens and Ones" chart, ask students to look at their work and decide whether they used this strategy. Ask students which strategy more closely matches what they did. MN3

Finally, ask students to consider what is happening with the tens and ones in this problem.

The problem was 48 + 33. If you add the tens, you get 4 tens plus 3 tens or 40 plus 30, and that's 7 tens or 70. Why wasn't our answer in the 70s?

Modeling the problem with sticker notation or cubes, as described above, can help students see that there is another ten in the 11 ones. That makes 8 tens, which puts the answer in the 80s.

3 ACTIVITY

More Addition Problems

Explain that students will now finish Addition Problems, Set 1 on *Student Activity Book* pages 335–336 and continue with Addition Problems, Set 2 on pages 337–338. Some of these pages ask students to solve each problem in two ways. Encourage students to use whatever strategy they are most comfortable with first and then to try using one of the strategies just discussed.

Because these pages include story problems as well as horizontal and vertical addition problems, remind students that the way a problem is written does not change what it is asking or the strategies that they can use to solve it.

Point out that the problems that are presented purely with numbers also ask students to write a story problem that matches. To introduce this idea, look together at problem 3 on *Student Activity Book* page 336, 44 + 26, and ask students to suggest a story or two. Encourage students to write a *different* story when they work on their own.

Continue to use **Assessment Checklist:** MP4 and MP7 (A38) in this activity.

ONGOING ASSESSMENT Observing Students at Work

Students add 2-digit numbers and record their work.

○ **Can students accurately write an equation or a story problem that represents the problem?**

○ **What strategies do students use to solve the problem?** Are they using the ideas and strategies just discussed, such as adding on one number in parts or adding tens and ones? 🔍 **MP7**

○ **Is their strategy efficient?** Are they adding on a multiple of 10, or are they adding on a group of 10 at a time? If they combine 10s and 1s, do they do it efficiently? Are they able to account for an extra group of 10 ones? 🔍 **MP7**

MATH NOTES

MN1 How Are They the Same? Most students begin with 40 + 30 or 30 + 40. Their second steps will vary (e.g., 8 + 3 = 11, 70 + 8 = 78, or 70 + 3 = 73), as will the ways they carry out these sub-problems (e.g., adding 11 as a whole vs. breaking it into 10 and 1). Focus students' attention on the first step (40 + 30) to help them see what is the same in each of these methods and to understand why they are all considered "adding tens and ones."

MN2 Add the Ones First If there are students who add the ones first and then the tens, record this strategy with equations as well. Some students may be using the steps and notation of the U.S. standard algorithm for addition. Help students see that this strategy also involves adding tens and ones. Although the strategies are the same, the shorthand notation used to record the steps of the standard algorithm can obscure both the place value of the numbers and the meaning of each step of the procedure.

MN3 Other Strategies Be sure to acknowledge other strategies used to solve the problem. For example, some students create an equivalent problem, reasoning, "I can take 2 from the 33 and give it to the 48. That's 50 plus 31, and that's 81." Others add a nearby "friendly" or "landmark" number and then compensate, thinking, "33 + 50 would be 83. I added 2 too many, so take 2 away from 83, and it's 81."

○ **How do students represent their solution strategy?** Do they use equations? If so are they using standard notation accurately? Vertical notation? A number line? Sticker notation? A combination? Can you tell how they solved the problem?

○ **Are students able to use a different strategy to solve the problem?**

Collect students' work to get a sense of the range of strategies they are using to solve addition problems.

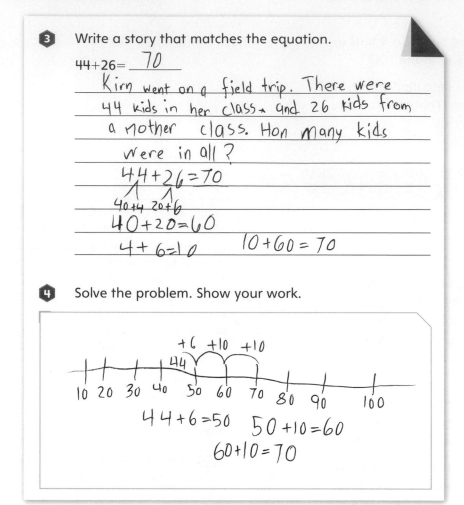

3 Write a story that matches the equation.

44 + 26 = ___70___

Kim went on a field trip. There were 44 kids in her class, and 26 kids from a nother class. How many kids were in all?

44 + 26 = 70

40 + 4   20 + 6

40 + 20 = 60

4 + 6 = 10   10 + 60 = 70

4 Solve the problem. Show your work.

+6 +10 +10

44

10 20 30 40 50 60 70 80 90 100

44 + 6 = 50   50 + 10 = 60

60 + 10 = 70

[Monisha's Work]

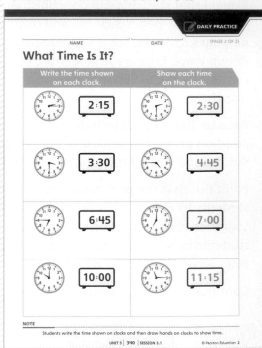

STUDENT ACTIVITY BOOK, P. 339

DAILY PRACTICE

NAME   DATE   (PAGE 1 OF 2)

What Time Is It?

Read each clock. Record what time it is, and write the time in words. Then record and draw what time it will be in 15 minutes.

What time is it now?	What time will it be in 15 minutes?
8:00 eight o'clock	8:15 eight fifteen
12:00 twelve o'clock	12:15 twelve fifteen
6:30 six thirty	6:45 six forty-five
2:30 two thirty	2:45 two forty-five
3:00 three o'clock	3:15 three fifteen

NOTE

Students practice telling, recording, and determining the time to the hour, half hour, and quarter hour.

Measuring Time; Parts of an Hour

UNIT 5 | 339 | SESSION 3.1   © Pearson Education 2

STUDENT ACTIVITY BOOK, P. 340

DAILY PRACTICE

NAME   DATE   (PAGE 2 OF 2)

What Time Is It?

Write the time shown on each clock.	Show each time on the clock.
2:15	2:30
3:30	4:45
6:45	7:00
10:00	11:15

NOTE

Students write the time shown on clocks and then draw hands on clocks to show time.

UNIT 5 | 340 | SESSION 3.1   © Pearson Education 2

1 Franco had a collection of 57 buttons. He bought 34 more buttons. How many buttons does he have now?

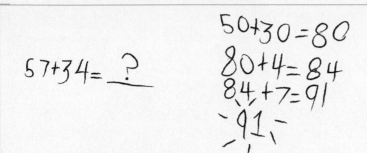

$$57+34= \underline{}\;?$$

$$50+30=80$$
$$80+4=84$$
$$84+7=91$$
$$-91-$$

2 Use a different strategy to solve this problem. Show your work.

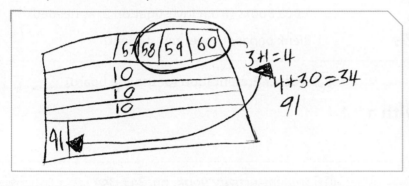

[Alberto's Work]

SESSION FOLLOW-UP: REVIEW AND PRACTICE

Daily Practice and Homework

DAILY PRACTICE For ongoing review, students complete *Student Activity Book* pages 339–340.

HOMEWORK Students solve two addition problems and show their work, and write a story problem and solve it on *Student Activity Book* pages 341–342.

STUDENT ACTIVITY BOOK, P. 341

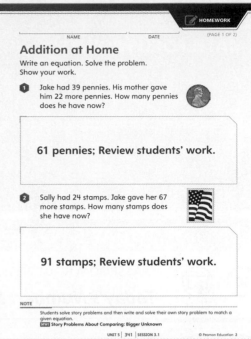

HOMEWORK

(PAGE 1 OF 2)

NAME   DATE

Addition at Home

Write an equation. Solve the problem. Show your work.

1 Jake had 39 pennies. His mother gave him 22 more pennies. How many pennies does he have now?

61 pennies; Review students' work.

2 Sally had 24 stamps. Jake gave her 67 more stamps. How many stamps does she have now?

91 stamps; Review students' work.

NOTE

Students solve story problems and then write and solve their own story problem to match a given equation.
Story Problems About Comparing: Bigger Unknown

UNIT 5 | 341 | SESSION 3.1   © Pearson Education 2

STUDENT ACTIVITY BOOK, P. 342

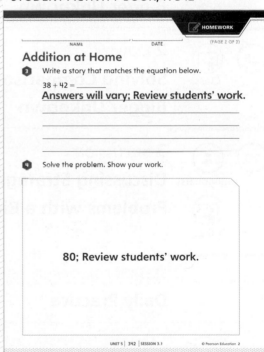

HOMEWORK

(PAGE 2 OF 2)

NAME   DATE

Addition at Home

3 Write a story that matches the equation below.

$$38+42=\underline{}$$
Answers will vary; Review students' work.

4 Solve the problem. Show your work.

80; Review students' work.

UNIT 5 | 342 | SESSION 3.1   © Pearson Education 2

Comparison Problems with the Bigger Amount Unknown

MATH FOCUS POINTS

○ Visualizing, representing, and solving comparison problems with a bigger unknown (more than/fewer than)

○ Developing efficient strategies for adding 2-digit numbers

○ Developing efficient methods for notating addition strategies

VOCABULARY

○ comparing
○ more than
○ greater than
○ fewer than
○ less than

TODAY'S PLAN	MATERIALS
CLASSROOM ROUTINES: REVIEW AND PRACTICE *Today's Number: Skip Counting by 5s*	1,000 Books (from Investigation 2; as needed) Blank paper (1 sheet per student)
1 ACTIVITY **Introducing Comparison Problems with a Bigger Unknown**	Teacher Presentation (or use the board)
2 ACTIVITY **Solving Comparison Problems with a Bigger Unknown**	Student Activity Book, pp. 343–344 A38 (from Session 1.3)
3 DISCUSSION **Discussing Strategies for Comparison Problems with a Bigger Unknown**	Teacher Presentation (or use Student Activity Book, pp. 343–344) Student Activity Book, pp. 341–342 Class number line
SESSION FOLLOW-UP: REVIEW AND PRACTICE **Daily Practice**	Student Activity Book, pp. 345–346

Common Core State Standards	**Classroom Routines:** 2.NBT.A.1, 2.NBT.A.2, 2.NBT.A.3, 2.NBT.B.5 **Session:** 2.OA.A.1, 2.NBT.B.5, 2.NBT.B.6, 2.NBT.B.9, 2.MD.B.6	**Daily Practice:** 2.NBT.A.2

CLASSROOM ROUTINES: REVIEW AND PRACTICE

Today's Number: Skip Counting by 5s

MATH FOCUS POINTS

○ Counting by 5s within 500

○ Identifying patterns in the skip counting sequence of 5s

○ Generating equivalent expressions for a number

Students count around the class by 5s beginning with the number 500. They can use their 1,000 Books to help them if they wish. As students count, record the numbers they say in a column. Encourage students to look at the list of numbers and share what they notice.

What numbers are on the list and not on the list? What patterns in the number sequence do you notice? Can you explain this pattern?

Count around the class by 5s again, this time beginning from 700. Again, record the numbers in a list, and discuss what students notice.

Now you and a partner can practice counting by 5s. You and your partner should pick a number in your 1,000 Books that ends with a 5 or a 0 as your start number.

Have students pair up and use their 1,000 Books to count by 5s, starting from a multiple of 5. After a few minutes of practice call the class together and explain that Today's Number is 125. Students generate equations using only multiples of 5 (e.g., $125 = 100 + 25$; $125 = 100 + 20 + 5$).

---

1 ACTIVITY

Introducing Comparison Problems with a Bigger Unknown

Display the Teacher Presentation (or write the following problem on the board) and read the problem aloud.

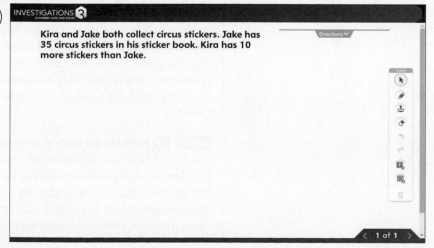

Kira and Jake both collect circus stickers. Jake has 35 circus stickers in his sticker book. Kira has 10 more stickers than Jake.

Turn and talk with a partner about what information we know about this problem.

Make a list of known information. As a piece of information is shared, relate it back to the story problem. MN MWI MPN1

> Jake and Kira both have circus stickers.
> Jake has 35 circus stickers.
> Kira has 10 more stickers than Jake.
> Kira has more stickers than Jake.

[Jacy] said that Kira has more stickers than Jake. What part of the problem tells us that information?

" STUDENTS MIGHT SAY "

"It says Kira has 10 *more* stickers than Jake. So that means Kira has more stickers."

"Right. 10 more stickers. Jake has 35, and Kira has 10 more than that."

Sometimes it is helpful to draw a sketch of a problem so that you can see it on paper in addition to seeing it in your mind. I'm just going to make a quick sketch of this problem using two bars. We know Jake and Kira both have stickers. (Draw two equal horizontal bars, one labeled Jake's stickers and the other labeled Kira's stickers.) And we are comparing the amount of stickers each of them has. MPN2

If they had the same amount of stickers, these bars would work because they are equal length. But you told me that Kira has more stickers than Jake so I'll make hers longer than Jake's. What else do we know? Right, we know Jake has 35 stickers.

Record 35 on the bar showing Jake's stickers.

Jake's Stickers	35	
Kira's Stickers		

MATH NOTE

MN **Comparison Problems with the Bigger Amount Unknown** Students are familiar with comparison problems where there are two known amounts, and the difference between them is the unknown (e.g., Sally has 10 stickers and Jake has 15 stickers. Who has more? How many more?). In this new problem, students know one amount (Jake has 35 stickers) and the difference (Kira has 10 more stickers than Jake). They need to figure out the other amount (how many stickers Kira has). The unknown amount is bigger than the known amount. For more information, see **Teacher Note 4:** Types of Story Problems.

MATH WORDS AND IDEAS

MWI Story Problems about Comparing: Bigger Unknown

MATH PRACTICE NOTES

MPN1 **MP1 Make sense of problems and persevere in solving them.** Because of the complexity of the language in comparison problems with bigger (or smaller) amounts unknown, it is necessary to spend more time discussing the meaning of these problems and making sure students understand the relationship between the quantities that are given and what is to be found.

MPN2 ▣ **MP4 Model with mathematics.** The use of two bars to represent a story problem is a kind of mathematical model. The mathematical elements of the problem are shown in relation to each other, revealing the missing quantity.

How can we show that Kira has 10 more stickers than Jake on our sketch?

Have a few students indicate which part of the sketch shows Kira's 10 additional stickers.

Several of you pointed out the part of Kira's bar that extends beyond Jake's as Kira's 10 extra stickers, and a few people showed the extra stickers as the space beyond Jake's bar.

Jake's Stickers	35
Kira's Stickers	10

Reread the problem again gesturing to each part of the sketch that corresponds to words. Then pose the final question for students to answer.

I think lots of you have figured out what question we are going to answer about this problem and that is, if Jake has 35 stickers and Kira has 10 more than Jake, how many stickers does Kira have?

Have students turn and talk with a partner to discuss the solution. When students share their solutions, listen for evidence that they are thinking about Kira's stickers as being 10 more than 35 or 45 stickers. Record the equation $35 + 10 = 45$ under Kira's bar on the sketch. Look back at the list of known information, and confirm that 45 stickers makes sense. **MPN**

What if I asked you a second question about Kira and Jake's circus stickers? What if I wanted to know how many circus stickers they would have if they combined their stickers? What equation would you write to show that problem?

Record the equation (i.e., $35 + 45 = $ _____), and let students know that they now will solve some similar story problems. Explain that for each problem, they should think about what information they know, what they are trying to figure out and then solve the problem and show their thinking so that someone looking at their paper could tell how they thought about the solution.

STUDENT ACTIVITY BOOK, P. 343

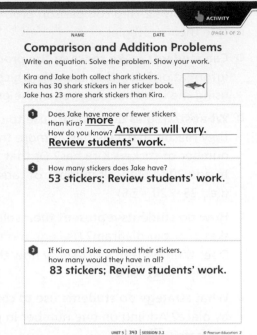

2 ACTIVITY

Solving Comparison Problems with a Bigger Unknown

Students solve the problems on *Student Activity Book* pages 343–344. Their work should show how they thought about the problem and include an equation that represents the problem.

Briefly read through both pages as a class. The first page is similar to the problem students just discussed. The second page, while also about a bigger unknown, presents known information in terms of how many fewer. Let students know that they will be discussing Problems 4–6 at the end of the session. **PD**

Continue to use **Assessment Checklist:** MP4 and MP7 (A38) in this activity.

MATH PRACTICE NOTE

MPN ☑ **MP4 Model with mathematics.**
An equation that represents a story problem is also a kind of mathematical model.

PROFESSIONAL DEVELOPMENT

PD TEACHER NOTE 4: Types of Story Problems

ONGOING ASSESSMENT Observing Students at Work

Students solve 2-step comparison problems with the bigger unknown and notate their strategies.

○ **Can students make sense of the problem?** Do they identify the known information? Can they identify which person has the larger/smaller quantity using the information given in the problem?

○ **What strategies do students use to determine the unknown quantity?** Do they reason that Jake has 23 more than Kira and add this amount to the number of stickers Kira has? Or that Franco has 20 fewer cans so they need to add 20 to Franco's number of cans to determine how many Sally has? (i.e., $35 + 20 = 55$)

○ **How do students represent their solution strategy?** Do they draw a quick sketch or bar diagram? Use equations? Sticker notation? A combination? Does their written work show how they thought about/solved the problem? 🔍 **MP4**

○ **What strategy do students use to combine the quantities?** Are they adding by place? Adding on one number in parts? Is their strategy efficient and accurate? 🔍 **MP7**

Make note of students who represent their solutions in clear and understandable ways so that you can call on them during the discussion that follows.

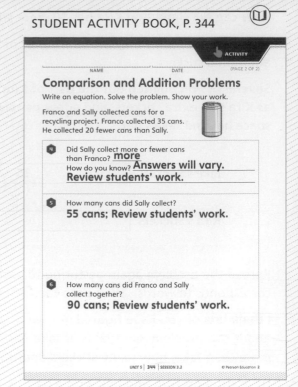

STUDENT ACTIVITY BOOK, P. 344

ACTIVITY

NAME _____ DATE _____ (PAGE 2 OF 2)

Comparison and Addition Problems

Write an equation. Solve the problem. Show your work.

Franco and Sally collected cans for a recycling project. Franco collected 35 cans. He collected 20 fewer cans than Sally.

4   Did Sally collect more or fewer cans than Franco? **more**
How do you know? **Answers will vary.**
Review students' work.

5   How many cans did Sally collect?
55 cans; Review students' work.

6   How many cans did Franco and Sally collect together?
90 cans; Review students' work.

UNIT 5 | **344** | SESSION 3.2   © Pearson Education 2

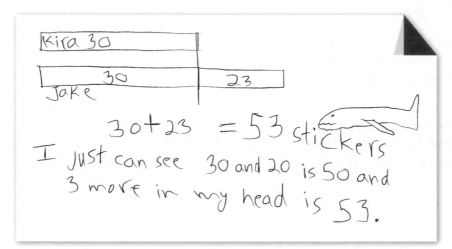

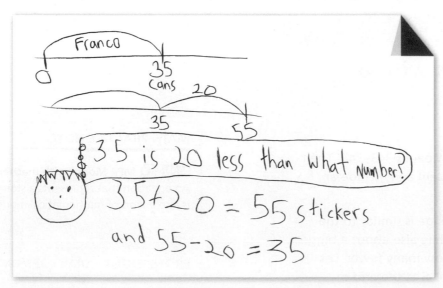

 **DIFFERENTIATION** Supporting the Range of Learners

INTERVENTION Scaffold a Solution It may help some students to think first about what the situation would look like if both people had the same number of stickers (or cans). **If Kira and Jake both had the same number of stickers how many would they have? (30) Do they have the same number? Who has more?** Clarifying whether or not the student knows whether Jake will have more or fewer than 30 stickers is an important first step in thinking about this problem. Encourage students to draw a sketch showing this information and help them label each part. **Who has more? How many more?** Help students show this information on their sketches.

ENGLISH LANGUAGE LEARNERS Provide Vocabulary Support Review the meanings of the terms *more, fewer,* and *combined* as they are encountered in the problems on *Student Activity Book* pages 343–344. Use simple definitions for each term. For example: **Remember, if Kira and Jake *combined* their stickers, it means they *put together* all of their stickers.** To check for understanding, have students draw a sketch to show what is happening. Then have students restate the problem before they begin to solve it.

3 DISCUSSION

Discussing Strategies for Comparison Problems with a Bigger Unknown

MATH FOCUS POINTS FOR DISCUSSION

○ Visualizing, representing, and solving comparison problems with a bigger unknown (more than/fewer than)

○ Developing efficient strategies for adding 2-digit numbers

Gather students to discuss the problems on *Student Activity Book* pages 343–344. Because Problems 1–3 are similar to the problem presented at the beginning of the session, the main focus of this discussion will be on Problems 4–6 (*Student Activity Book* page 344).

Display the Teacher Presentation (or use *Student Activity Book* page 343), and briefly discuss Problems 1–2 by asking students about the known information in the problem. Ask how they determined whether or not Jake would have more or fewer stickers than Kira.

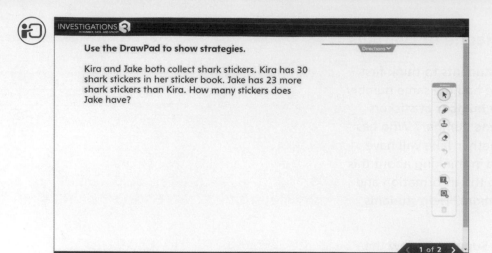

Use the DrawPad to show strategies.

Kira and Jake both collect shark stickers. Kira has 30 shark stickers in her sticker book. Jake has 23 more shark stickers than Kira. How many stickers does Jake have?

Once you figured out that Jake would have more stickers than Kira, how did you solve the problem?

STUDENTS MIGHT SAY

"If Kira has 30 and Jake has 23 more then I just wrote down 30 plus 23 equals what. I did it in my head and got 53. 53 is 23 more than 30."

"I knew if they both had the same, Jake would have 30 stickers, but he has 23 more than that. So I wrote this equation (30 + 23 = _____), and I just knew in my head 30 and 20 is 50 and 3 more is 53."

"I drew two lines and wrote 30 on them. Then I took a jump of 23 on this one see, and it got me to 53."

[Rochelle] can you show us your line drawing? [Rochelle] drew two lines, but on one of the lines [she] showed a "jump" of 23. Almost like we do when we are showing strategies on the number line.

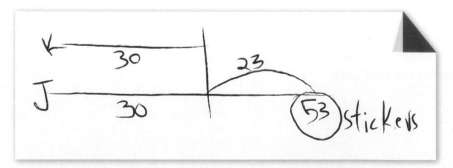

What does the jump of 23 stand for? And what about the 30? Where is the answer to the problem?

Ask students to help you record an equation that represents the problem, and then move on to discuss Problems 4–6 on *Student Activity Book* page 344.

Read the problem together, and then list the known information in the problem.

> **Franco and Sally collected cans.**
> **Franco collected 35 cans.**
> **Franco collected 20 fewer cans than Sally.**

One of the most important pieces of information in the problem is knowing whether the number of cans Sally collected is greater than the number of cans Franco collected or fewer than or less than that number. How did you think about that?

Identifying this piece of information is important in terms of choosing a solution strategy. As students explain their thinking, look for those who seem to understand the relationship between Franco's cans and Sally's cans. Ask specifically about the use of the word "fewer."

This problem said that Franco collected *fewer* cans than Sally. What does that tell you about the number of Franco's cans compared to the number of Sally's cans?

STUDENTS MIGHT SAY „

"Fewer than means the same thing as less than, so I just know that Franco collected less cans than Sally, and Sally collected more cans than Franco."

Listen for evidence that students understand the comparison and that Franco collected a smaller number of cans than Sally. Some students might express this by saying Sally collected more or that Sally will have a number that is greater than 35 or by understanding the words "fewer than" as meaning "less than." Add this information to the list of known information.

> **Franco and Sally collected cans.**
> **Franco collected 35 cans.**
> **Franco collected 20 fewer cans than Sally.**
> **Sally collected more cans than Franco.**

Then discuss students' strategies.

STUDENTS MIGHT SAY

"I thought of making a cube train with 35 cubes for Franco and then I knew I needed to add on the 20 more cubes to that train to make it show Sally's cans. But I didn't really make the cube train. I just thought it in my mind. Sally's cube train was longer."

"After I read the problem I thought, okay so what number is 20 more than 35 because I knew Sally's number had to be more."

"You can do it on the number line. See here is 35. And so you think what number is 20 away from 35. Since we know Franco collected less cans, so Sally's number has to be a bigger number. So I just thought 10 more is 45 and another 10 more is 55, and that's 20."

Look for images or representations students are thinking about as they solved the problem. Select one or two to highlight for the class.

[Tia] said [she] looked at the number line to help [her]. Let's use the class number line to think about this problem.

Use the class number line or make a sketch. Label 35 as Franco's cans.

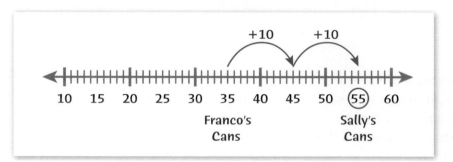

[Tia] said that [she] thought about what number was 20 away from 35. Why 20? What does that represent? [She] also said that [she] knew that 35 was less than Sally's number. So [she] added 20 on in two jumps of 10, and [she] landed on 55.

Record $35 + 10 + 10 = 55$. Ask students what each part of the equation represents, being sure to label 55 as Sally's cans. Record $35 + 20 = 55$ underneath.

[Malcolm] said that [he] thought about cube trains. Imagine that in your mind. Instead of building trains with cubes, I'm going to use lines to show the trains. Can you help me draw a sketch with lines that show Franco's cans and Sally's cans?

Have students direct you as you draw a quick sketch of two equal lines, adding known information to the sketch as students suggest.

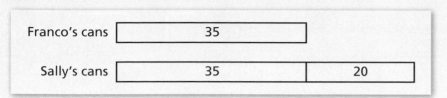

| Franco's cans | 35 | |
| Sally's cans | 35 | 20 |

Ask students for an equation that matches this representation, again relating each part to the sketch and to the problem.

Then discuss the last part of the problem about the total number of cans collected. Record an equation for the problem, and ask students to share their strategies for combining these numbers. Begin by asking a student who added by place to share his or her strategy. Record the steps using both horizontal and vertical notation.

$$35 + 55 =$$
$$30 + 50 = 80$$
$$5 + 5 = 10$$
$$80 + 10 = \boxed{90}$$

$$\begin{array}{r} 35 \\ + 55 \\ \hline 80 \quad (30 + 50) \\ + 10 \quad (5+5) \\ \hline \boxed{90} \end{array}$$

Several people added by place to find the total number of cans. You broke both the 35 and the 55 into 10s and 1s. You combined the tens and then the ones and then added those amounts. There are two ways we can record this strategy.

Talk through both forms of notation highlighting the same step in each form of notation. Then ask one or two students who kept one number whole and added the other on in parts to share. Record a strategy that shows adding on 55 to 35 and one that shows adding on 35 to 55.

$$35 + 55 =$$
$$35 + 5 = 40$$
$$40 + 50 = \boxed{90}$$

$$55 + 35 =$$
$$55 + 30 = 85$$
$$85 + 5 = \boxed{90}$$

Each of these shows adding one number in parts. Where can you see the 55 being added on? What about the 35?

Highlight this by drawing a loop around the +5 and the +50 and the +30 and the +5.

Let students know that they will be solving more problems like these during Math Workshop in the next session.

SESSION FOLLOW-UP: REVIEW AND PRACTICE

Daily Practice

DAILY PRACTICE For ongoing review, students complete *Student Activity Book* pages 345–346.

STUDENT ACTIVITY BOOK, P. 345

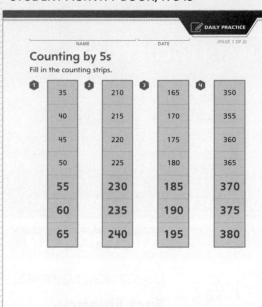

STUDENT ACTIVITY BOOK, P. 346

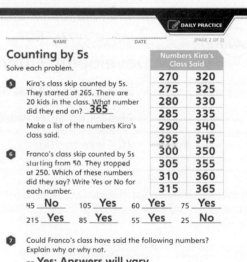

Capture 5 in the 1,000 Book

MATH FOCUS POINTS

○ Visualizing, representing, and solving comparison problems with a bigger unknown (more than/fewer than)
○ Developing efficient strategies for adding 2-digit numbers
○ Adding and subtracting a number of tens and/or ones to/from a 3-digit number
○ Using knowledge of place value to find pairs of 2-digit numbers that add to 100 or a number close to 100
○ Skip counting by 5s and 10s within 1,000 and noticing patterns in the counting sequence

VOCABULARY

○ count by 5s
○ count by 10s

TODAY'S PLAN	MATERIALS

  CLASSROOM ROUTINES: REVIEW AND PRACTICE
Fact Fluency

 Student Activity Book p. 349

Students' envelopes of "Facts I Know" and "Facts I Am Still Working On" (from Session 1.6)

---

  1 ACTIVITY
Introducing Math Workshop

---

 2 MATH WORKSHOP
Developing Fluency with Addition

   2A *Capture 5 in the 1,000 Book*

   2B Solving Story Problems

   2C *Close to 100*

2A G32*

G33

Change Cards (from Session 1.2)

1,000 Books (from Investigation 2)

Translucent colored chips (12 per pair)

Game pieces (1 per pair)

2B *Student Activity Book*, pp. 347–348

A38 (from Session 1.3)

2C G36 *

Materials from Session 2.1

Wild Cards from Digit Cards (optional; for the Extension)

---

  3 DISCUSSION
Skip Counting by 5s and 10s

Teacher Presentation (or use the board)

1,000 Books (from Investigation 2; as needed)

SESSION FOLLOW-UP: REVIEW AND PRACTICE
Daily Practice and Homework

Student Activity Book, pp. 349–350

---

* See *Materials to Prepare* in the Investigation 3 Planner.

Common Core State Standards	Classroom Routines: 2.OA.B.2 Session: 2.OA.A.1, 2.OA.B.2, 2.NBT.A.2, 2.NBT.B.5, 2.NBT.B.6, 2.NBT.B.8	Daily Practice: 2.NBT.B.5

CLASSROOM ROUTINES: REVIEW AND PRACTICE

Fact Fluency

MATH FOCUS POINT

○ Developing fluency with addition and subtraction within 20

Students review and practice the cards in their "Facts I Am Still Working On" envelope. They can work alone or with a partner. Work in a small group with students who have more than a few facts in their "Facts I Am Working On" envelopes. Help them select a fact and then discuss and write a clue. Students select up to six facts to practice at home and record these on *Student Activity Book* page 349. Explain that students will be practicing these facts for homework tonight.

ACTIVITY

NAME   DATE

Fact Practice

Choose 6 facts that are hard for you to
remember. Write them on the blank cards.

12 ☐ 6 = 7
Clue: 12 - 6 = 6

Use something you know to write a clue.
Practice these with someone at home.
Answers will vary.

___ ☐ ___ = ___   ___ ☐ ___ = ___
Clue: _____   Clue: _____

___ ☐ ___ = ___   ___ ☐ ___ = ___
Clue: _____   Clue: _____

___ ☐ ___ = ___   ___ ☐ ___ = ___
Clue: _____   Clue: _____

UNIT 5 | 349 | SESSION 3.3   © Pearson Education 2

1 ACTIVITY

Introducing Math Workshop

Introduce the three activities students will be working on during Math Workshop. In addition to *Close to 100*, students can play *Capture 5* using any page in their 1,000 Book as the game board. Briefly review the directions, and remind students of the materials they will need to play the game.

In addition to *Close to 100* and *Capture 5* in the 1,000 Book, you will also be working on a set of story problems similar to the ones you solved yesterday. Remember to read each problem and try to imagine it in your mind before you begin to solve it. Think about how to show your work for each problem so that someone looking at your paper would understand your thinking. **MPN1** **MPN2**

Let students know that they should spend some part of Math Workshop working on the story problems, in addition to playing one of the games.

2 MATH WORKSHOP

Developing Fluency with Addition

Students choose among the following activities, all of which focus on supporting the development of efficient and accurate strategies for adding 2-digit numbers.

MATH PRACTICE NOTES

MPN1 **MP1 Make sense of problems and persevere in solving them.** Given a story problem to solve, the first step is always to picture the situation in one's mind.

MPN2 **MP6 Attend to precision.** Being able to communicate one's mathematical ideas is an aspect of knowing, learning, and doing mathematics.

2 A *Capture 5* in the 1,000 Book

Pairs choose any chart in the 1,000 Book to use as their game board. They also need counters that fit on those squares, a deck of Change Cards (C53–C54), and a game piece. Each student needs a copy of the *Capture 5* Recording Sheet (G32). The directions are available on G33.

ONGOING ASSESSMENT Observing Students at Work

Students add and subtract multiples of 10 and single-digit numbers to 3-digit numbers.

○ **How do students move on the game board?** Do they fluently add or subtract 10 or multiples of 10 to or from a number and move their piece, or do they make jumps of 10? Are they comfortable adding and subtracting to/from 3-digit numbers? 🔍 **MP7**

○ **How do students capture a chip?** Are they playing more strategically? Do they determine the distance from their game piece to a chip and look for combinations of Change Cards that will make up that distance? 🔍 **MP7**

○ **Can students write equations that accurately reflect their moves from one number to another?**

○ **Are students demonstrating knowledge of the effect of combining forward and backward moves (e.g., using +30 and −10 cards to move forward 20 spaces)?** 🔍 **MP7**

---

2 B Solving Story Problems

Students solve story problems about comparing and adding on *Student Activity Book* pages 347–348.

For complete details about this activity, see Session 3.2. Continue to use **Assessment Checklist:** MP4 and MP7 (A38) in this activity.

---

2 C *Close to 100*

For complete details about this activity, see Session 2.1.

 DIFFERENTIATION Supporting the Range of Learners

EXTENSION Extend Thinking Students who are ready for more challenge can add Wild Cards to the deck of Digit Cards. A Wild Card can stand for any number. Explain that if students use a Wild Card to make a number they should write "W.C." above that number when they record the equation on their *Close to 100* Recording sheet (G36).

> For a more comprehensive extension activity to be done outside of class, see *Close to 100 with Wild Cards* at the end of this investigation.

STUDENT ACTIVITY BOOK, P. 347

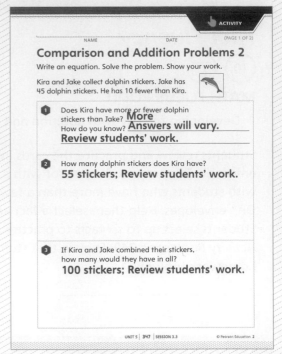

STUDENT ACTIVITY BOOK, P. 348

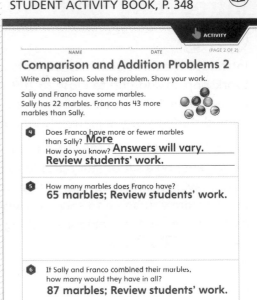

ENGLISH LANGUAGE LEARNERS Model Thinking Aloud Help students understand how to use a Wild Card. **A Wild Card can be any number you want it to be.** Model how to show and use a Wild Card. For example, write each number as you show and read your cards: **I got [2, 6, 8, 5, Wild Card, and 3]. I need to get as close to 100 as I can. I'll start by making [82].** Write **[82]. How much more do I need to get 100? That's right, I need [18] more to get 100.** Use a number line or 100 Chart to demonstrate how you know you need [18] to get to 100. **I have an [8], so I'll make my Wild Card be [1].** Write the equation as you say it: **Now I have [82] + [18] = [100]. My score for this round is [0]!**

3 DISCUSSION

Skip Counting by 5s and 10s

MATH FOCUS POINT FOR DISCUSSION

○ Skip counting by 5s and 10s within 1,000, and noticing patterns in the counting sequence

Display the Teacher Presentation (or write the number word four hundred sixty-five on the board), and ask students to talk with a partner about what Digit Cards you would need to show the number.

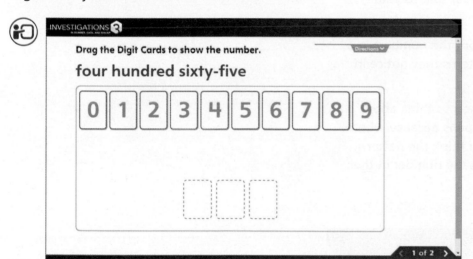

Record the number under the words, and ask students to explain how the words helped them know which numbers to use. Focus specifically on the number 6 in the tens place.

Can you explain why the word says "sixty" but we only used a 6 not a 6 and a zero?

At this point in the year, students should be able to talk about the 6 as representing 6 tens or 60. Next focus students on the counting by 5s number sequence. **PD**

PROFESSIONAL DEVELOPMENT

PD DIALOGUE BOX 6: Counting by 5s and 10s

Suppose we were going to count by 5s around our class starting from 400. Do you think someone would say "465?" Why or why not? MPN

Take a few ideas, and then begin the count. As students count, record a list of numbers beginning with 400 and ending with the last student's number. Verify that the number 465 is on the list, and ask students what they notice about this sequence of numbers.

" STUDENTS MIGHT SAY "

"They all end in 5 or 0, and the pattern goes 0, 5, 0, 5, 0."

"It does that because you keep adding 5 and 0 plus 5 is 5 then 5 + 5 is 10, so that's where the zero comes from."

"The first number stays the same, and the tens number goes 0, 0, 1, 1, 2, 2, 3, 3, 4, 4, 5, 5, and on like that."

This time, let's count by 10s around the class. We are going to start at 400 again. Do you think we will say 465 when we count by 10s? Talk to your partner, and then we will count. MWI

Begin the count again at 400, and as students count, record the numbers in a list next to the counting by 5s list. Ask students what patterns they notice in this list of numbers.

I have a question we aren't going to answer; it's a question to think about. [Jacy] noticed that the 0, 5 pattern in the ones place happens because when you count by 5s you are adding 5 each time. Why do you think the pattern [Chen] noticed in the tens place happens? And why does the number in the hundreds place stay the same for so many numbers?

SESSION FOLLOW-UP: REVIEW AND PRACTICE

Daily Practice and Homework

 DAILY PRACTICE For reinforcement of this unit's content, students complete *Student Activity Book* page 350.

 HOMEWORK Students practice the facts they recorded on *Student Activity Book* page 349 with someone at home.

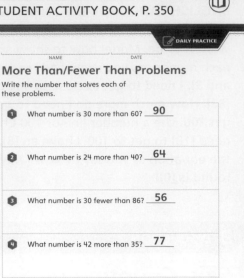

MATH PRACTICE NOTE

MPN 🔍 **MP7 Look for and make use of structure.** When students explain *why* the patterns they notice hold, they are identifying structures of the number system.

MATH WORDS AND IDEAS

MWI Skip Counting by 5s and 10s

Adding Tens and Ones

MATH FOCUS POINTS

○ Developing efficient strategies for adding 2-digit numbers

○ Developing efficient methods for notating addition strategies

○ Visualizing, representing, and solving comparison problems with a bigger unknown (more than/fewer than)

TODAY'S PLAN	MATERIALS
(10) Class **CLASSROOM ROUTINES: REVIEW AND PRACTICE** *Today's Number: Skip Counting by 5s*	1,000 Books (from Investigation 2; as needed) Blank paper (1 sheet per student)
(20) Class **1 ACTIVITY** **Practicing Adding by Place**	📖 *Student Activity Book* pp. 351–352 📄 S73* (optional; for the Extension) Chart: "Adding Tens and Ones" (from Session 3.1) 🔧 Connecting cubes (optional; for the Intervention)
(10) Class **2 DISCUSSION** **Adding Tens and Ones**	📲 Teacher Presentation (or use *Student Activity Book*, p. 351) 📖 *Student Activity Book*, p. 351 🔧 Connecting cubes (in towers of 10)
(30) **3 MATH WORKSHOP** **Developing Fluency with Addition** 3A Solving Story Problems 3B *Capture 5* in the 1,000 Book 3C *Close to 100*	📖 3A *Student Activity Book* pp. 353–354 ☑️📄 A38 (from Session 1.3) 3B Materials from Session 3.3 3C Materials from Session 3.3
SESSION FOLLOW-UP: REVIEW AND PRACTICE **Daily Practice**	📖 *Student Activity Book*, p. 355

* See *Materials to Prepare* in the Investigation 3 Planner.

Common Core State Standards	Classroom Routines: 2.NBT.A.2 Session: 2.OA.A.1, 2.NBT.B.5, 2.NBT.B.9	Daily Practice: 2.OA.A.1, 2.NBT.B.5

CLASSROOM ROUTINES: REVIEW AND PRACTICE

Today's Number: Skip Counting by 5s

MATH FOCUS POINTS

○ Counting by 5s within 1,000

○ Identifying patterns in the skip counting sequence of 5s

○ Generating equivalent expressions for a number

Students count around the class by 5s beginning with the number 800. They can use their 1,000 Books to help them if they wish. As students count, record the numbers they say in a column. Encourage students to look at the list of numbers and share what they notice.

What numbers are on the list and not on the list? What patterns in the number sequence do you notice? Can you explain this pattern? MPN1

Count around the class by 5s again, this time beginning from 685. Again, record the numbers in a list, and discuss what students notice.

Now you and a partner can practice counting by 5s. You and your partner should pick a number in your 1,000 Books that ends with a 5 or a 0 as your start number.

Have students pair up and use their 1,000 Books to count by 5s, starting from a multiple of 5. After a few minutes of practice, call the class together and explain that Today's Number is 100. Students generate equations using only multiples of 5 and 10 (e.g., 100 = 75 + 25; 100 = 120 − 20; and so on).

---

1 ACTIVITY

Practicing Adding by Place

Display the "Adding Tens and Ones" chart, and remind students of the work they have been doing with learning how to add 2-digit numbers efficiently and accurately and how they have been working to show their strategies using equations or a number line or with sticker notation or sketches.

Display the following problem horizontally and vertically. Remind students that a problem written vertically means the same thing as a problem written horizontally.

$$\begin{array}{r} 56 \\ + 25 \\ \hline \end{array} \qquad\qquad 56 + 25 =$$

I want everyone to think about this question: How could you explain to someone how to use the strategy of adding tens and ones to solve this problem? MPN2 MWI

MATH PRACTICE NOTES

MPN1 🔍 **MP7 Look for and make use of structure.** Noticing patterns in counting sequences and explaining why they hold helps students develop fluency in the number system.

MPN2 MP8 Look for and express regularity in repeated reasoning. The strategy of adding tens and ones (or adding by place) is an application of the commutative and associative properties of addition.

$56 + 25 = (50 + 6) + (20 + 5) =$

$50 + (6 + 20) + 5 =$

$50 + (20 + 6) + 5 =$

$(50 + 20) + (6 + 5)$

Grade 2 students are not expected to know and use such terminology, but they can recognize that when they break up the 56 and 25, they have a new problem with four addends that can be combined in any order.

MATH WORDS AND IDEAS

MWI Strategies for Adding 2-Digit Numbers: Adding Tens and Ones

Together as a class, with students offering ideas, briefly describe the steps for solving the problem using tens and ones. Remind students of the discussions from the previous sessions about breaking the numbers apart and combining the tens and then the ones.

Then, ask students to solve the problems on *Student Activity Book* pages 351–352 using the strategy of adding tens and ones. Point out that they will need to write a story problem for the second problem. **MPN**

ONGOING ASSESSMENT ▸ Observing Students at Work

Students practice adding tens and ones and notating their strategies.

○ **Can students write an equation or story problem that represents the problem?**

○ **Are students able to add by place?** Do they accurately combine tens with tens and ones with ones? How do they keep track? What tools, models, or representations do they use? Do they get the right answer? **MP7**

○ **How do students represent their strategies and record their work?** Do they use equations? Is their notation clear and accurate? Do they use representations such as a number line or sticker notation to explain their strategies?

 **DIFFERENTIATION** Supporting the Range of Learners

INTERVENTION Adapt the Problem If students are unable to engage productively in the strategy, try to discern if they understand what it means to break apart a number into tens and ones. If they are able to do this, it might be that the numbers in these problems are too large for students to think about in a meaningful way. Choose a problem such as 38 + 22. Ask students to model the problem with cubes, and use equations or use sticker notation to represent their work with cubes.

EXTENSION Vary the Problem Students who solve the problems efficiently and accurately and who notate their strategies in a clear and understandable way can solve the more challenging problems on S73.

ENGLISH LANGUAGE LEARNERS Allow Varied Responses Students may need additional support writing story problems. Encourage students to draw sketches of their story problems, write the story problems in their first languages, and/or tell their story problems to partners and work with partners to write the story problems in English. Provide sentence stems, words, or phrases that students can use in their stories. If students use their first languages to label pictures, help them write the information in English under their labels.

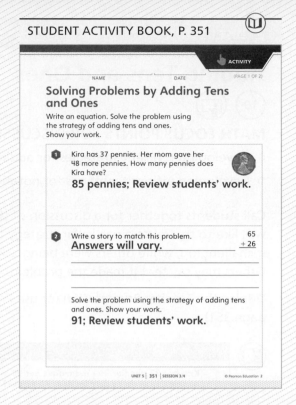

STUDENT ACTIVITY BOOK, P. 351

Solving Problems by Adding Tens and Ones

Write an equation. Solve the problem using the strategy of adding tens and ones. Show your work.

1. Kira has 37 pennies. Her mom gave her 48 more pennies. How many pennies does Kira have?
85 pennies; Review students' work.

2. Write a story to match this problem.
Answers will vary.
$$65 + 26$$

Solve the problem using the strategy of adding tens and ones. Show your work.
91; Review students' work.

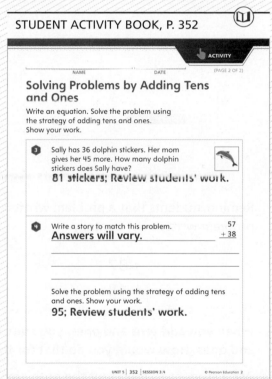

STUDENT ACTIVITY BOOK, P. 352

Solving Problems by Adding Tens and Ones

Write an equation. Solve the problem using the strategy of adding tens and ones. Show your work.

3. Sally has 36 dolphin stickers. Her mom gives her 45 more. How many dolphin stickers does Sally have?
81 stickers; Review students' work.

4. Write a story to match this problem.
Answers will vary.
$$57 + 38$$

Solve the problem using the strategy of adding tens and ones. Show your work.
95; Review students' work.

MATH PRACTICE NOTE

MPN MP2 Reason abstractly and quantitatively. Writing a story problem for a numerical expression deepens students' understanding of operations and can become a strategy they use for interpreting problems presented using only numbers and notation.

2 DISCUSSION

Adding Tens and Ones

MATH FOCUS POINTS FOR DISCUSSION

○ Developing efficient strategies for adding 2-digit numbers

○ Developing efficient methods for notating addition strategies

Call students together for a discussion of their work. Begin by asking what it was like to try to use a particular strategy to solve the problems. Some find it challenging, while others were being asked to use their strategy of choice. Others may say that it made the problems easier to solve.

Display the Teacher Presentation (or use Problem 1 from *Student Activity Book* page 351).

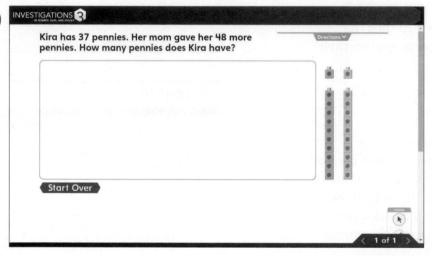

Remind students that a problem written vertically means the same thing as a problem written horizontally.

$$37 \qquad\qquad 37 + 48 =$$
$$+\ 48$$

When you add tens and ones, you start by breaking the numbers into tens and ones. How would you do that for this problem?

Ask a student to represent the problem with cubes.

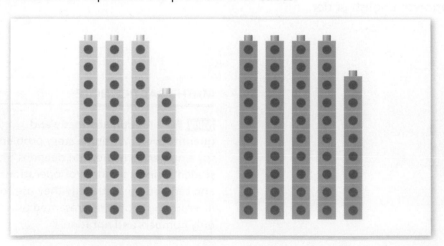

RESOURCE MASTERS, S73

ACTIVITY

Solving Problems by Adding Tens and Ones

Write an equation. Solve the problem using the strategy of adding tens and ones. Show your work.

1. Franco had 66 car stickers. Jake gave him 59 car stickers. How many car stickers does Franco have now?

125 stickers; Review students' work.

2. Kira found 74 shells, and Sally found 67 shells. How many shells did they find in all?

141 shells; Review students' work.

UNIT 5 | 573 | SESSION 3.4 © Pearson Education 2

After you broke the numbers into tens and ones, what did you do next?

Talk through the strategy with students, having volunteers model each step with the cubes. **MN**

$$37 + 48 =$$

$$\begin{array}{r} 37 \\ + \ 48 \\ \hline 70 \\ + \ 15 \\ \hline 85 \end{array}$$ (30 + 40) (7 + 8)

$$30 + 40 = 70$$
$$7 + 8 = 15$$
$$70 + 15 = 85$$

Finally, ask students to consider what is happening with the tens and ones in this problem.

The problem was 37 plus 48. If you add the tens, you get 30 plus 40. That's 70. Why wasn't our answer in the 70s?

Listen for explanations that account for the extra 10 in 15. Modeling the problem with cubes can help students see that there is another 10 in the 15 ones, which makes a total of 8 tens. Therefore, the answer is in the 80s.

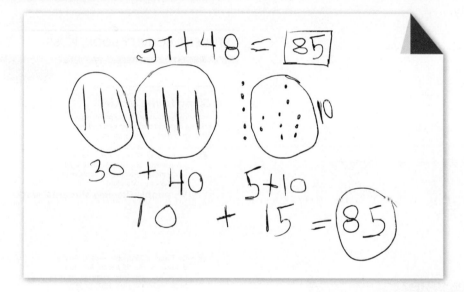

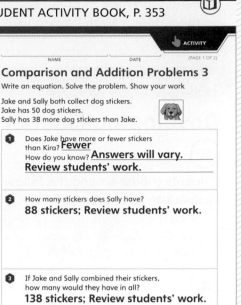

STUDENT ACTIVITY BOOK, P. 353

Comparison and Addition Problems 3
Write an equation. Solve the problem. Show your work

Jake and Sally both collect dog stickers.
Jake has 50 dog stickers.
Sally has 38 more dog stickers than Jake.

1. Does Jake have more or fewer stickers than Kira? **Fewer**
How do you know? **Answers will vary. Review students' work.**

2. How many stickers does Sally have?
88 stickers; Review students' work.

3. If Jake and Sally combined their stickers, how many would they have in all?
138 stickers; Review students' work.

MATH NOTE

MN **Different Second Steps** After adding 30 + 40 or 40 + 30, some students may add 7 to 70 and then 8 to 77. Others may add 8 to 70 and then 7 to 78.

Students who have not finished solving the problems can continue working on them during Math Workshop.

3 MATH WORKSHOP

Developing Fluency with Addition

 30

Students choose among the following activities, which include a new set of comparison story problems.

---

3 A Solving Story Problems

Student Activity Book pages 353–354 offer additional story problems about comparing and adding.

For complete details about this activity, see Session 3.2. Continue to use **Assessment Checklist:** MP4 and MP7 (A38) in this activity.

---

3 B *Capture 5* in the 1,000 Book

For complete details about this activity, see Session 3.3.

---

3 C *Close to 100*

For complete details about this activity, see Session 3.3.

SESSION FOLLOW-UP: REVIEW AND PRACTICE

Daily Practice

✎ **DAILY PRACTICE** For reinforcement of this unit's content, students complete *Student Activity Book* page 355.

STUDENT ACTIVITY BOOK, P. 354

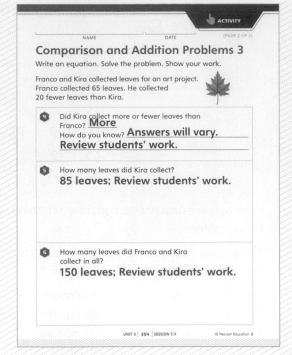

ACTIVITY

NAME   DATE   (PAGE 2 OF 2)

Comparison and Addition Problems 3

Write an equation. Solve the problem. Show your work.

Franco and Kira collected leaves for an art project. Franco collected 65 leaves. He collected 20 fewer leaves than Kira.

4 Did Kira collect more or fewer leaves than Franco? **More**
How do you know? **Answers will vary.**
Review students' work.

5 How many leaves did Kira collect?
85 leaves; Review students' work.

6 How many leaves did Franco and Kira collect in all?
150 leaves; Review students' work.

UNIT 5 | 354 | SESSION 3.4   © Pearson Education 2

STUDENT ACTIVITY BOOK, P. 355

DAILY PRACTICE

NAME   DATE

Going to the Movies

Write an equation. Solve the problem by keeping one number whole and adding the other on in parts. Show your work.

1 On Monday, 38 people went to see the scary movie. 56 people went to see the funny movie. How many people went to the movies on Monday?
94 people; Review students' work.

2 On Tuesday, 23 people went to see the dinosaur movie. 49 people went to see the shark movie. How many people went to the movies on Tuesday?
72 people; Review students' work.

NOTE
As students solve two story problems, they write equations, add 2-digit numbers, and find different ways to solve problems.
Strategies for Adding 2-Digit Numbers

UNIT 5 | 355 | SESSION 3.4   © Pearson Education 2

Adding One Number On in Parts

MATH FOCUS POINTS

○ Developing efficient strategies for adding 2-digit numbers

○ Developing efficient methods for notating addition strategies

○ Skip counting, writing multiples of 5 and 10 within 1,000, and noticing patterns in the counting sequence

○ Visualizing, representing, and solving comparison problems with a bigger unknown (more than/fewer than)

○ Adding and subtracting a number of tens and/or ones to/from a 3-digit number

TODAY'S PLAN	MATERIALS
(10) Class CLASSROOM ROUTINES: REVIEW AND PRACTICE ***Today's Number: More or Less?***	Teacher Presentation (or use the board) Blank paper (1 sheet per student)
(20) Class **1** ACTIVITY **Practicing Adding On in Parts**	*Student Activity Book*, pp. 357–358 S74* (optional; for the Extension) Chart: "Adding One Number On in Parts" (from Session 3.1) Connecting cubes (optional; for the Intervention)
(10) Class **2** DISCUSSION **Adding On in Parts**	Teacher Presentation (or use *Student Activity Book*, p. 355) *Student Activity Book*, p. 357 Connecting cubes (as needed) Number lines (as needed)
(30) **3** MATH WORKSHOP **Developing Fluency with Addition** **3A** Counting Strips: 5s and 10s **3B** Solving Story Problems **3C** *Capture 5* in the 1,000 Book **3D** *Close to 100*	**3A** Counting strips* Tape (as needed) **3B** *Student Activity Book*, pp. 359–360 Materials from Sessions 3.2, 3.3, and 3.4 **3C** Materials from Session 3.3 **3D** Materials from Session 3.3
SESSION FOLLOW-UP: REVIEW AND PRACTICE **Daily Practice and Homework**	*Student Activity Book*, pp. 361–364

* See *Materials to Prepare* in the Investigation 3 Planner.

Common Core State Standards	**Classroom Routines:** 2.NBT.A.4, 2.NBT.B.5, 2.NBT.B.9 **Session:** 2.OA.A.1, 2.NBT.A.2, 2.NBT.A.3, 2.NBT.B.5, 2.NBT.B.8, 2.NBT.B.9, 2.MD.B.6	**Daily Practice:** 2.NBT.A.2

CLASSROOM ROUTINES: REVIEW AND PRACTICE

Today's Number: More or Less?

MATH FOCUS POINTS

○ Estimating the sum of two 2-digit numbers using known combinations, place value, and properties of operations

○ Using standard notation (<, >) to express the relationship between quantities

○ Generating equivalent expressions for a number

I'm going to display an addition problem. The sum is Today's Number. Today, before we figure out the exact answer, I want you to think about whether Today's Number is more or less than 100.

Display the Teacher Presentation (or write 27 + 82 on the board).

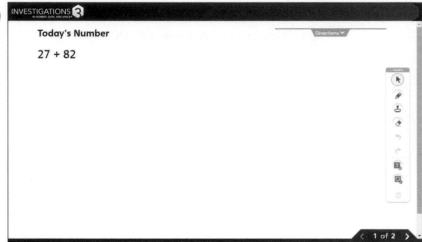

Students think about the problem individually, discuss their thinking with a partner, and then share strategies as a class.

What did you pay attention to when you were thinking about whether or not 27 + 82 was more or less than 100?

Listen for evidence that students' reasoning about the sum is based on the number of tens (e.g., there are 10 tens, and that's 100) or the sum of the tens (e.g., 20 + 80 = 100) and that they are also considering the number of ones. Once students agree that the sum is more than 100, determine the exact amount as a class. Use equations to record.

$$27 + 82 = \underline{}$$
$$20 + 80 = 100$$
$$7 + 2 = 9$$
$$100 + 9 = 109$$

Finally use symbols to compare Today's Number to 100:

$$109 > 100 \qquad 100 < 109$$

CLASSROOM ROUTINES: REVIEW AND PRACTICE

Display 63 + 35 and repeat the above steps. Once again, students think on their own and then with a partner. Discuss strategies as a class, highlighting the importance of looking first at the number of tens by looking at the digits in the tens place and then at the number of ones by looking at the digits in the ones place.

Find the exact answer as a class, using equations to record, and then use the less than and greater than signs to compare that number to 100.

If time permits, students generate equations for one of Today's Numbers: 109 or 98. Alternatively, they can work on Today's Number at some other point in the day or for homework.

1 ACTIVITY

Practicing Adding On in Parts

Display the "Adding One Number On in Parts" chart from Session 3.1. Point out examples of breaking one number into useful parts, such as tens and ones or an amount that gets you to a multiple of 10.

Display the following problem horizontally and vertically. Remind students that a problem written vertically means the same thing as a problem written horizontally.

$$49 + 21 = \qquad \begin{array}{r} 49 \\ + 21 \\ \hline \end{array}$$

Yesterday you practiced the strategy of breaking numbers into 10s and 1s to combine two numbers. Today we are going to practice a different strategy that we have been using this year. I want everyone to think about this: How could you solve this problem by keeping one number whole and adding the other on in parts? MWI

Give students a few minutes to think about this question, and discuss it with a partner.

Together as a class, with students offering ideas, briefly describe the steps for solving the problem by adding on one number in parts. Remind students of the discussions from the previous sessions about breaking one number into parts and then adding those parts.

Then ask students to use the strategy of keeping one number whole and adding on the other in parts as they solve problems on *Student Activity Book* pages 357–358.

STUDENT ACTIVITY BOOK, P. 357
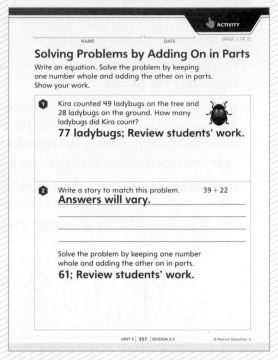

STUDENT ACTIVITY BOOK, P. 358

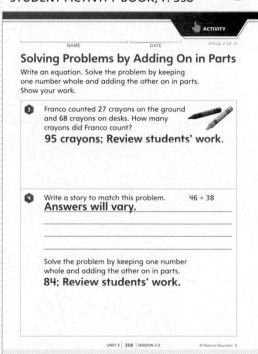

MATH WORDS AND IDEAS

MWI Strategies for Adding 2-Digit Numbers: Adding One Number On in Parts

ONGOING ASSESSMENT Observing Students at Work

Students practice keeping one number whole and adding on the other in parts to solve problems and work on notating their solution strategies.

- ○ **Can students accurately write an equation or story problem that represents the problem?**

- ○ **Are students able to keep one number whole and add on the other?** How do they add on? Do they add on 10s and then 1s? Do they break apart the other number to make a 10? How do they keep track? What tools, models, or representations do they use? Do they get the right answer? 🔍 **MP7**

- ○ **How do students record their work?** Do they use equations? Is their notation clear and accurate? Do they use representations such as a number line or sticker notation to explain their strategy?

 DIFFERENTIATION Supporting the Range of Learners

INTERVENTION Scaffold a Solution Encourage students who are unsure how to begin to think about the first step. **Let's say that we keep 49 whole. How could we think about adding on the 28?** If students typically use a tens and ones strategy, suggest they begin by breaking the 28 into tens and ones and adding on each part to the 49. Have cubes available for students to model the problem as they work. When students work through this first problem suggest they apply the same strategy as they work on Problem 2.

Some students might require further step-by-step scaffolding. **How will you add 22 in parts? What if you add 10 of the 22 onto the 39?** Move one tower of 10 cubes. **Can you add another 10? Now how many do you have left to add?** Or, provide these students with an easier problem such as 27 + 22, and see if they are able to apply the strategy.

EXTENSION Vary the Problem Students who solve the problems efficiently and accurately and notate their strategies in a clear and understandable way can solve the more challenging problems on S74.

2 DISCUSSION

Adding On in Parts

MATH FOCUS POINTS FOR DISCUSSION

○ Developing efficient strategies for adding 2-digit numbers

○ Developing efficient methods for notating addition strategies

Begin by asking students about the experience of trying to use a particular strategy to solve the problems. Ask if it was difficult or whether knowing which strategy to use made the problems easier to solve.

Display the Teacher Presentation (or use Problem 1 from *Student Activity Book* page 357).

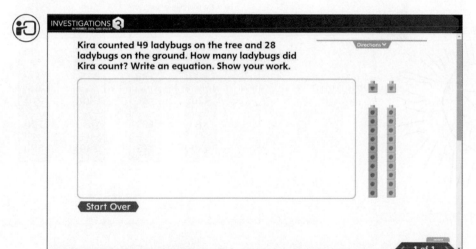

As you did in Session 3.4, use equations to record the strategies that students suggest, and ask students to model their strategies using the cubes or a number line. The number line is a particularly useful tool for modeling the strategy of keeping one number whole. Focus on where you can see the 28 that is being added in each strategy and on each representation. **MPN**

Select a few students who represented their strategy on the number line in different ways. Talk through the different ways students were being efficient in their solution strategies. For example, two students may add on the 28 and be accurate in their solutions, but they may differ in their efficiency. Encourage students who are taking jumps of 10 or several jumps of small numbers to think about how they could add on one larger amount.

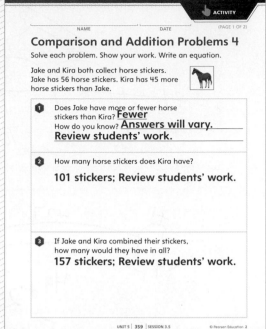

STUDENT ACTIVITY BOOK, P. 359

ACTIVITY

NAME   DATE   (PAGE 1 OF 2)

Comparison and Addition Problems 4

Solve each problem. Show your work. Write an equation.

Jake and Kira both collect horse stickers. Jake has 56 horse stickers. Kira has 45 more horse stickers than Jake.

1 Does Jake have more or fewer horse stickers than Kira? **Fewer**
How do you know? **Answers will vary. Review students' work.**

2 How many horse stickers does Kira have?
101 stickers; Review students' work.

3 If Jake and Kira combined their stickers, how many would they have in all?
157 stickers; Review students' work.

UNIT 5 | **359** | SESSION 3.5   © Pearson Education 2

MATH PRACTICE NOTE

MPN **MP8 Look for and express regularity in repeated reasoning.** Keeping one number whole and adding the other number on in parts is an application of the associative property of addition.

$49 + 28 = 49 + (20 + 8) = (49 + 20) + 8 = 69 + 8$

$49 + 28 = 49 + (1 + 27) = (49 + 1) + 27 = 50 + 27$

Grade 2 students are not expected to know and use such terminology as *associative property*, but they can recognize that when they break up the number 28, they have a new problem with multiple addends that they can add in any order.

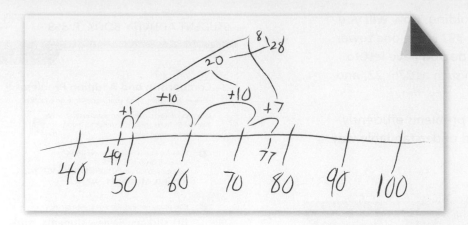

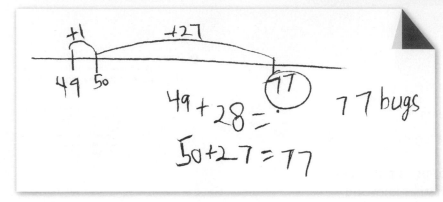

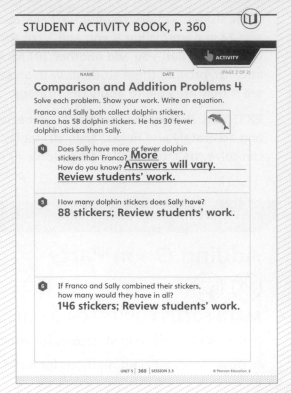

NAME   DATE   (PAGE 2 OF 2)

Comparison and Addition Problems 4

Solve each problem. Show your work. Write an equation.

Franco and Sally both collect dolphin stickers. Franco has 58 dolphin stickers. He has 30 fewer dolphin stickers than Sally.

4 Does Sally have more or fewer dolphin stickers than Franco? **More** How do you know? **Answers will vary. Review students' work.**

5 How many dolphin stickers does Sally have? **88 stickers; Review students' work.**

6 If Franco and Sally combined their stickers, how many would they have in all? **146 stickers; Review students' work.**

UNIT 5   360   SESSION 3.5   © Pearson Education 2

[Roshaun] used equations. [He] broke the 28 apart by place to add it on to the 49. Can you see the 28 in [his] solution?

[Roshaun's Work]

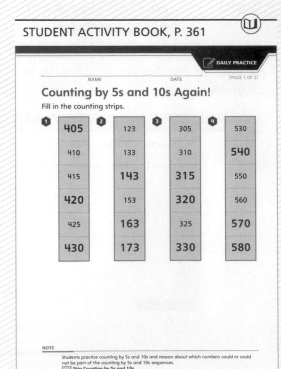

DAILY PRACTICE

NAME   DATE   (PAGE 1 OF 2)

Counting by 5s and 10s Again!

Fill in the counting strips.

1 405	**2** 123	**3** 305	**4** 530
410	133	310	540
415	143	315	550
420	153	320	560
425	163	325	570
430	173	330	580

NOTE

Students practice counting by 5s and 10s and reason about which numbers could or could not be part of the counting by 5s and 10s sequences.
Skip Counting by 5s and 10s

UNIT 5   361   SESSION 3.5   © Pearson Education 2

If some students have recorded their solution using vertical notation, compare that notation to a similar strategy notated with equations. If not, offer the example yourself.

We could also represent [Roshaun]'s strategy like this:

$$
\begin{array}{r}
49 \\
+\ 28 \\
\hline
69\ (49 + 20) \\
+\ 8 \\
\hline
77\ (69 + 1 + 7)
\end{array}
$$

3 MATH WORKSHOP

Developing Fluency with Addition

 30

Students choose among the following activities, all of which focus on supporting the development of efficient and accurate strategies for adding 2-digit numbers.

Explain the one new activity by connecting it with work students did earlier in the year when they made counting strips for counting by 1s. In this activity they will write the counting-by-5s numbers on one side of the strip and the counting-by-10s numbers on the other. They should begin with zero for both numbers and write the sequence as high as they can. **MN**

Tape a piece of adding machine tape vertically to the board and write several multiple-of-5 numbers, one underneath the other, starting with zero. Remind students that looking at the patterns in the numbers they have already written can also help them write more numbers. **MPN1** **MPN2**

---

3 A Counting Strips: 5s and 10s

Students begin at zero, write the multiples of 5, and make a vertical counting strip. They can add additional paper strips if they run out of space. On the reverse side, they write multiples of 10.

ONGOING ASSESSMENT Observing Students at Work

Students practice counting, writing, and reading the multiples of 5 and 10 within 1,000. They notice and use patterns in the sequence to think about what comes next.

○ **Are students fluent with the rote counting sequence?** As they read numbers aloud, do they say the right names for numbers?

○ **Are students able to make the transition between decades [. . . 170, 175, 180, 185, 190] and across centuries [. . . 290, 295, 300, 305, 310]?** Can students continue counting upwards of 1,000? Do they write these numbers correctly? **TN**

○ **Do students recognize and use any patterns in the counting sequence?** Do they reason why those patterns occur? (e.g., why do the multiples of 5 end in 0 and 5 but the 10s all end in zero?) **MP7**

○ **How accurate and legible are students' written numbers?**

 DIFFERENTIATION Supporting the Range of Learners

INTERVENTION Adapt the Problem For some students, writing a long list of numbers may be a fine motor challenge. Suggest that these students write several shorter sequences between a given set of numbers so that you can determine their familiarity with counting, reading, and writing 3-digit numbers.

EXTENSION Adapt the Problem Just as some students will find it a challenge to physically sustain number strips, others will embrace the idea and want to continue to 1,000 and beyond.

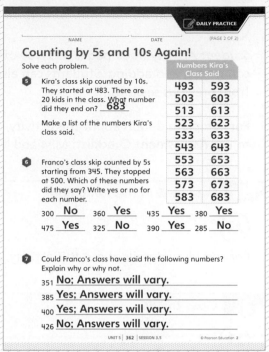

STUDENT ACTIVITY BOOK, P. 362

DAILY PRACTICE

NAME   DATE   (PAGE 2 OF 2)

Counting by 5s and 10s Again!

Solve each problem.

Numbers Kira's Class Said	
493	593
503	603
513	613
523	623
533	633
543	643
553	653
563	663
573	673
583	683

5 Kira's class skip counted by 10s. They started at 483. There are 20 kids in the class. What number did they end on? __683__

Make a list of the numbers Kira's class said.

6 Franco's class skip counted by 5s starting from 345. They stopped at 500. Which of these numbers did they say? Write yes or no for each number.

300 __No__   360 __Yes__   435 __Yes__   380 __Yes__

475 __Yes__   325 __No__   390 __Yes__   285 __No__

7 Could Franco's class have said the following numbers? Explain why or why not.

351 __No; Answers will vary.__

385 __Yes; Answers will vary.__

400 __Yes; Answers will vary.__

426 __No; Answers will vary.__

UNIT 5   362   SESSION 3.5   © Pearson Education 2

MATH NOTE

MN Vertical Counting Strips Writing numbers vertically, rather than horizontally, highlights the patterns that exist in the number sequence.

MATH PRACTICE NOTES

MPN1 MP6 Attend to precision. In creating their counting strips, students must attend to a variety of factors, including following the counting sequence and writing numerals legibly.

MPN2 MP7 Look for and make use of structure. Noticing patterns in the numbers of their counting strip, students become aware of the structure of those patterns to continue counting.

TEACHING NOTE

TN Skip Counting and Writing Numbers to 1,000 As students work on skip counting strips, observe to see how they are writing the numbers and how fluent they are with the counting sequences. Pay particular attention to how students handle crossing from one decade or century into another.

3 B   Solving Story Problems

Student Activity Book pages 359–360 offer more challenging problems about comparing and adding. Students can also work on any sets of story problems from previous sessions.

For complete details about this activity, see Sessions 3.2, 3.3, and 3.4. Continue to use **Assessment Checklist: MP4 and MP7 (A38)** in this activity.

3 C   *Capture 5* in the 1,000 Book

For complete details about this activity, see Session 3.3.

3 D   *Close to 100*

For complete details about this activity, see Session 3.3.

SESSION FOLLOW-UP: REVIEW AND PRACTICE

Daily Practice and Homework

DAILY PRACTICE For reinforcement of this unit's content, students complete *Student Activity Book* pages 361–362.

HOMEWORK Students find sets of numbers that add to 100, showing their work on *Student Activity Book* pages 363–364.

STUDENT ACTIVITY BOOK, P. 363

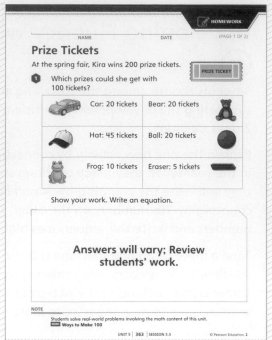

STUDENT ACTIVITY BOOK, P. 364

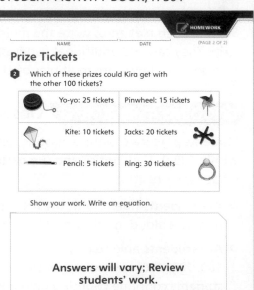

Enough for the Grade?

MATH FOCUS POINTS

○ Solving 2-step story problems that involve comparison and finding the difference

○ Developing efficient strategies for adding 2-digit numbers and notating strategies

○ Skip counting and writing multiples of 5 and 10 within 1,000, and noticing patterns in the counting sequence

○ Visualizing, representing, and solving comparison problems with a bigger unknown (more than/fewer than)

○ Adding and subtracting a number of tens and/or ones to/from a 3-digit number

TODAY'S PLAN	MATERIALS
CLASSROOM ROUTINES: REVIEW AND PRACTICE *Today's Number: Skip Counting by 10s*	*Student Activity Book*, p. 365 1,000 Books (from Investigation 2; as needed)
1 ACTIVITY **Introducing Enough for the Grade?**	Teacher Presentation (or use the board)
2 MATH WORKSHOP **Developing Fluency with Addition and Skip Counting** 2A Enough for the Grade? 2B Counting Strips: 5s and 10s 2C *Capture 5* in the 1,000 Book 2D *Close to 100*	**2A** *Student Activity Book*, pp. 366–369 A38 (from Session 1.3) S75–S76* (optional; for the Extension) **2B** Materials from Session 3.5 Additional strips of adding machine tape (as needed) **2C** Materials from Session 3.3 **2D** Materials from Session 3.3
3 DISCUSSION **What Went Wrong?**	Teacher Presentation (or use the board) Erroneous skip counting strips*
SESSION FOLLOW-UP: REVIEW AND PRACTICE **Daily Practice**	*Student Activity Book*, p. 370

* See *Materials to Prepare* in the Investigation 3 Planner.

Common Core State Standards	Classroom Routines: 2.NBT.A.1b, 2.NBT.A.2, 2.NBT.A.3, 2.NBT.B.5	Session: 2.OA.A.1, 2.NBT.A.1, 2.NBT.A.1b, 2.NBT.A.2, 2.NBT.A.3, 2.NBT.B.5, 2.NBT.B.8, 2.NBT.B.9, 2.MD.B.6 Daily Practice: 2.NBT.B.6

CLASSROOM ROUTINES: REVIEW AND PRACTICE

Today's Number: Skip Counting by 10s

MATH FOCUS POINTS

○ Counting by 10s within 1,000

○ Identifying patterns in the skip counting sequence of 10s

○ Generating equivalent expressions for a number

Ask students to predict whether or not they will land exactly on the number 200 if they skip count around the class by 10s. They can use their 1,000 Books to help them if they wish. As students count by 10s, make a vertical list of the numbers they say. Compare the final number said to 200. Is it more or less? Each student then completes *Student Activity Book* page 365, *Today's Number: 200*. Students generate expressions for the number 200 using only two multiples of 10 (two numbers from the list). For example: 100 + 100; 10 + 190; 150 + 50. Collect this work as the fifth in a series of *Today's Number* samples that will be collected throughout the year.

---

1 ACTIVITY

Introducing Enough for the Grade?

Remind students of the work they did earlier in the year on Enough for the Class? problems. Then introduce them to a new version of the problem: Enough for the Grade? **TN1** **TN2**

During Math Workshop you will have a chance to solve a new kind of problem. These problems are like the Enough for the Class? problems that we solved earlier this year but these are called Enough for the Grade? problems.

Display the Teacher Presentation (or write the problem on the board) and read it aloud with the class.

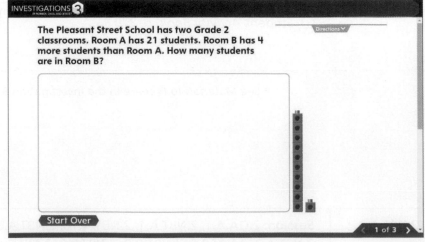

The Pleasant Street School has two Grade 2 classrooms. Room A has 21 students. Room B has 4 more students than Room A. How many students are in Room B?

TEACHING NOTES

TN1 **Enough for the Grade?** These multi-step problems build on the Enough for the Class? context introduced in Unit 1 and bring together many of the problem types students have been working on thus far in Grade 2. Each begins with a comparison problem with the bigger amount unknown and then asks students to combine two quantities to determine the number of students in the grade. Part 3 presents two amounts to compare to the number in the grade. While some add and then compare, Grade 2 students often have other ways they make sense of such situations. This is part of what make Enough for the Grade? problems interesting and challenging.

TN2 **Enough for *Our* Grade?** As with all story problems, these can be adapted to be about your school, class, or grade. Personalizing problems can make them more engaging. Changing the name of the school or teacher or the items involved does not change the underlying mathematical structure of the problems. However, numbers have been chosen because they suggest a specific combination or strategy or relate to the other numbers in the problem (e.g., one addend is a multiple of 10 or the ones in both addends combine to make a 10). If you choose to adapt Enough for the Grade? problems, care should be given to preserving the overall mathematical structure and intent of the problem, as well as to the size of the numbers involved.

Think about what information you know and what information you are trying to figure out. Talk with a partner about the problem. Explain how you would figure out how many students are in Room B.

After a few minutes, bring the class together to discuss the number of students in Room B. Discuss what information is known, and make a list. Then ask students to share their thinking. Because the difference between the two rooms is small (4 students), it is likely that students will "just know" there are 25 students in Room B. Encourage them to say how they would explain how they know to someone else.

How could you use cubes to show that Room B has 4 more students? What about a quick line sketch? How could you show this on the number line?

Add the number of students in Room B (25) to the list of known information.

> ### Room A — 21 students
>
> ### Room B has 4 more students than Room A.
>
> ### Room B has more kids than Room A.
>
> ### There are more than 21 kids in Room B.
>
> ### There are 25 kids in Room B.

Next, present the second part of the problem:

How many students are in Grade 2 at the Pleasant Street School? Talk with your partner about *how* you would figure this out.

After a few minutes, ask a few students to share how they would figure out the total number of students in Grade 2. Students will likely agree that they would need to combine the number of students in each class. Record this in the form of an equation, or use vertical notation.

$$21 + 25 = \underline{\quad\quad} \qquad\qquad \begin{array}{r} 21 \\ + 25 \\ \hline \end{array}$$

Here is the third part of this problem.

The gym teacher at the Pleasant Street School has a bin of jump ropes. She has 26 red jump ropes and 18 blue jump ropes. Are there enough jump ropes for every student in Grade 2 at the Pleasant Street School to have one jump rope? Are there Enough for the Grade?

Would there be any extras? Would they need to get more?

Have students briefly talk with their partner about how they would figure this out. The goal of this introduction is not to solve each problem but instead to introduce students to problems that have more than one part.

Explain to students that Enough for the Grade? problems will be a new activity during Math Workshop. Let them know that there are four different problems; they will receive two today and two in the next Math Workshop session.

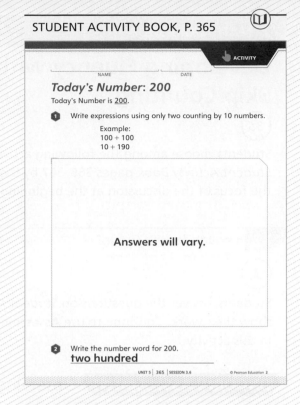

STUDENT ACTIVITY BOOK, P. 365

> ACTIVITY
>
> NAME   DATE
>
> *Today's Number:* **200**
>
> Today's Number is <u>200</u>.
>
> **1**   Write expressions using only two counting by 10 numbers.
> > Example:
> > 100 + 100
> > 10 + 190
>
> **Answers will vary.**
>
> **2**   Write the number word for 200.
> **two hundred**
>
> UNIT 5 | 365 | SESSION 3.6   © Pearson Education 2

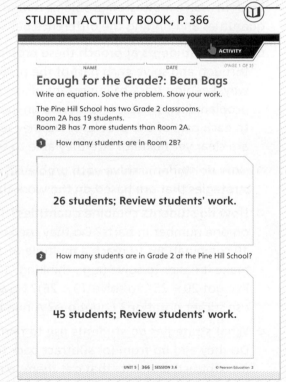

STUDENT ACTIVITY BOOK, P. 366

> ACTIVITY   (PAGE 1 OF 2)
>
> NAME   DATE
>
> **Enough for the Grade?: Bean Bags**
>
> Write an equation. Solve the problem. Show your work.
>
> The Pine Hill School has two Grade 2 classrooms.
> Room 2A has 19 students.
> Room 2B has 7 more students than Room 2A.
>
> **1**   How many students are in Room 2B?
>
> **26 students; Review students' work.**
>
> **2**   How many students are in Grade 2 at the Pine Hill School?
>
> **45 students; Review students' work.**
>
> UNIT 5 | 366 | SESSION 3.6   © Pearson Education 2

2 MATH WORKSHOP

Developing Fluency with Addition and Skip Counting

Students choose among the following activities. They need to complete *Student Activity Book* pages 366–367 by the end of this session, as they will be the focus of the discussion at the beginning of Session 3.7.

2 A   Enough for the Grade?

Students answer the questions on *Student Activity Book* pages 366–369 and show their work. Continue to use **Assessment Checklist: MP4 and MP7 (A38)** in this activity.

ONGOING ASSESSMENT Observing Students at Work

Students solve multi-step problems that involve combining and comparing quantities and finding the difference between two amounts.

○ **How do students approach these problems?** Are they able to work through and solve each part of the problem? Do they work in an organized way, keeping track of important pieces of information related to the problem (i.e., what is known and unknown) and then relating each solution to each part of the problem? Do they seem to have solution pathways that are clear yet flexible? Are they able to shift their thinking if they lose track?

○ **How do students solve each problem?** Are they accurate? Do they use strategies that are based on the work they have been doing in this unit?

○ **How do students combine quantities?** Do they add tens and ones? Add on one number in parts? Do they use known information such as Make 10 combinations to reach a multiple of 10? Do they adapt the problem to make it easier to solve (e.g., thinking "If I take 1 from 26 and give it to 19, I've got 20 + 25" to solve 19 + 26)? How do they show their work? Do they use sticker notation? Equations? A number line? 🔍 **MP7**

○ **What strategies do students use to find the difference between quantities?** Do they add up from (or subtract back to) the given number? Do they add (or subtract) amounts that get them to multiples of 10 (e.g., to find the difference between 45 and 56, do they add 5 to 45 first to get to 50, an easy number to work with)? 🔍 **MP7**

○ **How do students show their work for each part of the problem?** Is their solution strategy apparent? Do they use equations to record? Represent their thinking on a number line? Make a quick sketch to show the comparison of two quantities?

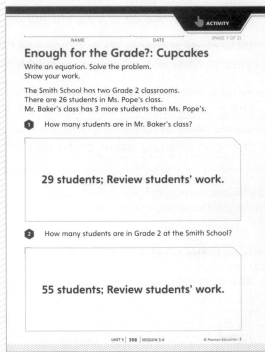

STUDENT ACTIVITY BOOK, P. 367

ACTIVITY

NAME   DATE   (PAGE 2 OF 2)

Enough for the Grade?: Bean Bags

Write an equation. Solve the problem.
Show your work.

The gym teacher at the Pine Street School has a basket of bean bags. He has 38 green bean bags and 18 yellow bean bags.

3 Are there enough bean bags for the grade?

> **Yes; Review students' work.**

4 Are there any extra bean bags? If yes, how many? If no, how many more are needed?

> **Yes; 11 extra bean bags; Review students' work.**

UNIT 5 | 367 | SESSION 3.6   © Pearson Education 2

STUDENT ACTIVITY BOOK, P. 368

ACTIVITY

NAME   DATE   (PAGE 1 OF 2)

Enough for the Grade?: Cupcakes

Write an equation. Solve the problem.
Show your work.

The Smith School has two Grade 2 classrooms. There are 26 students in Ms. Pope's class. Mr. Baker's class has 3 more students than Ms. Pope's.

1 How many students are in Mr. Baker's class?

> **29 students; Review students' work.**

2 How many students are in Grade 2 at the Smith School?

> **55 students; Review students' work.**

UNIT 5 | 368 | SESSION 3.6   © Pearson Education 2

DIFFERENTIATION Supporting the Range of Learners

INTERVENTION Vary the Problem It may be appropriate for some students to focus on the first two parts of a problem, determining how many students are in each class and then in the grade. Problems can also be adapted by using smaller numbers or using only some of the information (e.g., creating an Enough for the Class? problem).

EXTENSION Extend Thinking Each of the Enough for the Grade? problems has an optional fifth part that poses a more challenging question that may be appropriate for some but not all students. These questions are on S75 and S76 and correspond to each of the problems on *Student Activity Book* pages 366–369.

ENGLISH LANGUAGE LEARNERS Repeat and Clarify Help students understand the problems on *Student Activity Book* pages 366–369 by reading the problems with students working in pairs. For each problem, have students retell the information to each other and discuss how they will solve the problem. Ask questions to stimulate partner discussions. For example: **What do you know? What do you need to find? How will you solve the problem? What will you do first? Next? Why? Tell your partner the steps you will take to solve the problem.**

---

2 B Counting Strips: 5s and 10s

For complete details about this activity, see Session 3.5.

---

2 C *Capture 5 in the 1,000 Book*

For complete details about this activity, see Session 3.3.

---

2 D *Close to 100*

For complete details about this activity, see Session 3.3.

STUDENT ACTIVITY BOOK, P. 369

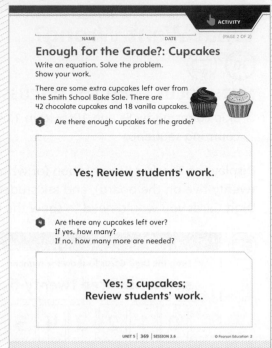

RESOURCE MASTERS, S75

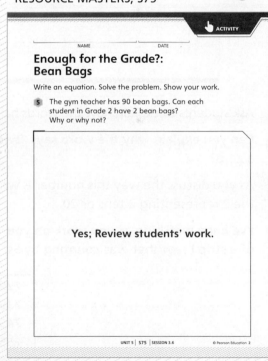

3 DISCUSSION

What Went Wrong?

MATH FOCUS POINT FOR DISCUSSION

○ Skip counting by 5s and 10s within 1,000, and noticing patterns in the counting sequence

Display the Teacher Presentation (or write the number word seven hundred twenty-five on the board), and ask students to talk with a partner about what Digit Cards you would need to show the number.

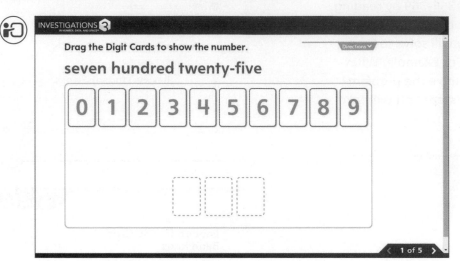

Ask students to explain how the words helped them know which numbers to use.

Can you explain why the word says "twenty" but we used a 2, not a 2 and a zero?

As you discuss the way this number is written in words, be sure to talk about the 2 representing 2 tens or 20.

I've been watching as you work on your skip counting strips. Here's a section of a strip I saw that was counting by 5s. It starts with 725.

| 725 |
| 735 |
| 745 |
| 755 |
| 765 |
| 775 |
| 785 |
| 795 |

ACTIVITY

NAME   DATE

Enough for the Grade?: Cupcakes

Write an equation. Solve the problem. Show your work.

5 There are 100 cupcakes leftover from the Grade 2 Bake Sale.
Are there enough cupcakes for each student to have 2? Why or why not?

No; Review students' work.

UNIT 5 | S76 | SESSION 3.6   © Pearson Education 2

Ask students what went wrong, how they know, and how they could fix it. Focus the discussion on why someone might have made the errors.

" STUDENTS MIGHT SAY "

 "The person was thinking that counting by 5 numbers end in 5 but it's every *other* number that ends in 5."

 "Counting by 10 numbers always end in 0, but counting by 5 numbers end in either a 5 or a 0."

 "Yeah, they're missing the numbers that end in 0."

 "That person counted by 10s from 725!"

Follow the same process with another strip or two. Use errors you have seen students making.

510	910	255
520	920	260
530	930	265
540	940	270
550	950	275
560	960	280
570	970	285
580	980	290
590	990	295
600	10100	300
700		310
800		320
900		330

SESSION FOLLOW-UP: REVIEW AND PRACTICE

Daily Practice

✒ **DAILY PRACTICE** For ongoing review, students complete *Student Activity Book* page 370.

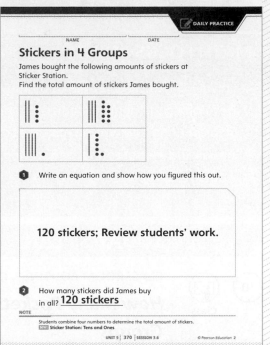

STUDENT ACTIVITY BOOK, P. 370

✏ DAILY PRACTICE

NAME _____ DATE _____

Stickers in 4 Groups

James bought the following amounts of stickers at Sticker Station.
Find the total amount of stickers James bought.

1   Write an equation and show how you figured this out.

120 stickers; Review students' work.

2   How many stickers did James buy in all? **120 stickers**

NOTE   Students combine four numbers to determine the total amount of stickers.
Sticker Station: Tens and Ones

UNIT 5 | 370 | SESSION 3.6   © Pearson Education 2

Fluency with Addition

MATH FOCUS POINTS

○ Solving 2-step story problems that involve comparison and finding the difference

○ Developing efficient strategies for adding 2-digit numbers and notating strategies

○ Skip counting and writing multiples of 5 and 10 within 1,000, and noticing patterns in the counting sequence

○ Visualizing, representing, and solving comparison problems with a bigger unknown (more than/fewer than)

○ Adding and subtracting a number of tens and/or ones to/from a 3-digit number

TODAY'S PLAN	MATERIALS
(10) Class CLASSROOM ROUTINES: REVIEW AND PRACTICE **_How Many Pockets?: Adding Four Groups_**	📖 _Student Activity Book_, p. 371 🔧 Connecting cubes (4 bins) Chart: "How Many Pockets?" (from Session 2.3)
(20) Class **1** DISCUSSION **Are There Enough Bean Bags for the Grade?**	🖥 Teacher Presentation (or use _Student Activity Book_, pp. 366–367) 📖 _Student Activity Book_, pp. 366–367 (completed; from Session 3.6)

(30)   **2** MATH WORKSHOP
Developing Fluency with Addition and Skip Counting
   2A Enough for the Grade?
   2B Counting Strips: 5s and 10s
   2C _Capture 5_ on the 1,000 Book
   2D _Close to 100_
	📖 **2A** _Student Activity Book_, pp. 372–375
	📄 S77–S78* (optional; for the Extension)
	☑📄 A38 (from Session 1.3)
	2B Materials from Session 3.5
	   Additional strips of adding machine tape (as needed)
	2C Materials from Session 3.3
	2D Materials from Session 3.3

(10) Individuals **3** ASSESSMENT ACTIVITY **Quiz 2**	☑📄 A41–A42*
SESSION FOLLOW-UP: REVIEW AND PRACTICE **Daily Practice**	📖 _Student Activity Book_, p. 376

* See _Materials to Prepare_ in the Investigation 3 Planner.

Common Core State Standards	
Classroom Routines: 2.OA.B.2, 2.NBT.B.5, 2.NBT.B.6 **Session:** 2.OA.A.1, 2.NBT.A.1, 2.NBT.A.2, 2.NBT.A.3, 2.NBT.B.5, 2.NBT.B.6, 2.NBT.B.8, 2.NBT.B.9	**Daily Practice:** 2.OA.B.2

CLASSROOM ROUTINES: REVIEW AND PRACTICE

How Many Pockets?: Adding Four Groups

MATH FOCUS POINTS

○ Collecting, counting, representing and comparing data

○ Adding four 2-digit numbers

Organize students into four groups and give each a bin of cubes. Students take as many cubes as they have pockets and then figure out how many pockets in their group. Encourage them to think about facts they know as they combine their pockets.

Ask each group to share their total and to give you their cubes, in towers of 10 and a tower of leftovers. Record the four totals, and display the cube towers beneath them.

Students work independently to determine the total number of pockets the class is wearing. They record their work on *Student Activity Book*, page 371. Encourage students to use what they know about adding tens and ones to determine the total number of pockets. **TN**

When students are finished, discuss a few strategies for combining the 4 quantities. Model each with the cubes, and record equations. If students do not suggest finding the total of two groups and then adding the two subtotals, suggest it as a strategy. Confirm the total by counting the cube towers by 10s and then 1s, and record the data on the Pocket Data Chart.

---

1 DISCUSSION

Are There Enough Bean Bags for the Grade?

MATH FOCUS POINTS FOR DISCUSSION

○ Visualizing, representing, and solving comparison problems with a bigger unknown (more than/fewer than)

○ Developing efficient strategies for adding 2-digit numbers and notating strategies

Gather students to discuss their work on *Student Activity Book* pages 366–367. Display the Teacher Presentation (or use the problem on *Student Activity Book* page 366), and read part 1 aloud.

> **The Pine Hill School has two Grade 2 classrooms.**
> **Room 2A has 19 students.**
> **Room 2B has 7 more students than Room 2A.**
> **How many students are in Room 2B?**

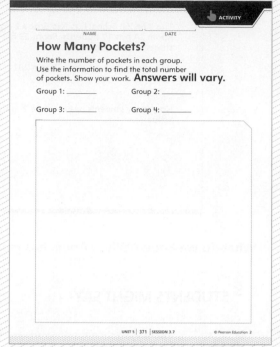

How Many Pockets?
Write the number of pockets in each group.
Use the information to find the total number
of pockets. Show your work. **Answers will vary.**

Group 1: _____   Group 2: _____

Group 3: _____   Group 4: _____

UNIT 5 | 371 | SESSION 3.7   © Pearson Education 2

STUDENT ACTIVITY BOOK, P. 372

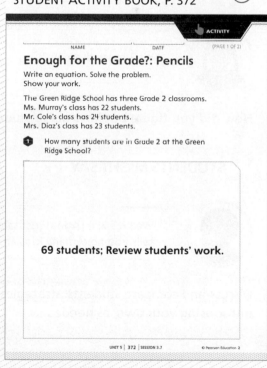

Enough for the Grade?: Pencils
Write an equation. Solve the problem.
Show your work.

The Green Ridge School has three Grade 2 classrooms.
Ms. Murray's class has 22 students.
Mr. Cole's class has 24 students.
Mrs. Diaz's class has 23 students.

1   How many students are in Grade 2 at the Green Ridge School?

69 students; Review students' work.

UNIT 5 | 372 | SESSION 3.7   © Pearson Education 2

TEACHING NOTE

TN **Pockets** Save this work, as it will provide additional information about fluency with addition within 100 (Benchmark 5), assessed in 3.8.

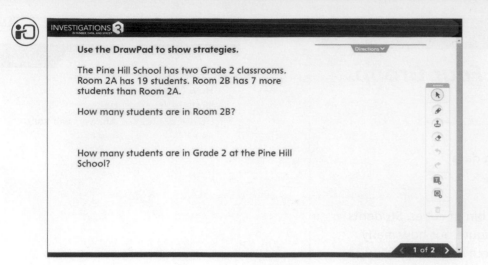

Use the DrawPad to show strategies.

The Pine Hill School has two Grade 2 classrooms. Room 2A has 19 students. Room 2B has 7 more students than Room 2A.

How many students are in Room 2B?

How many students are in Grade 2 at the Pine Hill School?

What do we know? Which Room has more students? How do you know?

STUDENTS MIGHT SAY

"It says Room B has 7 more students than Room A. So there have to be more kids in that class."

"It's 7 more than 19."

How did you figure out how many students were in Room B?

STUDENTS MIGHT SAY

"Well it's like [Anita] just said. Room B has 7 more kids. So 19 + 7 tells you how many kids are in Room B."

Discuss and compare students' strategies, using their methods of recording or introducing your own, as needed.

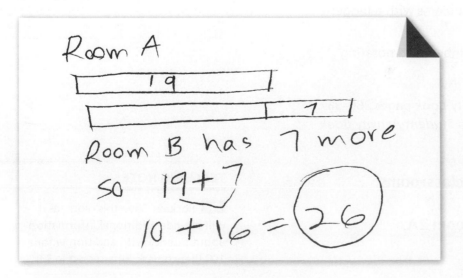

STUDENT ACTIVITY BOOK, P. 373

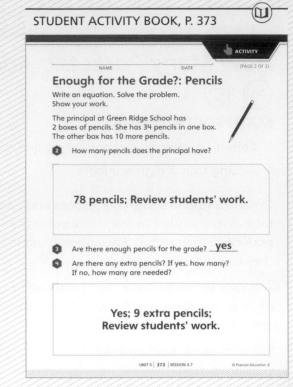

Enough for the Grade?: Pencils

Write an equation. Solve the problem. Show your work.

The principal at Green Ridge School has 2 boxes of pencils. She has 34 pencils in one box. The other box has 10 more pencils.

2 How many pencils does the principal have?

78 pencils; Review students' work.

3 Are there enough pencils for the grade? _yes_
4 Are there any extra pencils? If yes, how many? If no, how many are needed?

Yes; 9 extra pencils; Review students' work.

STUDENT ACTIVITY BOOK, P. 374

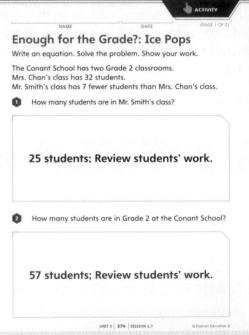

Enough for the Grade?: Ice Pops

Write an equation. Solve the problem. Show your work.

The Conant School has two Grade 2 classrooms. Mrs. Chan's class has 32 students. Mr. Smith's class has 7 fewer students than Mrs. Chan's class.

1 How many students are in Mr. Smith's class?

25 students; Review students' work.

2 How many students are in Grade 2 at the Conant School?

57 students; Review students' work.

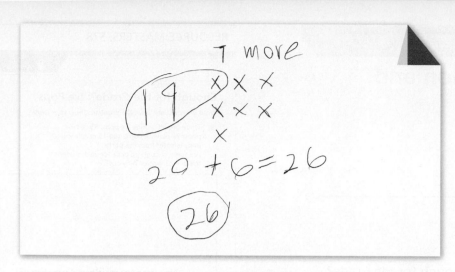

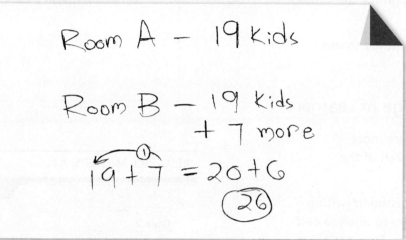

STUDENT ACTIVITY BOOK, P. 375

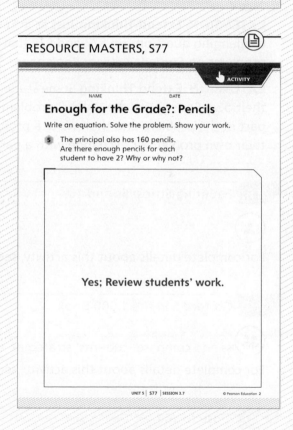

Once students agree that Room B has 26 students, ask how they figured out how many second graders there were in the Pine Hill School.

STUDENTS MIGHT SAY

"I added 19 + 26 by doing tens and ones. 10 + 20 is 30, 9 + 6 = 15, and 30 + 15 = 45."

"I added the 19 on in parts. 26 + 10 = 36. To add the 9, instead I added 10 and then took away 1. 36 + 10 = 46 minus the extra one is 45."

"I take one from the 26 to the 19, then I had 20 + 25 and that's 45."

Again, notate students' strategies. Encourage others to rephrase strategies in their own words, to compare one strategy to another, or to show it with another tool or representation (e.g., Can you show what [Esteban]'s strategy would look like on the number line?).

If time remains, discuss parts 3 and 4 in a similar manner.

2 MATH WORKSHOP

Developing Fluency with Addition and Skip Counting

Students choose among the following four activities.

2 A   Enough for the Grade?

Student Activity Book pages 372–375 offer additional Enough for the Grade? Problems.

For complete details about this activity, see Session 3.6. Continue to use **Assessment Checklist:** MP4 and MP7 (A38) in this activity.

DIFFERENTIATION Supporting the Range of Learners

EXTENSION Extend Thinking Just as in Session 3.6, there are more challenging questions on S77 and S78 that correspond to each of the problems on *Student Activity Book* pages 372–375.

EXTENSION Extend Thinking Some students may be interested in writing their own Enough for the Grade? problems. Challenge them to analyze each part of the problem and then write a problem that is similar. They can solve their own problem or exchange with a partner.

2 B   Counting Strips: 5s and 10s

For complete details about this activity, see Session 3.5.

2 C   *Capture 5* in the 1,000 Book

For complete details about this activity, see Session 3.3.

2 D   *Close to 100*

For complete details about this activity, see Session 3.3.

RESOURCE MASTERS, S78

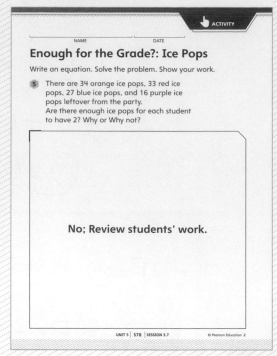

RESOURCE MASTERS, A41

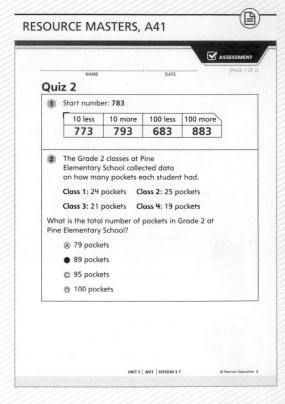

3 ASSESSMENT ACTIVITY

Quiz 2

Explain that students will end the session by solving some problems on their own, so you can get a sense of how much they have learned and grown in their math thinking so far this year.

Distribute Quiz 2 (A41–A42), review the format with students, and read the problems aloud.

These questions provide additional information about Benchmarks 2, 3, 4, 5, and 7. Use this information, along with other information you have collected during this unit, when assessing a student's progress towards these Benchmarks. PD

BENCHMARKS	QUESTIONS
2: Understand that three-digit numbers represent amounts of hundreds, tens, and ones.	5
3: Read, write, count, and compare numbers to 1,000.	1, 5
4: Add/subtract 10 or 100 to/from numbers within 1,000.	1
5: Add fluently within 100.	2
7: Counting by 5s, 10s, and 100s within 1000.	3–4

SESSION FOLLOW UP: REVIEW AND PRACTICE

Daily Practice

 DAILY PRACTICE For ongoing review, students complete *Student Activity Book* page 376.

RESOURCE MASTERS, A42

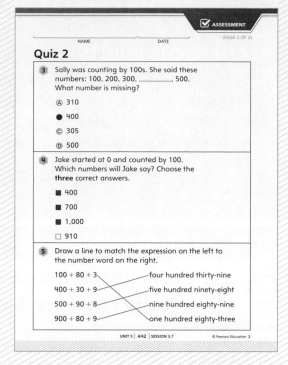

STUDENT ACTIVITY BOOK, P. 376

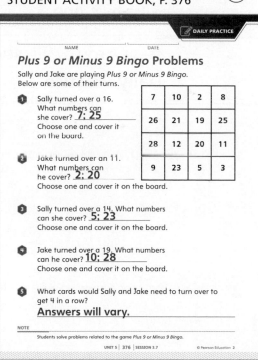

PROFESSIONAL DEVELOPMENT

PD TEACHER NOTE 5: Place Value in Second Grade

<table>
<tr>
<td>

SESSION 3.8

</td>
<td>

Adding within 100, Counting within 1,000

</td>
</tr>
</table>

MATH FOCUS POINTS

○ Solving a comparison problem with a bigger unknown

○ Adding 2-digit numbers using accurate and efficient strategies

○ Skip counting and writing multiples of 5 and 10 within 1,000

TODAY'S PLAN	MATERIALS
(10) Class CLASSROOM ROUTINES: REVIEW AND PRACTICE ***Today's Number: More or Less?***	Teacher Presentation (or use the board) Blank paper (1 sheet per student)
(60) Individuals **1** ASSESSMENT ACTIVITY **Adding within 100, Counting within 1,000**	A43–A45*
SESSION FOLLOW-UP: REVIEW AND PRACTICE **Daily Practice**	*Student Activity Book*, p. 377

* See *Materials to Prepare* in the Investigation 3 Planner.

Common Core State Standards	**Classroom Routines:** 2.NBT.A.4, 2.NBT.B.5, 2.NBT.B.9 **Session:** 2.OA.A.1, 2.NBT.A.2, 2.NBT.B.5	**Daily Practice:** 2.NBT.A.1b, 2.NBT.A.3, 2.NBT.A.4, 2.NBT.B.5

CLASSROOM ROUTINES: REVIEW AND PRACTICE

Today's Number: More or Less?

MATH FOCUS POINTS

○ Estimating the sum of two 2-digit numbers using known combinations, place value, and properties of operations

○ Using standard notation (<, >) to express the relationship between quantities

○ Generating equivalent expressions for a number

I'm going to display an addition problem. The sum is Today's Number. Today, before we figure out the exact answer, I want you to think about whether Today's Number is more or less than 100.

Display the Teacher Presentation (or write 47 + 58 on the board).

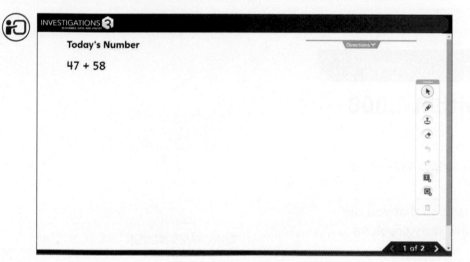

Students think about the problem individually, discuss their thinking with a partner, and then share strategies as a class.

What did you pay attention to when you were thinking about whether or not 47 + 58 was more or less than 100?

Listen for evidence that students' reasoning about the sum is based on the number of tens (e.g., there are 9 tens, and that's 90) or the sum of the tens (e.g., 40 + 50 = 90) and that they are also considering the number of ones. Once students agree that the sum is more than 100, determine the exact amount as a class. Use equations to record.

$$47 + 58 = \underline{\hspace{1cm}}$$
$$40 + 50 = 90$$
$$7 + 8 = 15$$
$$90 + 15 = 105$$

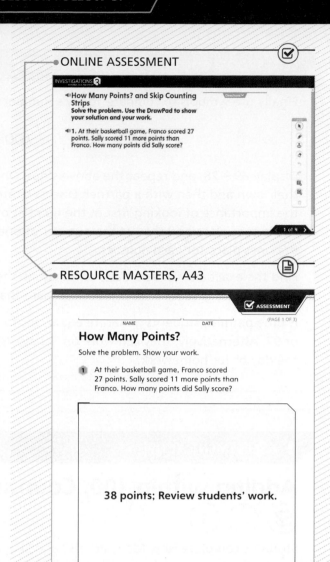

● ONLINE ASSESSMENT

How Many Points? and Skip Counting Strips
Solve the problem. Use the DrawPad to show your solution and your work.

◄1. At their basketball game, Franco scored 27 points. Sally scored 11 more points than Franco. How many points did Sally score?

1 of 4

● RESOURCE MASTERS, A43

☑ ASSESSMENT

NAME   DATE   (PAGE 1 OF 3)

How Many Points?
Solve the problem. Show your work.

1. At their basketball game, Franco scored 27 points. Sally scored 11 more points than Franco. How many points did Sally score?

38 points; Review students' work.

UNIT 5 | A43 | SESSION 3.8   © Pearson Education 2

Finally use symbols to compare Today's Number to 100:

$$105 > 100 \qquad 100 < 105$$

Display $69 + 28$, and repeat the above steps. Once again, students think on their own and then with a partner. Discuss strategies as a class, highlighting the importance of looking first at the number of tens by looking at the digit in the tens place and then at the number of ones by looking at the digit in the ones place for each number.

Find the exact answer as a class, using equations to record, and then use the less-than and greater-than signs to compare that number to 100.

If time permits, students generate equations for one of Today's Numbers: 105 or 97. Alternatively, they can work on Today's Number at some other point in the day or for homework.

1 ASSESSMENT ACTIVITY

Adding within 100, Counting within 1,000

Students complete How Many Points? and Skip Counting Strips (A43–A45 or the Online Assessment).

Explain that students will work on several tasks, individually, so that you can get a sense of how they have grown in their ability to solve story problems and add within 100. **TN1** **TN2** **TN3**

BENCHMARKS	QUESTIONS
3: Read, write, count, and compare numbers to 1,000.	4
5: Add fluently within 100	2–3
6: Solve comparison story problems with a bigger unknown.	1
7: Count by 5s, 10s, and 100s within 1,000.	4

Problem 1: At their basketball game, Franco scored 27 points. Sally scored 11 more points than Franco. How many points did Sally score?

Problem 2: Kira and Jake are on the same basketball team. During the game, Kira scored 48 points. Jake scored 34 points. How many points did they score?

Problem 3: presents the same problem with horizontal and vertical notation.

Problem 4: asks students to complete four skip counting strips.

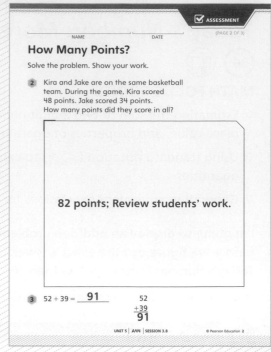

RESOURCE MASTERS, A44

☑ ASSESSMENT
(PAGE 2 OF 3)
NAME   DATE

How Many Points?
Solve the problem. Show your work.

2 Kira and Jake are on the same basketball team. During the game, Kira scored 48 points. Jake scored 34 points. How many points did they score in all?

82 points; Review students' work.

3 $52 + 39 =$ __91__ $\begin{array}{r} 52 \\ +39 \\ \hline 91 \end{array}$

UNIT 5 | A44 | SESSION 3.8   © Pearson Education 2

TEACHING NOTES

TN1 Assessing Students' Use of the Number Line These problems also provide an opportunity to see whether and how students are making use of the number line as a tool for representing, solving, and/or recording strategies for solving problems involving addition and subtraction.

TN2 Assessing Students' Ability to Explain Their Strategy These problems also provide an opportunity to observe students' growing ability to explain their strategies for solving addition and subtraction problems. Note whether students' strategies rely on place value and/or properties of operations.

TN3 Assessing Fluency within 100 In addition to A43–A44, use students' work from the Pocket Routine (*Student Activity Book* p. 369) from Session 3.7, and Problem 2 from Quiz 2 (A41–A42) to assess students' fluency with addition within 100 (Benchmark 5).

ONGOING ASSESSMENT Observing Students at Work

Students solve a comparison problem with a bigger unknown and two addition problems, presented in a context and without a context. They also complete skip counting strips that count by 5s and 10s. **PD**

○ **Can students make sense of what the problems are asking?**

○ **What strategies do students use to add?** Do they add by place, combining tens and ones? Keep one number whole and add the other on in parts? Another strategy? Are they working efficiently and accurately?

○ **How do students show their work?** Do they use sticker notation? Number lines? Equations? Vertical notation? Can you tell how they solved the problem?

○ **Can students accurately skip count and write numbers within 1,000?**

 DIFFERENTIATION Supporting the Range of Learners

ENGLISH LANGUAGE LEARNERS **Repeat and Clarify** Students may need additional support in order to understand the story problems and represent what each problem is asking. Reread the information to students, while using gestures and visuals to support comprehension. Then have students restate each problem in their own words before they begin to solve it. After students understand each problem, they should use numbers and equations to solve it. Discern students' mathematical knowledge from their understanding of English.

SESSION FOLLOW-UP: REVIEW AND PRACTICE

Daily Practice

 DAILY PRACTICE For ongoing review, students complete *Student Activity Book* page 377.

RESOURCE MASTERS, A45

ASSESSMENT (PAGE 3 OF 3)

NAME _____ DATE _____

Skip Counting Strips

4 Fill in the counting strips.

345	560	800	630
350	565	810	640
355	570	820	650
360	575	830	660
365	580	840	670
370	585	850	680
375	590	860	690
380	595	870	700
385	600	880	710
390	605	890	720
395	610	900	730
400	615	910	740

UNIT 5 | A45 | SESSION 3.8   © Pearson Education 2

STUDENT ACTIVITY BOOK, P. 377

DAILY PRACTICE

NAME _____ DATE _____

Today's Number: Guess the Number

[4] [5] [8]

1 Write all of the possible numbers you can make with the three numbers above.
458, 485, 548, 584, 845, 854

2 Today's Number is less than 600.
Which numbers could it be? **458, 485, 548, and 584**

3 Today's Number also has more 1s than 10s.
Which numbers could it be? **458 and 548**

4 Today's Number solves this equation: 52 + _____ = 600.
What is Today's Number? **548**

5 Write at least 5 equations for Today's Number, including one that shows Today's Number as the sum of 100s, 10s, and 1s.
Answers will vary.

6 Write the number word for Today's Number.
five hundred forty-eight

NOTE
Students use clues to figure out Today's Number.
MW8 Representing Place Value: Hundreds, Tens, and Ones

UNIT 5 | 377 | SESSION 3.8   © Pearson Education 2

PROFESSIONAL DEVELOPMENT

PD **TEACHER NOTE 9:** How Many Points? and Skip Counting Strips

INTERVENTION

Use anytime after Session 3.1.

Adding Tens and Ones

(25) (person)

MATH FOCUS POINTS

○ Visualizing, representing, and solving add to story problems with the result unknown

○ Developing efficient strategies for adding 2-digit numbers

○ Developing efficient methods for notating addition strategies

MATERIALS: connecting cubes organized into single color towers of 10 (9 towers per student), S79

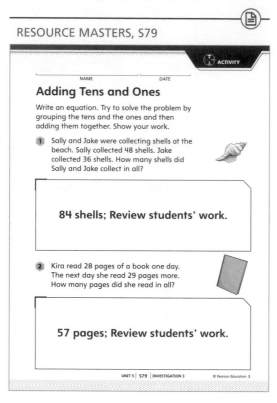

RESOURCE MASTERS, S79

Read the following problem aloud. **Kira had 37 rocks in her collection. Her brother gave her 25 more rocks. How many rocks did Kira have in all?** Ask students to visualize the action and retell the story. Identify and record the known and unknown information.

Distribute cubes, and have students represent the two quantities. **Show the number of rocks Kira had. How many towers of 10 is that? How many single cubes? Now show the number of rocks her brother gave her.** Verify this number in terms of tens and ones. Record these two amounts using sticker notation.

We can add numbers by grouping the tens and the ones. How many tens in 37? In 25? How many tens in all? Have students show the answer to each question with their cubes. **What equation shows this?** Record 30 + 20 = 50. Repeat these questions for grouping the ones.

$$30 + 20 = 50$$
$$7 + 5 = 12$$
$$50 + 10 = 60$$
$$60 + 2 = 62$$

How many cubes do we have now? How many groups of 10s and how many 1s? Do you have enough ones to make a tower of 10? If so, snap them together. How many towers of 10 do you have? How many ones? How many in all? Ask students what the 62 cubes represent. Direct them back to the problem to remind them about the context. Ask students to explain how they know there are 62 cubes.

〝 STUDENTS MIGHT SAY 〞

"There are 5 towers of 10, and that's 50, and then 12 more. I can put 10 single cubes together to make another tower of 10, which would be 60. Then there are 2 more left over, which makes 62 in all."

Ask students to reassemble their cubes into single color towers of 10. Then display the this problem: **Jake had 49 rocks in his collection. Then Sally gave him 36 more. How many rocks did Jake have in all?**

Review the problem. Using cubes, students model then solve the problem by combining the tens and then the ones. When students have finished, ask a volunteer to show their strategy using cubes. As students share, record their steps using equations.

$$40 + 30 = 70$$
$$9 + 6 = 15$$
$$70 + 10 = 80$$
$$80 + 5 = 85$$

Distribute copies of S79 for students to complete.

DIFFERENTIATION

ENGLISH LANGUAGE LEARNERS **Repeat and Clarify** Have students restate the problem in their own words before they solve it. If students need additional support, ask questions to guide them. **What will you do first? What will you do next?**

ADDITIONAL RESOURCES

Math Words and Ideas Strategies for Adding 2-Digit Numbers: Adding Tens and Ones (MWI)

Adding On in Parts

MATH FOCUS POINTS

○ Visualizing, representing, and solving add to story problems with the result unknown

○ Developing efficient strategies for adding 2-digit numbers

○ Developing efficient methods for notating addition strategies

MATERIALS: connecting cubes organized into single color towers of 10, blank paper (as needed), S80

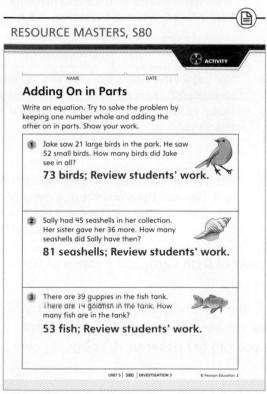

RESOURCE MASTERS, S80

Read this problem aloud: **Jake found 46 shells. Franco found 37 shells. How many shells did Jake and Franco find in all?**

Are groups being combined or separated? Ask students to help you write an equation to represent the problem (i.e., 46 + 37 = _____). Ask a student to represent each quantity with cubes.

Today we will use the addition strategy of keeping one number whole and adding the other one on in parts. Does it matter if we keep 46 whole and add on 37 or if we keep 37 whole and add on 46?

STUDENTS MIGHT SAY

"You can start with either 37 or 46. No matter which number you start with, you will get the same answer."

"I would start with 46 because you don't have to add on as much as if you started with 37."

What part of 37 should we add to 46 first? Some students might suggest adding on 4 from the 37 to get to 50 and then add on the remaining 33 either in parts or whole (50 + 33). Others are likely to suggest adding the 37 on by breaking it into tens (30) and ones (7). Use cubes and number lines to demonstrate both of these ways of adding on the 37.

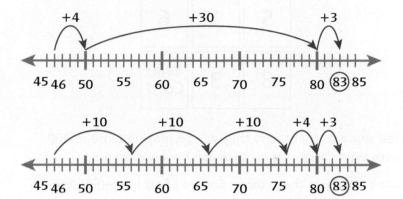

Then have students help you record each using equations. How can we show this first way of adding 37 onto 46 in parts? What did we add first? What did we add next? How would you show those steps using equations?

46 + 4 = 50	46 + 30 = 76
50 + 30 = 80	76 + 4 = 80
80 + 3 = 83	80 + 3 = 83

Where in these equations do you see the 46 shells Jake found? Where do you see the 37 shells Franco found?

Give students similar problems to solve on their own using the strategy of keeping one number whole. Remind them to record their work using equations. Supply cubes and blank paper as needed. Then distribute copies of S80.

DIFFERENTIATION

ENGLISH LANGUAGE LEARNERS Repeat and Clarify Read the problems with students. Then restate the problems using simpler language. For example: **Jake saw 21 birds. Then he saw 52 birds. How many birds did Jake see in all?**

ADDITIONAL RESOURCES

Math Words and Ideas Strategies for Adding 2-Digit Numbers: Adding One Number On in Parts

EXTENSION Use anytime after Session 3.3.

Close to 100 with Wild Cards

⏱️30 👥

MATH FOCUS POINT

○ Using knowledge of place value to find pairs of 2-digit numbers that add to 100 or a number close to 100

MATERIALS: Digit Cards with Wild Cards added (1 deck per pair), G36

Display the following cards:

5	1	6
8	3	Wild Card

Tell students that today they will be playing *Close to 100* with Wild Cards. A Wild Card can be any digit 0–9.

Look closely at these cards. Can you find a combination with a sum of 100 exactly? Can you find a combination that uses the Wild Card? If so, what digit would the Wild Card represent?

Have students share their thinking with a partner. Then collect students' ideas. Record possible combinations noting how different combinations can result in the same total.

 STUDENTS MIGHT SAY

"You can make 100 if you use the Wild Card. I used the 6 and the 3 in the tens place. Together they add to 90. Then I used the 8 in the ones place to make 98. The Wild Card would be 2. 98 + 2 = 100."

"I made 100 differently. I used the 8, the 1, the 5 and the Wild Card to make 85 + 15 = 100."

Display the following cards:

2	3	5
Wild Card	1	0

Look at these cards. Talk with a partner. Can you find a combination with a sum of 100 exactly? Would you use the Wild Card? If so, which digit would it be?

 STUDENTS MIGHT SAY

"You can't make 100 exactly with these cards. The closest we got was 95. First we made the biggest number we could, which was 53. Then we used the Wild Card to make 42. 53 + 42 = 95, which is 5 less than 100."

"We got a little closer. We used the Wild Card to make 90. Then we used the 1 and the 2 to make 12. 90 + 12 = 102, which is 2 more than 100."

"We got even closer, but we still couldn't make 100. We used the 5 and the 0 to make 50. Then we used the wild card and the 1 to make 51. 50 + 51 = 101. We were just 1 away!"

Distribute decks of Digit Cards and 2 copies of G36 to each pair.

As you play, think carefully about your cards. If you cannot make 100 exactly, how close can you get? Sometimes you can get closer to 100 by going over 100 slightly.

DIFFERENTIATION

ENGLISH LANGUAGE LEARNERS Provide Sentence Stem Provide a sentence stem to help students explain their reasoning for the numbers they made. For example: *I made the numbers _____ and _____ because _____.* If students need additional support, then read the sentence, pausing so they can fill in the missing information. If students point to their numbers, then restate the information using the sentence stem and have students repeat after you.

ADDITIONAL RESOURCES

Math Words and Ideas Ways to Make 100

HOW MANY TENS? HOW MANY HUNDREDS?

Algebra Connections in This Unit

In this unit, your students have opportunities to engage with ideas that lay a foundation for algebra. Seven- and eight-year-olds can and do think algebraically. Part of the work of Grade 2 is helping students learn to verbalize those thoughts and begin to consider such questions as: Is this statement always true? Does it work for all numbers? How can we know? Such skills will provide the basis for making sense of algebraic notation and proof when it is formally introduced, years from now.

As illustrated in the Algebra Connections Teacher Notes in Units 1 and 3, implicit in students' calculation strategies are generalizations about the behavior of operations. For example, addition strategies in which addends are decomposed and the parts added together in a different order can be viewed as applications of the commutative and associative properties of addition. When students are challenged to notice and verbalize such a generalization and then to explain how they know the generalization is true, they engage in proof, a core practice of mathematics. Proving is at the heart of MP3, Construct viable arguments and critique the reasoning of others.

Consider the following vignette in which students discuss a generalization that often arises in *Close to 100*:

Teacher: I know that 80 + 20 = 100. I wanted to use that fact, but I didn't have the right cards. But I had a 7 and a 9, and 79 is pretty close to 80. What number could go with 79 to make 100? Talk to a partner about what you think.

When the class comes together, students offer ideas.

Anita: You have one number down, so you need one number up, so 21.

Henry: You take 80 − 1 = 79, so you take 20 + 1. 79 + 21 = 100.

Teacher: But let's say I don't have a 1. Are there other numbers I could look for?

Rochelle: Do the same thing. Go 1 down and 1 up. 78 + 22 equals 100.

Henry: You're just taking one from one number and giving it to the other.

The teacher writes on the board, "You're taking 1 from one number and giving it to the other."

Teacher: Henry, is this what you said? What happens when you do that?

Carla: You get the same sum.

The statement on the board now reads, "You're taking 1 from one number and giving to the other, and you get the same sum."

Teacher: Does it work for only 80 and 20? Or are you saying that you can *always* do that?

Rochelle: You can always do it.

Teacher: Use a picture or cubes to show me how you know that when you're adding any two numbers, you can take one from one number and add it to the other and get the same sum.

The students have made an assertion—mathematicians call such an assertion a conjecture—that the sum of two addends remains the same if you subtract 1 from one addend and add 1 to the other. The teacher has challenged the class to show that this conjecture is true not just for 80 + 20 and 79 + 21 but for *all* numbers.

How do Grade 2 students respond to such a question? Consider how the students above respond to their teacher's challenge to justify their conjecture. Alberto begins, using a tower of ten cubes to demonstrate his ideas.

Alberto: I started with 10 + 0.

If you move one over, it's 9 + 1.

Move another one over, and now it's 8 + 2.

Rochelle: You can keep going. You take 1 from one number and give it to the other.

Teacher: Alberto used ten cubes. What if he started with 100? Could he still subtract 1 from one number and add it to the other?

Anita: Yes. Because you're still using the same amount, the same number of cubes.

Henry: It doesn't matter how many cubes you start with. It will still work because you're just changing them around. You keep taking from one number and adding it to the other.

Tia: It has to be the same because, whatever number you start with, you don't put any more cubes in, and you don't take any away.

Alberto presents a model of addition—joining two sets of cubes—that shows how he knows that $10 + 0 = 9 + 1 = 8 + 2$. Anita sees that the same representation can show why $80 + 20 = 79 + 21 = 78 + 22$. Henry and Tia point out that it does not matter what the original numbers are. The model could be used to make a similar argument for any two whole numbers. Later these students might refer back to such visual models to show why the same action—subtracting from one number and adding to the other—does not produce the same results with other operations.

The Grade 2 students' argument justifies the claim that if you subtract 1 from one addend and add 1 to another addend, the total remains the same. The sum of the numbers n and m is represented by the total number of cubes in two stacks. By moving one cube from one stack to another, Alberto demonstrated subtracting 1 from n and adding 1 to m. The total number of cubes remains unchanged; therefore, $n + m = (n - 1) + (m + 1)$. Alberto's demonstration, along with his classmates' explanations, validates the claim not only for particular numbers but for any whole numbers, and it easily conveys why the claim is true.

Grade 2 students may extend this generalization to say that if *any amount* is subtracted from one addend and added to the other, the total stays the same (written algebraically, $n + m = (n - x) + (m + x)$. Some students use this generalization to solve addition problems, thinking, for example, $38 + 25 = 40 + 23 = 63$. They may show that this works as Alberto did, but instead of moving one cube, they can move any number of cubes to prove that the total is unchanged.

For most adults, notation such as $n + m = (n - x) + (m + x)$ is the chief identifying feature of algebra. The notation, however, expresses rules about how operations work, which students can reason out for themselves. This *reasoning*—about how numbers can be put together and taken apart under different operations—*not* the notation is the work of elementary students in algebra.

These examples illustrate the kind of early algebraic reasoning that is fully accessible to elementary-aged students. *Investigations* students are encouraged to verbalize the generalizations they see about numbers and operations and to explain and justify them by using materials and tools such as cubes and number lines. These discussions are not so much about finding an answer to a particular problem but about describing a way to address a whole class of problems.

Note: In the text for the sessions, you will find Math Notes that identify where these early algebra discussions are likely to arise. Some of the **Teacher Notes** and **Dialogue Boxes** further elaborate the ideas and illustrate students' conversations about them. These discussions also engage students in MP7, Look for and make use of structure, MP8, Look for and express regularity in repeated reasoning, and MP3, Construct viable arguments and critique the reasoning of others. The Math Practice Notes provide more information about these practices.

Learning Addition and Subtraction Facts in Second Grade

Efficient computation strategies are based, in part, on developing fluency with addition and subtraction facts. Fluency means that facts are quickly accessible mentally, either because they are immediately known or because the calculation that is used is so effortless as to be essentially automatic (in the way that some adults quickly derive one combination from another—for example, thinking $8 + 9 = 8 + 8 + 1$). In *Investigations*, the development of fluency begins in Kindergarten where students are expected to fluently add and subtract within 5. Fluency within 10 is expected in Grade 1 and within 20 by the end of Grade 2.

More Than Just "Facts"

Addition combinations and their subtraction counterparts are traditionally referred to as "the facts," and that terminology is used in this curriculum. However, "fact" often implies something that can only be memorized (such as the first president of the United States or the capital of Nebraska) and not something that can be learned through reasoning. In *Investigations*, students learn addition and subtraction facts by using what they already know about numbers and number relationships, about the properties of addition and subtraction, and about the relationship between these two operations. Relying on memory alone is not sufficient. If students forget answers, they are left with no way to think about the problem. If, however, their learning of the facts is based on reasoning, they have a way to determine the answer.

For example, the sum of $7 + 8$ can be determined in many ways. If we forget that $7 + 8 = 15$, but understand what addition is and know some related combinations, we can reason to find the sum. For example, if we know that $7 + 7 = 14$, we can add 1 more to get 15. If we know that $8 + 8 = 16$, we can take 1 away and get 15. If we know that $7 + 3 = 10$, we can add the 5 that's left to get 15 ($7 + 8 = 7 + 3 + 5 = 15$). In K–2, students use the facts repeatedly, in a variety of contexts, while also building an understanding of the properties of the operations, specifically the commutative and associative properties and the relationship between addition and subtraction.

Practicing the Facts

As in K–1, students encounter many activities, games, and story problems that involve adding and subtracting within 20. In Grade 2, designated time to review and practice the facts is built into the curriculum, in sessions and as a recurring Classroom Routine, *Fact Fluency*.

Fact Cards are also introduced as a tool to support fluency as well as independent responsibility for keeping track of "Facts I Know" and "Facts I Am Still Working On." Fact Cards for addition present two related problems—except for the Doubles, which have one—building on and strengthening students' understanding of the commutative property of addition. Subtraction Cards present only one problem. While Grade 2 students come to see that $10 - 4$ and $10 - 6$ are related not only to each other but also to their addition counterparts (i.e., $4 + 6$ and $6 + 4$), they develop this understanding of the relationship between the operations of addition and subtraction over time. Because students often view these as unrelated problems early in the year, when students first get the cards, they are purposely presented on two different Fact Cards.

$$1 + 2$$
$$2 + 1$$

Clue: _____

$$2 - 1$$

Clue: _____

Over the course of the year, students receive sets of Fact Cards that represent various groups of addition and subtraction facts and sort them into two envelopes: "Facts I Know" and "Facts I Am Still Working On". In this way, students determine which facts they know and which they need to practice. After opportunities to practice, the clue line provides scaffolding for challenging facts that remain hard to remember.

In Unit 1, the fact work focuses on reviewing addition and subtraction within 10, a Grade 1 benchmark, plus a few additional facts, and on thinking about categories of facts. The focus on groups of related facts helps students learn effective strategies for finding solutions.

Fact Cards: Set 1*	Fact Cards: Set 2
Doubles	Minus Half
Plus 1	Minus 1
Plus 2	Minus 2
Make 10	10 Minus
Other $3 + 4$ and $4 + 3$ $3 + 5$ and $5 + 3$ $3 + 6$ and $6 + 3$ $4 + 5$ and $5 + 4$	Other $4 - 3$ $5 - 3, 5 - 4$ $6 - 4, 6 - 5$ $7 - 3, 7 - 4, 7 - 5, 7 - 6$ $8 - 3, 8 - 5, 8 - 6, 8 - 7$ $9 - 3, 9 - 4, 9 - 5, 9 - 6,$ $9 - 7, 9 - 8$

* Some combinations fall into more than one category.
For example, $1 + 9$ and $9 + 1$ is a Make 10 and a Plus 1 Fact.

Later units provide practice with these facts, and introduce and practice the remaining facts.

Fact Cards: Set 3*	Fact Cards: Set 4
Near Doubles	Plus 10
	Minus 10

Fact Cards: Set 5	Fact Cards: Sets 6 and 7
Plus 9	Remaining Facts
Minus 9	

* Some combinations fall into more than one category.
For example, $9 + 8$ and $8 + 9$ is a Near Double and a Plus 9 Fact.

Every unit in the Grade 2 sequence includes practice of the facts so that, by the end of the year, students have no (or very few) cards left in their "Facts I Am Still Working On" envelopes. The ongoing nature of this work provides teachers many opportunities to assess students' fluency with these problems. If, over time, there are students who are not moving many cards from their "Facts I Am Still Working On" to their "Facts I Know" envelopes, that is important information and an opportunity to provide focused support and practice.

In *Investigations*, developing fluency with the addition and subtraction facts is based on work that is focused and deep. Learning a set of facts is not distinct from developing an understanding about quantities and operations and the relationship between them. In fact, even when students are engaged in an activity that might seem like pure number practice, for example solving Number Strings, they are working to make sense of and understand the task. This flexibility and sense making results in fluency with the addition and subtraction facts that contributes to the development of computational fluency in the primary grades and beyond.

Stickers: A Context for Place Value

In Unit 3, students were introduced to a new context, a store that sells stickers individually (as singles, or ones), in strips of ten, or in sheets of 100. This context helps students think about place value, the principle upon which whole numbers in our base-10 number system are structured (in tens and ones; in hundreds, tens, and ones; etc.).

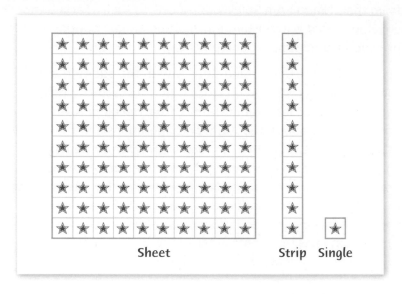

Sheet   **Strip**   **Single**

In this unit, students see a set of stickers and figure out how many there are, or they figure out how to show a particular number with stickers. As students count stickers and represent quantities with them, they are working in a context that promotes counting by 10s and helps them consolidate the idea that 53 is made up of five tens and three ones.

This work helps students develop more efficient strategies for solving addition and subtraction problems. For example, consider a problem like this:

Kira has two strips of ten stickers and 5 stickers. For her birthday her brother gave her another strip of ten stickers and three singles. How many does she have now?

The context helps students keep in mind the tens-and-ones structure of numbers, supporting their use of such strategies as breaking numbers into tens and ones and adding like groups.

$$25 + 13 = 20 + 5 + 10 + 3$$
$$20 + 10 = 30$$
$$5 + 3 = 8$$
$$30 + 8 = 38$$

The sticker context is extended to 100 as students are introduced to sheets of 100 stickers organized in rows of ten. This helps students achieve a strong understanding of how 100 is composed (e.g., 1 hundred is equivalent to 10 tens or 100 ones). Using sticker books with pages that hold 100 stickers helps students understand multiples of 100 and the structure of the 3-digit numbers. In this unit, the model is extended as students represent 3-digit numbers and add and subtract 100 to any number within 1,000. This work, and the work in Unit 8, extend their thinking about place value, or how numbers in our number system are structured (in ones, tens, hundreds, and so on). In later grades, students build on this foundation as they investigate the structure of much larger numbers (thousands, hundred thousands, and millions).

Types of Story Problems

Students encounter a variety of addition and subtraction problem types in the early grades. The context of some problems involves actions like combining, removing, or comparing; others involve a static situation of two parts and a whole. Problems can also vary in terms of what information is known and unknown.

ADD TO/TAKE FROM: PROBLEMS ABOUT COMBINING AND REMOVING These problems involve an action. In their most familiar form, they ask students to combine two amounts (Add To) or to remove one amount from another (Take From) and determine how many there are at the end of the story (Result Unknown). In other words, students need to find the sum or the difference. In other variations, the unknown is the amount added or removed (Unknown Change) or the amount at the beginning of the story (Unknown Start).

PUT TOGETHER/TAKE APART: PROBLEMS ABOUT PARTS AND WHOLES These stories do not involve actions like combining or removing; nothing is joined or amassed, given away or used up. Rather, students are asked to consider two parts (e.g., the number of red flowers in a vase and the number of blue flowers in a vase) that make up one whole (e.g., the number of flowers in a vase). Students can be asked to determine the whole when the two parts are known (Total Unknown); one of the parts when the other part and the whole are known (Addend Unknown, also commonly known as Finding a Missing Part); or how a given whole could be broken into two parts (Both Addends Unknown).

	RESULT UNKNOWN	CHANGE UNKNOWN	START UNKNOWN
Add To	Two bunnies sat on the grass. Three more bunnies hopped there. How many bunnies are on the grass now? $2 + 3 = ?$ GK G1 G2	Two bunnies were sitting on the grass. Some more bunnies hopped there. Then there were five bunnies. How many bunnies hopped over to the first two? $2 + ? = 5$ G1 G2	Some bunnies were sitting on the grass. Three more bunnies hopped there. Then there were five bunnies. How many bunnies were on the grass before? $? + 3 = 5$ G1 G2
Take From	Five apples were on the table. I ate two apples. How many apples are on the table now? $5 - 2 = ?$ GK G1 G2	Five apples were on the table. I ate some apples. Then there were three apples. How many apples did I eat? $5 - ? = 3$ G1 G2	Some apples were on the table. I ate two apples. Then there were three apples. How many apples were on the table before? $? - 2 = 3$ G1 G2

Adapted from © Copyright 2010. National Governors Association for Best Practices and Council of Chief State School Officers. All rights reserved.

Note: Each skill is assessed at the grade levels in purple and is not assessed at the grade levels in black.

	TOTAL UNKNOWN	ADDEND UNKNOWN	BOTH ADDENDS UNKNOWN
Put Together/ Take Apart	Three red apples and two green apples are on the table. How many apples are on the table? $3 + 2 = ?$ GK G1 G2	Five apples are on the table. Three are red and the rest are green. How many apples are green? $3 + ? = 5, 5 - 3 = ?$ G1 G2	Grandma has five flowers. How many can she put in her red vase and how many in her blue vase? $5 = 0 + 5, 5 = 5 + 0$ $5 = 1 + 4, 5 = 4 + 1$ $5 = 2 + 3, 5 = 3 + 2$ GK G1 G2

Adapted from © Copyright 2010. National Governors Association for Best Practices and Council of Chief State School Officers. All rights reserved.

Note: Each skill is assessed at the grade levels in purple.

COMPARE: PROBLEMS ABOUT COMPARISON These problems ask students to compare two quantities to determine how many more (or fewer) one has than the other (Difference Unknown). Other variations give one quantity, and a difference, and ask students to find the other quantity (Bigger Unknown, Smaller Unknown).

	DIFFERENCE UNKNOWN	BIGGER UNKNOWN	SMALLER UNKNOWN
Compare version with more	Lucy has two apples. Julie has five apples. How many more apples does Julie have than Lucy? $2 + ? = 5, 5 - 2 = ?$ **G1** **G2**	Julie has three more apples than Lucy. Lucy has two apples. How many apples does Julie have? $2 + 3 = ?, 3 + 2 = ?$ **G1** **G2**	Julie has three more apples than Lucy. Julie has five apples. How many apples does Lucy have? $5 - 3 = ?, ? + 3 = 5$ **G1** **G2**
Compare version with fewer	Lucy has two apples. Julie has five apples. How many fewer apples does Lucy have than Julie? $2 + ? = 5, 5 - 2 = ?$ **G1** **G2**	Lucy has 3 fewer apples than Julie. Lucy has two apples. How many apples does Julie have? $2 + 3 = ?, 3 + 2 = ?$ **G1** **G2**	Lucy has 3 fewer apples than Julie. Julie has five apples. How many apples does Lucy have? $5 - 3 = ?, ? + 3 = 5$ **G1** **G2**
Adapted from © Copyright 2010. National Governors Association for Best Practices and Council of Chief State School Officers. All rights reserved.			
Note: Each skill is assessed at the grade levels in purple and is not assessed at the grade levels in black.			

Note that the information above is intended to describe the problem types and to help teachers distinguish among them; students should not be expected to name these categories or say to which category a problem belongs. What is important is that they can visualize the relationship among the quantities in all types of situations, regardless of which quantities are given and which must be determined. From that ability to visualize, students can then apply the operations of addition and subtraction appropriately.

It is also important to note that, if teachers choose to personalize the text of story problems (e.g., using names of students in the class or situations or topics that are more relevant to your particular group of students), it is important to retain the structure of the original problem.

Place Value in Second Grade

Understanding the place-value structure of our base-10 number system and how it applies to and supports number composition and computation is a central piece of work in the number and operations strand of the *Investigations* curriculum. The base-10 number system is a "place value" system. That is, any numeral, say 2, can represent different values, depending on where it appears in a written number: it can represent 2 ones, 2 tens, 2 hundreds, 2 thousands, and so forth. Understanding our place-value system requires coordinating the way we write numbers —e.g., 217—and the way we name numbers in words—two hundred seventeen—with how the value of each place represents quantities.

In order to successfully work with place value, students need to know that 1 ten is equal to 10 ones and be able to coordinate groups of tens and ones. Consider, for example, the number 32: one aspect of understanding the value of each place in this number is knowing that the 3 represents 3 groups of ten, the 2 represents 2 ones, and this can be expressed as $30 + 2$. It is also important for students to understand 32 as 2 groups of ten and 12 ones ($20 + 12$). Similarly, as students work with greater numbers such as 132, they must recognize the number of hundreds, tens, and ones ($100 + 30 + 2$) but also know that 132 can also be thought of as 13 groups of ten and 2 ones. The compactness of the base-10 system is what makes it powerful, but that very compactness means it is dense with ideas, which young students must put together.

Foundational Ideas of Place Value

In Kindergarten, students develop fluency with ones as they master the counting sequence and count quantities. They use Ten Frames to reinforce the foundational idea that 10 ones can also be thought of as a *group* of 10 ones, and explore the two-addend combinations of 10. These are precursors to work with place value. Similarly, representing teen numbers on Ten Frames, seeing them as 10 ones and some leftover number of ones, and using equations (e.g., $15 = 10 + 5$) to represent this information helps students notice important regularities in these numbers and the way we write them (i.e., the 1 in 15 refers to the group of ten, and the 5 refers to the number of leftover ones).

In Grade 1, students make a critical shift from thinking and working primarily in ones to thinking and working with *groups* of tens and ones. They strengthen their understanding of this critical 10:1 relationship as they work with contexts and models (e.g., fingers, Ten Frame cards, connecting cubes organized into towers of ten) that represent groups of tens and ones.

With these models in mind, Grade 1 students represent 2-digit quantities and discuss how 15 and 51 are different as they build the understanding that numbers have different values depending on their place and that the way we write, read, and say 2-digit numbers is connected to the number of tens and ones. Grade 1 students also use these place-value models to represent addition and subtraction of 2-digit numbers. In doing so, they connect a model to notation and use the model to explain their thinking.

While much of the foundation for work with place value is laid in Kindergarten and Grade 1, coming to *understand* and *know* that 10 ones is equivalent to 1 ten, *applying* this 10:1 relationship to larger quantities and multidigit numbers (e.g., 10 tens is 1 hundred, and 10 hundreds is 1 thousand), *coordinating* these multiple units (i.e., groups of tens and groups of ones), and *using* these ideas to develop and refine strategies for addition and subtraction is the focus of the place-value work in Grade 2.

Grade 2 and the Base-10 Number System

In Grade 2, students continue to work with models that represent the place-value structure of our base-10 number system. In Unit 1, students are introduced to coins and coin values, which they later use to model problems with pennies, dimes, and dollars and they revisit the work with tens and ones from Grade 1. In Unit 3 they continue this work and are also introduced to a "sticker" context, where stickers come in singles, strips of ten, and sheets of 100. They use both contexts to think about the composition of 2-digit and 3-digit numbers (to 500 in Unit 3 and 1,000 in Unit 5). Numbers are composed as they focus on making different combinations of stickers or coins to equal a given quantity. For example, 87 (or 87¢) can be composed of 8 strips of 10 and 7 individual stickers (or 8 dimes and 7 pennies), but it can also be composed of 7 strips of 10 and 17 individual stickers (or 7 dimes and 17 pennies). Students also work with other models including connecting cubes organized into towers of 10, the 100 chart, and a shorthand notation for the sticker context. The purpose of these models is to help students build mental images that they can then use in visualizing and solving problems. While no single model is a perfect match for every idea, the purpose of these contexts and models is to give students different examples to use and compare. With these models in mind, students can more easily discuss how 15, 51 and 510 are different as well as learn to read and write numbers to 1,000. For example, in Unit 3 students "fill in" targeted numbers on a series of 100 charts, each representing numbers in the 100s, 200s, 300s etc. as they play a game that involves adding or subtracting 10 to or from a number they have assembled with digit cards. With the goal of covering five numbers in a row, students must first decide whether starting on 258 or 285 is more advantageous and then determine whether adding or subtracting 10 to this number will land them closer to their goal. This and other games not only provides students with an engaging way to practice reading and writing numbers, but it also provides a context for discussing what happens to a 2- or 3-digit number when 10 or 100 is added or subtracted, looking at both how the digit in the tens or hundreds place changes (increases/decreases by 1), and how the value of the number changes (increases/decreases by 10 or 100). Throughout Grade 2, students engage in a variety of activities and games that develop and reinforce the hundreds, tens, and ones structure of the base-10 number system.

Place Value and Computational Fluency in Grade 2

A thorough understanding of the base-10 number system is one of the critical building blocks for developing computational fluency. The composition of numbers from multiples of 1, 10, 100, 1,000, and so forth, is the basis of most of the strategies students use for computation with whole numbers. In all units of Grade 2, students refine strategies for addition (e.g., adding by place and adding on one number in parts), and for subtraction (e.g., keeping one number whole and subtracting the other in parts) and develop fluency for adding

and subtracting 2-digit numbers. Students apply these same strategies as they work with 3-digit numbers, using familiar models and contexts to represent and explain their strategies for addition and subtraction of greater numbers as they solve story problems of all types with unknowns in all positions. In Grade 2, story problem contexts, introduced in Units 1 and 3, such as Enough for the Class? and How Many Stickers?, evolve in Units 5 and 8 into Enough for the Grade? and sticker problems with 3-digit numbers, providing students with opportunities to solve addition and subtraction problems with greater numbers using familiar contexts. Supporting the development of fluency with addition and subtraction is an array of games, such as *Close to 100* (adding 2-digit numbers that total close to 100) and *Capture 5* (adding and subtracting 10 and multiples of 10 to/from 2- and 3-digit numbers), which offer repeated practice adding and subtracting 100s, 10s, and 1s.

For many reasons, Grade 2 is a turning point for the work students are doing with number and operations. In Kindergarten and first grade, students developed many of the foundational pieces necessary to shift their thinking primarily from working with single units (ones) to thinking and working with groups. In Grade 2, students deepen this work with 2-digit numbers and extend the work to 3-digit numbers. They need the time and opportunity to solidify these ideas and relationships as they represent numbers in a variety of ways using hundreds, tens, and ones and as they think flexibly about how numbers can be combined and separated. Building a solid understanding of 2-digit numbers and having fluent and accurate strategies for adding and subtracting them is the basis for developing fluency with 3-digit numbers in Grade 3 and beyond.

Assessment: How Much More to $1.00?

Benchmark Addressed:

Benchmark 1: Solve a 2-step story problem that involves finding the difference between a 2-digit number and 100.

In order to meet the benchmark, students' work should show that they can:

○ Accurately determine the difference between a 2-digit number and 100;

○ Demonstrate how they solved the problem.

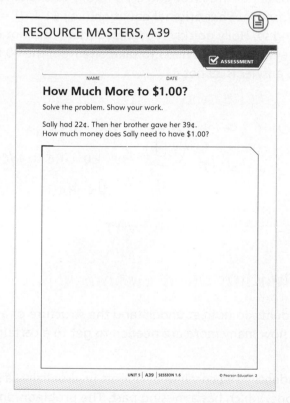

By the end of this unit, students are expected to fluently add 2-digit numbers within 100 using numerical strategies. Most students solve this problem by first combining 22 and 39. Use students' work to gather information about the kinds of strategies students are using to combine two 2-digit numbers at this point in the unit. If you see students using cubes, coins, 100 charts, or 100 grids to add, plan to provide these students with additional opportunities to practice and review numerical strategies such as breaking numbers apart by place, adding one number on in parts, and changing one number and adjusting, in *Investigations* 2 and 3.

Meeting the Benchmark

Many students add on in groups to determine the difference between 61 and 100. A few may use what they know about a similar problem to reason through this problem. The following examples of student work provide a range of typical responses. All of these students met the benchmark—they were able to interpret the problem, solve it accurately, and show their work.

Tia uses a combination of 10 (i.e., 1 + 9) to get from 61 to 70, then adds 30 to get to $1.00.

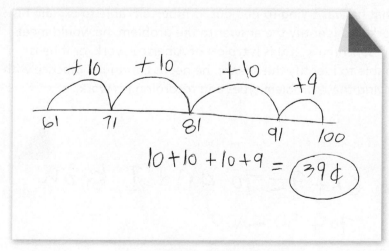

[Tia's Work]

Paige adds 10s first and then ones to arrive at the total.

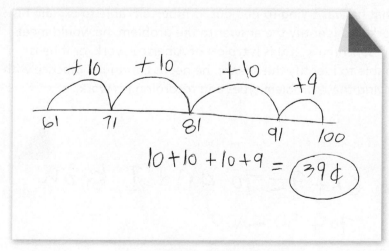

[Paige's Work]

Malcolm uses the related combination 60 + 40 to solve the problem, as well as what he knows about addition. He reasons that if you take one from the 40 and give it to the 60, you create an equivalent problem: 61 + 39.

60 + 40 = 100
so
61 + (39) = 100

you can take the 1 from the 40 and give it to 61.

[Malcolm's Work]

A few students use a different strategy, perhaps subtracting 22 and then 39 (or vice versa) from 100.

Partially Meeting the Benchmark

Some students understand the action of the problem—that they are figuring out how many more are needed. However, as they record their work, they struggle to connect the original problem with the work they have done. For example, Alberto appears to understand that the problem is about determining the difference between 61 and 100, but it is not clear what his answer is. Ask Alberto to retell the original story and describe what he was trying to find out. If Alberto is able to explain his work and identify the answer to the problem, he would meet the benchmark. If this is typical of Alberto's work, or if he is unable to identify the answer, he needs continued practice with solving these problem types and recording his work.

61 + 9 = 70 and I know
70 + 30 = 100

[Alberto's Work]

Other students appear to understand the structure of the problem (i.e., that they are trying to find the difference between 61 and 100 or how much to add to 61 to get 100), but their work indicates an error.

Holly's work suggests that she understands the problem she is trying to solve (i.e., 61 + ? = 100) and that she uses a known fact, 60 + 40 = 100, to help. Her work suggests that she is adjusting by 1 (perhaps because of the relationship between 60 and 61), and she ends up with an answer of 41. Holly's teacher was curious about this error and asked Holly to explain her work and then complete her original equation (i.e., 61 + 41 = 100). Upon doing so, Holly quickly recognized that it did not equal 100 and remarked "Oh, I need to take one from the 40 to make 61, so the answer is 39 not 41."

61 + ? = 100   (41¢)
60 + 40 = 100

I took 1 from the 60 and gave it to the 40.

[Holly's Work]

Not Meeting the Benchmark

Some students do not yet understand the structure of a problem that asks how many more are needed to get to a certain amount.

These students need continued support in visualizing a problem like this one, which has a missing part. The problems on *Student Activity Book* pages 307–310 provide this kind of practice and examples for designing additional ones. As students work on such problems, ask how many cents are needed in all, and then ask the students to show that amount on a 100 grid, helping them see how those 100 represent the situation.

Teacher: If these 100 cubes represent $1.00, how many cubes would represent the amount of money Sally has? (61) Can you show me the 61¢? Next we need to figure out how many more cents Sally would need to have $1.00 and how many more make $1.00?

TEACHER NOTE 7

Students' Addition Strategies

As students work on the activities in this unit, you will likely see a range of addition strategies. By the end of Grade 2, all students should be fluent with at least one strategy for solving 2-digit addition problems within 100 and notating their work. In Grade 2, fluency means that they have a strategy that they understand, that is efficient and accurate, and that is based on place value and an understanding of the operation. At this point, efficiency means that students are working with groups of tens and one as opposed to adding on one group of 10 at a time or counting by ones. Students will vary in terms of flexibility; some are quite flexible, choosing a strategy based on the numbers in the problem, and others use one strategy exclusively. See Unit 1, Teacher Note 7: Strategies for Addition and Subtraction, for descriptions of foundational strategies.

Students' strategies for addition fall into three basic categories. Note that at this point in the year, it is assumed that students understand that addition is commutative and, therefore, that they can solve the following problem as 66 + 52 or 52 + 66:

> *Franco had 66 car stickers. Jake gave him 52 car stickers. How many car stickers does Franco have now?*

Adding One Number in Parts

At the end of Grade 2, many students keep one number whole and add the other one *in parts.* Fluency with this strategy means that students add on the other number in parts; that is, they do not count on by ones. Some students add on the tens first and then the ones. Others are more comfortable adding on to a number that is a multiple of 10, as Simon did. They add on enough to the other number to get to a multiple of 10 and then proceed.

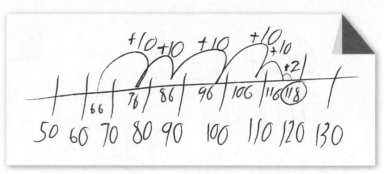

[Chen's Work]

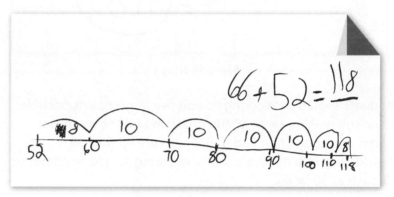

[Carla's Work]

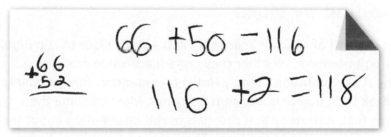

[Darren's Work]

$$66 + 4 = 70$$
$$70 + 40 = 110$$
$$110 + 8 = \boxed{118}$$

[Simon's Work]

$$66 + 52$$
$$60 + 50 = 110$$
$$6 + 2 = 8$$
$$110 + 8 = \boxed{118}$$

[Esteban's Work]

Students should be working to add the largest parts possible while still making sense of the problem and the numbers. Students such as Chen and Carla, who are adding each individual group of 10, should be working to add multiples of 10, such as 50 or 60.

$$60 + 50 = 110$$
$$110 + 2 = 112$$
$$112 + 6 = 118$$

[Henry's Work]

Adding by Place

At the end of Grade 2, many students add by place to combine 2-digit numbers. Whether they use a place-value model (e.g., the sticker notation used by Holly) or equations, these students break both numbers into tens and ones. Most combine the tens first, a strategy that provides useful information about the approximate size of the total. Their second step varies. Some, like Esteban, combine the ones (6 + 2) and then the subtotals (110 + 8), and others, like Henry, add each group of ones onto the total (110 + 2 = 112, 112 + 6 = 118).

Some students may use a place-value strategy but add the ones first and then the tens. There are several ways that students notate this strategy.

6 + 2 = 8	66 + 52	66
60 + 50 = 110	8	+ 52
110 + 8 = 118	+ 110	118
	118	

[Holly's Work]

Some students use vertical notation to record. As you model their strategies, record what was added (e.g., 60 + 50) to help students make sense of both the strategy and the notation. Emphasize that you are doing this for demonstration purposes. Students who use vertical notation do not need to write this extra information when they record.

$$
\begin{array}{r}
66 \\
+\ 52 \\
\hline
110 \quad (60 + 50) \\
+\quad 8 \quad (6 + 2) \\
\hline
118
\end{array}
$$

The U.S. Standard algorithm for addition, which some second grade students may be familiar with, is also an example of adding by place. Rather than beginning with the largest place, as students often do naturally, this algorithm begins with the smallest place. It includes a shorthand way of notating the value of numbers as the digits in each place are added. For many Grade 2 students, the compressed notation of this algorithm can obscure both the place value of the numbers and the meaning of each step of the procedure. This can lead to a more rote approach to solving addition problems. Grade 2 students are still solidifying their understanding of the base-10 number system and the operation of addition. Such understanding is critical to the development of computational fluency and takes time and practice.

After students have developed good, efficient algorithms that they understand and can carry out easily, such as adding by place, some may also become fluent in the traditional or standard algorithm. Others will continue to use adding by place or adding on in parts fluently, which will also serve them well for their computation needs now and as adults. The U.S. Standard algorithm for addition is not addressed directly until Grade 4, although some Grade 2 students may be able to use it with understanding. Note that the vertical notation of adding by place value shown on the previous page, in which the ones are added first, is closely related to the steps in the standard algorithm but makes these steps more transparent. When students use the standard algorithm, demonstrate this form of notation and help students compare the two. Students who use the standard algorithm should also learn other strategies that demonstrate their flexibility with and understanding of addition. The U.S. algorithm is included in a study of strategies for addition in Grade 4.

Changing and Adjusting

At the end of Grade 2, a few students may "take" an amount from one of the addends and "give" it to the other addend, creating an equivalent problem that is easier to solve. For example, Jacy takes six from the 66 and gives it to the 52.

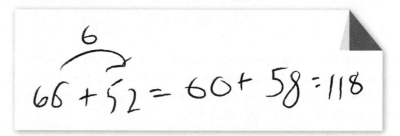

[Jacy's Work]

Similarly, Nadia takes 2 from the 52 and gives it to the 66, and Lonzell takes 4 from the 52 to turn 66 into 70.

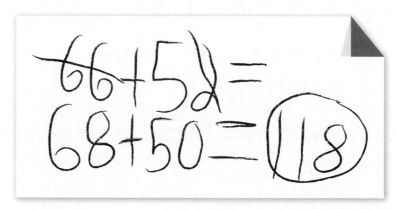

[Nadia's Work]

[Lonzell's Work]

Depending on how this strategy is conceptualized and carried out, it can also be seen as a variation of keeping one number whole and adding the other on in parts.

$$66 + 52$$
$$66 + \ 4 = 70$$
$$70 + 48 = 118$$

Other students change one or both of the numbers to make nearby friendly or landmark numbers, add the new numbers, and then compensate for the changes. For example, consider these students' work with 66 + 52.

66 + 52
70 + 52 = 122
I added 4 too many, so subtract 4
122 − 4 = 118

[Juanita's Work]

66 + 52 = (118)

If it was 50+50 that would = 100 but there was an extra 10 from the 66 and 6 +2 equels 8 and 8+10 = 18 so add a hundred and you get 118.

[Nate's Work]

To some, Juanita's strategy seems similar to changing the numbers to create an equivalent problem, and Nate's looks like a variation of adding by place. It is not important that everyone agree on categorizing student strategies; rather, it is important that the strategy be accurate, efficient, and understandable to the student.

In Grades 3 and 4, students will study these strategies and others in more depth.

Flexibility

At the end of Grade 2, some students can use only one of the above strategies fluently. Others are comfortable enough with several strategies to choose a method based on the structure of the problem or the numbers in it. For example, you may see a student who adds on one number in parts when combining a large number and a small number but who otherwise adds by place, or you may see a student who always adds by place unless the problem involves numbers close to landmark numbers, such as 25 or 50. Developing fluency with all these strategies is a focus of the Grade 3 work on addition.

Notation

All students should be able to write an equation (horizontally or vertically) that represents a given problem situation and interpret and solve a problem presented in either horizontal or vertical form. However, Grade 2 students often use a variety of notational systems—including numbers, equations, the number line, and stickers as a model for representing the place value of our base-ten number system—to solve problems and record their work. See **Teacher Note 8:** Notating Addition Strategies for more information.

Notating Addition Strategies

One challenge students face as they refine and consolidate their strategies for addition in Grade 2 and beyond is finding ways to communicate their mathematical thinking on paper that are clear and efficient. Grade 2 students have several models and representations available to them as they record their work, including the 100 chart, number line, sticker notation, numbers, equations, and vertical notation. See Unit 1, Teacher Note 14: Notating Students' Strategies, for information about recording and helping students record their work, particularly early in the year.

The 100 Chart

At this point in the year, students should not be using the 100 chart to *solve* problems. For example, students should "just know" that 48 + 10 = 58 without finding 48 on the 100 chart and moving down one row. However, some students use this tool to orient and organize themselves and their thinking. Many of these students have difficulty recording what they did on paper. Some say, "I used the 100 chart" or "I counted on the 100 chart." Others try to draw the 100 chart—in whole or in part. Still others include a description of their strategy, "I started at 48 and added on 33."

Encourage students to describe the math of their strategy in writing; for example, "You said you counted on the 100 chart. *How* did you count? Did you count by ones? By tens?" The real focus, however, should be on helping students write equations and helping them connect those equations to the jumps they are making on the 100 chart; for example, "You said that you started at 48 and then jumped 10. Where did you land? What did you do next?"

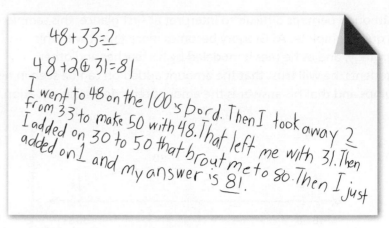

[Carolina's Work]

The Number Line

Many Grade 2 students use the number line to solve addition problems and to show how they solved them. The number line is a particularly useful tool for using and representing the strategy of keeping one number whole and adding the other on in parts. While clear and concise notation is the goal, students often encounter predictable challenges when representing their strategies on a number line. For some students, drawing and labeling a number line and then showing a solution on it can be a challenging fine-motor task. For others, the challenge lies in showing how they added on the other number, showing how they know that they added on all of it and making their answer clear—all in such a way that someone else can read and understand their strategy. For example, to solve 48 + 33, Gregory kept the 48 whole and added on the 33 in groups of 2, 10, 10, 10, and 1 (48 + 2 + 10 + 10 + 10 + 1). He shows that the 3 tens make 30, 2 and 1 makes 3, 30 and 3 makes 33, and his answer is 81.

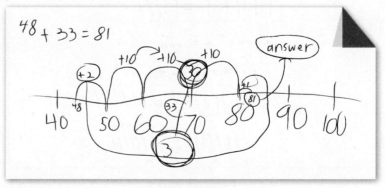

[Gregory's Work]

[Luis's Work]

Although perhaps difficult to interpret at first glance, this sample is quite complete. As Gregory becomes more fluent with this strategy, and as he sees it modeled by his teacher and other students, he will trust that the amount added on can be seen in his jumps and that his answer is the amount recorded in his equation.

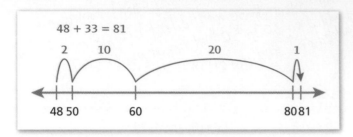

Sticker Notation

Many Grade 2 students use a base-10 model (stickers in strips of 10 and singles or cubes in towers of 10 and single cubes) to solve addition problems efficiently and accurately and/or to represent their strategy. These tools are particularly effective for adding by place. But using sticker notation to record what they did can be challenging and cumbersome. Some students painstakingly show *every* step and draw out every amount in the form of stickers.

For example, Amaya shows 49 and 14 and then combines the tens ($10 + 40 = 50$). Then she takes a 1 from the 4 ($4 - 1 = 3$) and gives it to the 9 to make another 10 ($9 + 1 = 10$). She adds that 10 to the others ($50 + 10 = 60$) and then adds the 3 ones that are still left ($60 + 3 = 63$).

[Amaya's Work]

Again, this is a very complete description and, while accurate, is not efficient. Students such as Amaya should be encouraged to add equations to their work and think about how the equations represent the sticker notation. As Amaya becomes more fluent with this strategy and sees it modeled by her teacher and other students, she will develop more efficient ways of notating her work.

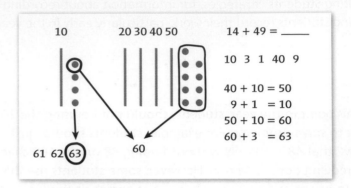

Numbers, Equations, and Vertical Notation

At this point in the year, most students use equations or vertical notation to show their strategies. There are some typical issues to look for as students use numbers and equations to record their work.

RUN-ON EQUATIONS Because students have been thinking about the meaning of the equal sign all year long, particularly during their work on *Today's Number*, you should not see many who record in this way.

[Alberto's Work]

It is clear that Alberto is saying that he added (49 + 1) + 10, but 49 + 1 does *not* equal 50 + 10. Question students who record in such a way. Focus on equality and what the equal sign means. For example, "I see here that you have an equation that says 49 + 1 = 50 + 10. Does 49 + 1 *equal* 50 + 10?"

LINES, CARETS, AND ARROWS Some students use lines, carets, or arrows to clearly and efficiently show their strategy for adding 2-digit numbers. Like Travis, they keep track of the place value of the numbers, and their steps and answer are clear.

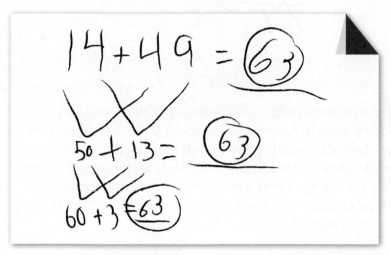

[Travis's Work]

Note that although carets can be a clear and efficient method for recording addition strategies, using carets becomes far more complicated and problematic when subtracting. For this reason—and because the field of mathematics agrees on certain notational conventions—all students should move toward using horizontal equations or vertical notation, with meaning, as they are ready.

Some students "try on" these methods of recording and use them accurately, but it is harder for others to clearly see and make sense of their strategies.

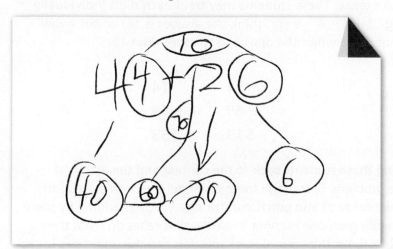

[Anita's Work]

[Lonzell's Work]

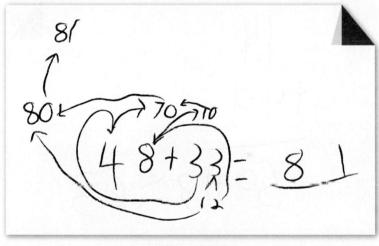

[Malcolm's Work]

These students need support in developing clearer ways to record their strategies. Anita and Malcolm should be encouraged to use equations to show their steps, and Lonzell may benefit from vertical notation.

$$
\begin{array}{r}
14 \\
+\ 49 \\
\hline
50 \\
+\ 13 \\
\hline
63
\end{array}
$$

VERTICAL NOTATION It is important that students be comfortable solving addition problems presented with vertical and horizontal notation by the end of Grade 2. Students should see both kinds of notation as efficient ways to record a problem and its solution, not as a directive to carry out a particular strategy. Some students believe that when they see a problem written in the vertical form, they must carry out a particular algorithm rather than consider what they know about the numbers in the problem. As with any problem, students must first think about what the problem is asking and use what they know about numbers and the operation to solve the problem. *Investigations* students are often more familiar with horizontal equations. Therefore, as they begin to see and use vertical notation, there are some common problems to watch for.

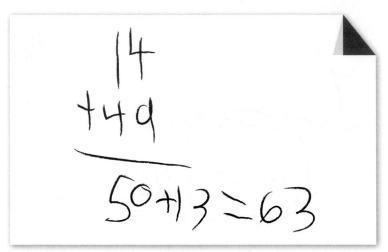

[Katrina's Work]

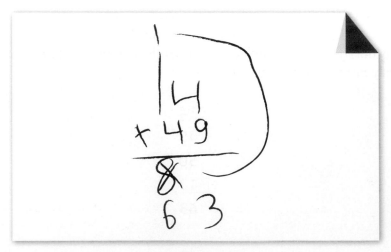

[Leo's Work]

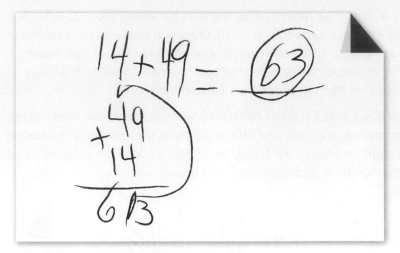

[Paige's Work]

These students compute accurately, but they need help finding ways to notate what happens to the extra group of ten. Consider modeling the slightly expanded form of the conventional notation to help students understand the steps they are taking as they add by place. This understanding is critical to understanding the compact notation of the U.S. Standard algorithm for addition.

$$
\begin{array}{r} 14 \\ + 49 \\ \hline 13 \\ + 50 \\ \hline 63 \end{array}
\qquad
\begin{array}{r} \overset{1}{1}4 \\ + 49 \\ \hline 63 \end{array}
$$

Some Grade 2 students use the U.S. standard algorithm and its notation with understanding. This is fine, although they are also expected to understand and be able to use other strategies and notations. Others misapply it and end with answers that do not make sense. These students may treat each digit individually (e.g., 1 + 4 + 4 + 9 and think the answer is 18) or not know what to do when the ones add to more than 10.

$$
\begin{array}{r} 14 \\ + 49 \\ \hline 513 \end{array}
\qquad
\begin{array}{r} \overset{10}{1}4 \\ + 49 \\ \hline 153 \end{array}
$$

Bring these students back to the context and the action of the problem. Encourage them to model the problem and to make sense of and practice a strategy—such as adding by place or adding on one number in parts—that relies on what they know about the operation of addition and the quantities in the problem and offers a clear and efficient way to notate their work.

Assessment: How Many Points? and Skip Counting Strips

PROBLEM 1

Benchmark addressed:

Benchmark 6: Solve comparison story problems with a bigger unknown.

In order to meet the benchmark, students' work should show that they can:

○ Solve the problem accurately;

○ Show how they solved the problem.

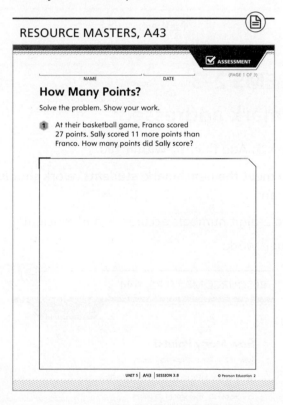

RESOURCE MASTERS, A43

NAME   DATE   (PAGE 1 OF 3)

☑ ASSESSMENT

How Many Points?

Solve the problem. Show your work.

1. At their basketball game, Franco scored 27 points. Sally scored 11 more points than Franco. How many points did Sally score?

UNIT 5 | A43 | SESSION 3.8   © Pearson Education 2

This problem also provides additional information about how students are adding two 2-digit numbers (**Benchmark 5**).

Meeting the Benchmark

The following examples of student work provide a range of typical responses. All of these students met the benchmark— they were able to interpret the problem, solve it accurately, and show their work.

These students reason that Sally's total will be 11 more than Franco's total of 27 and efficiently combine these amounts to determine the answer. Strategies include adding by place, adding 11 on in parts, or taking 1 from 11 and giving it to 27, resulting in 28 + 10.

Carla uses bars to model and make sense of the problem. She reasons that Sally will have 11 more points than Franco and adds by place to determine Sally's total score.

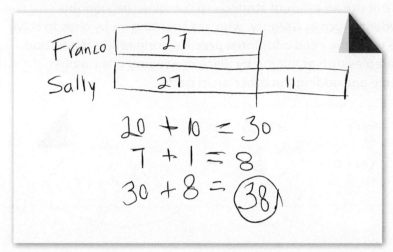

[Carla's Work]

Lonzell and Monisha both add on 11 in parts. Lonzell uses 27 + 10, a fact he knows, to combine the amounts. Monisha uses the same strategy on a number line.

> Franco = 27 points
> Sally = 27 points and 11 more
> I know 27 + 10 = 37 and 1 more is 38
> Sally scored 38 points

[Lonzell's Work]

> Sally has 11 more
> 27 + 11 = 38
> +10   +1
> 27   37 (38)
> Franco   Sally

[Monisha's Work]

Partially Meeting the Benchmark

Some students understand the structure of the problem, but do not use an efficient strategy to combine the amounts. Students, such as Gregory, who are counting on by ones to solve the problem, need additional practice using efficient addition strategies such as adding by place or keeping one number whole and adding the other on in parts.

[Gregory's Work]

Other students solve the problem accurately, but do not represent their solution strategy. Though her work is correct, it is unclear how Leigh thought about the problem and arrived at her answer.

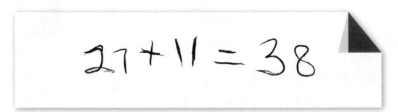

[Leigh's Work]

Meet with students like Leigh to determine how they made sense of the problem and what strategy they used to combine the quantities in the problem. Ask these students if they can go back and model their steps. If students do not understand the structure of the problem, they do not meet the benchmark.

Not Meeting the Benchmark

Some students may have difficulty interpreting and modeling a comparison story with a bigger part unknown. These students may simply state that Sally has 11, as Jeffrey does, or they may add the numbers or subtract one number from the other with no understanding of how these operations relate to the meaning of the problem.

These students need continued support visualizing and modeling comparison problems with a bigger unknown. Comparison Problems on *Student Activity Book* pages 343–344 provide a comparison story problem with a bigger unknown and a model for making other problems that students can solve in class and for homework.

[Jeffrey's Work]

PROBLEMS 2–3

Benchmark addressed:

Benchmark 5: Add fluently within 100.

In order to meet the benchmark, students' work should show that they can:

○ Add two 2-digit numbers accurately and efficiently;

○ Show their work.

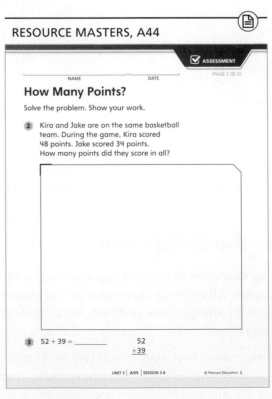

Some students add by place, others keep one number whole, and still others change the numbers to make the problem easier. They use a variety of methods—equations, stickers notation, and the number line—to show their work.

Meeting the Benchmark

The following examples of student work provide a range of typical responses. All of these students meet the benchmark— they were able to interpret the problem and solve it accurately and efficiently.

ADDING TENS AND ONES Many students add by place to solve these problems. They break both numbers into tens and ones, combine the tens, and then add on the ones in a variety of ways.

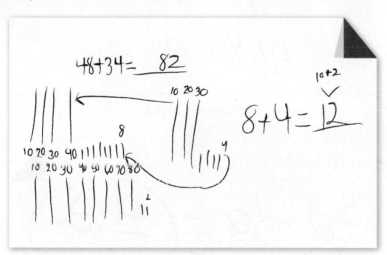

[Jacy's Work]

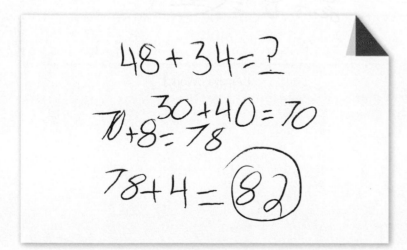

[Carla's Work]

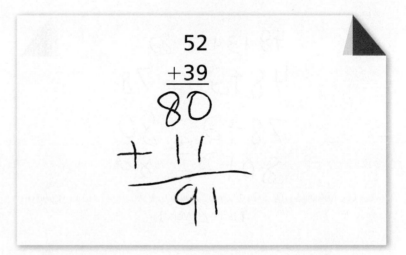

[Darren's Work]

[Alberto's Work]

KEEPING ONE NUMBER WHOLE Some students keep one of the numbers whole and add the other on in parts. Many, like Leigh and Jeffrey, break the number they are adding on into tens and ones (52 + 30 + 9). Others, like Chen, add on enough to get to a multiple of 10 (48 + 2 = 50), then add on tens (50 + 10 + 10 + 10 = 80) or a multiple of 10 (50 + 30 = 80), and then add on the remaining amount (80 + 2 = 82).

52
+39
91

$$52 + 30 = 82$$
$$82 + 9 = 91$$

[Leigh's Work]

$$48 + 34 = \underline{82}$$
$$48 + 30 = 78$$
$$78 + 2 = 80$$
$$80 + 2 = 82$$

[Jeffrey's Work]

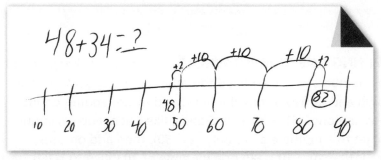

48 + 34 = ?

[Chen's Work]

MAKING AN EQUIVALENT PROBLEM A few students change the numbers to create a multiple of 10, thus making the problem easier to solve. Students may say the following:

○ Take 2 from the 34, and give it to the 48. 50 + 32 = 82.

○ Take 6 from the 48, and give it to the 34. That's 40 + 42, and that's 82.

Partially Meeting the Benchmark

Some students understand the structure of the problem—that it is about combining to find the total—but make errors as they add and keep track of the quantities in the problem. For example, Monisha adds 38 + 4 and gets 41, Amaya gets 12 when she combines 2 and 9, and Gregory forgets the 2 ones from the 52 when he finds the total number of stickers.

$$48 + 34 = \underline{81}$$
$$34 + 4 = 38$$
$$38 + 4 = 41$$
$$41 + 40 = 81$$

[Monisha's Work]

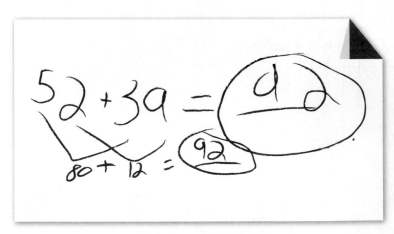

52 + 39 = ?
80 + 12 = 92

[Amaya's Work]

[Gregory's Work]

After you have reviewed their work, ask these students to see whether they can find and correct such errors on their own. Encourage them to take their time and work carefully to avoid such errors in the future. In addition, note whether these kinds of errors are consistent across problems or more of a one-time occurrence.

Not Meeting the Benchmark

Some students understand the structure of the problem but do not have efficient strategies for solving it.

$$52$$
$$+39$$
$$\overline{91}$$

I used the Hundreds Board.

[Yama's Work]

When the teacher questioned Yama about *how* she "used the 100 chart" to solve 52 + 39, Yama demonstrated counting on from 52 by ones.

Students who count on by ones at the end of Grade 2 no longer meet the benchmark. However, it is important to consider each student's growth. Successfully solving this problem may

represent a high level of work for a particular student. It is important to support these students in learning to count on in more efficient ways. Ask questions such as these:

○ "You said that you would start on 52 on the 100 chart and then count on 39. What if you started on 52 and you added 10? Where would you land?"

○ "If you start on 52, how many would you have to add to get to 60?"

You can also model such problems with cubes in towers of 10 or with a set of paper stickers. For example, "If we start with 52 stickers, how many would we have if we add another strip of 10?"

Other students understand the structure of the problem but do not have accurate strategies for solving it.

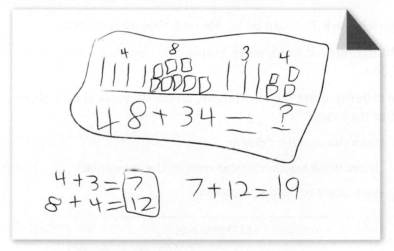

[Henry's Work]

Henry can write an equation to represent the first problem and can represent that problem in stickers. He also seems to have ideas about adding by place. However, he does not see the 4 in the tens place as 40 and the 3 in the tens place as 30. Instead of adding (40 + 30) + (8 + 4), he adds (4 + 3) + (8 + 4).

Other students who struggle with the place value of 2-digit numbers and/or with the vertical notation commonly associated with the U.S. standard algorithm for addition may end up with answers that are similarly unreasonable.

$$52$$
$$+39$$
$$\overline{811}$$

$$\overset{10}{52}$$
$$+39$$
$$\overline{181}$$

These students are following a series of steps that are disconnected from the quantities in the problem and the properties of the operation of addition. Ask them to use a different strategy to solve the problem. If they cannot do this on their own, ask them to use cubes (in towers of 10) or stickers to represent the problem. Then ask these students to use the adding by place strategy to solve the problem. Help them use numbers and equations to record, as needed. Students who struggle with this need more practice adding smaller 2-digit numbers. Spend time working with them on smaller problems that do not require regrouping and then move on to problems that do. Increase the size of the numbers as they become able to combine smaller 2-digit numbers.

PROBLEM 4
Benchmarks addressed:

Benchmark 7: Count by 5s, 10s and 100s within 1,000.

Benchmark 3: Read, write, count, and compare numbers to 1,000.

In order to meet the benchmark, students' work should show that they can:

○ Read the numbers given;

○ Know what numbers come next in the sequence;

○ Accurately write the numbers.

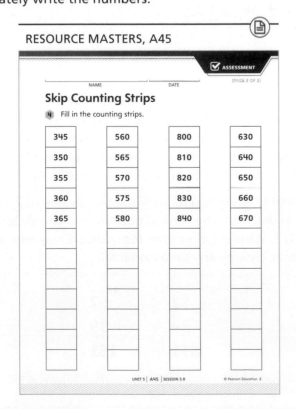

RESOURCE MASTERS, A45

NAME   DATE

Skip Counting Strips

4 Fill in the counting strips.

345	560	800	630
350	565	810	640
355	570	820	650
360	575	830	660
365	580	840	670

UNIT 5 | A45 | SESSION 3.8   © Pearson Education 2

Meeting the Benchmarks

Most students should be able to read the given numbers, determine what number to write next, and complete the sequence accurately.

345	560	800	630
350	565	810	640
355	570	820	650
360	575	830	660
365	580	840	670
370	585	850	680
375	590	860	690
380	595	870	700
385	600	880	710
390	605	890	720
395	610	900	730
400	615	910	740

[Chen's Work]

Not Meeting the Benchmarks

Some students understand the problem—that it is about completing the given skip-counting strips—but make a mistake as they count or write a particular number. For example, you may see students who do the following:

- Skip or repeat numbers;
- Have difficulty transitioning from one decade or century to another;
- Write only numbers that end in 5 on their multiple-of-5 strips;
- Count by tens when they reach a number that is a multiple of 10;
- Count by 100s when they reach 100.

As you review their work, note the types and number of errors students make. Afterward, ask students who made errors to double-check their work. Often, students will discover such errors when counting aloud and fix them on their own. Note whether they can do this. Encourage those who can to take their time and work carefully to avoid such errors in the future. In addition, note whether these kinds of errors are consistent across problems or more of a onetime occurrence.

Instruct students who cannot find and fix their own errors to use their 1,000 Book to correct their work. These students need more practice seeing and using the number sequences – oral, numerical, and written – to make sense of how these expressions of number are coordinated. These students should continue working on skip counting strips and playing games in the 1,000 Book.

Adding Nine

To introduce the plus 9 combinations at the beginning of Session 1.1, this teacher presents a pair of related problems that encourage students to use the relationship between adding 10 and adding 9. She writes 4 + 10 = _____ on chart paper.

Teacher: What do we know about adding 10 to another number?

Leigh: It becomes like 14, a 10 and a number.

Amaya: You replace the 0 with the 4 that's in the ones place. Because 0 plus 4 is 4.

Teacher: And when you put the 10 back in, what is the total?

Amaya: 14.

Teacher: How can you think about this using strips of 10 and singles?

Darren: If you add 10, you add 1 strip. So 4 plus 10 is 1 strip and 4 singles.

Teacher: I'm going to put up another problem. Remember that we've been talking about how things are related and about using what we know to solve a problem.

The teacher writes 4 + 9 = _____ on chart paper. Several students call out 13.

Teacher: Travis, you gave me an answer. Did you use anything you know to get the answer?

Travis: I know that 4 + 10 equals 14. And I took the 1 away to get 13.

Teacher: Why did you have to take away the 1?

Travis: Because it isn't 10, it's 9, and 10 minus 1 is 9.

Anita: Yes, 10 and 4 is 14. Nine and 4 is 1 less, so it's 13.

The teacher records 4 + 10 = 14 and 14 − 1 = 13 and then directs students' attention to the number line.

Teacher: Travis and Anita said that 4 + 10 is 14 [draws an arc from 4 to 14 and labels it +10] and 14 − 1 is 13 [draws an arc from 14 to 13 and labels it −1]. But the problem was 4 + 9. I see plus 10 [points to the +10 arc] and minus 1 [points to the −1 arc], but where's the plus 9?

Simon: From 4 to 13.

After asking Simon to count from 4 to 13 on the number line, the teacher draws a dotted line arcing from 4 to 13 and labels it +9.

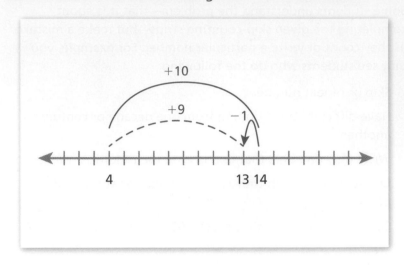

Teacher: Did anyone solve this a different way?

Jacy: You can flip the numbers for addition. So I thought 9 and 1 more makes 10, and then there's only 3 left to add.

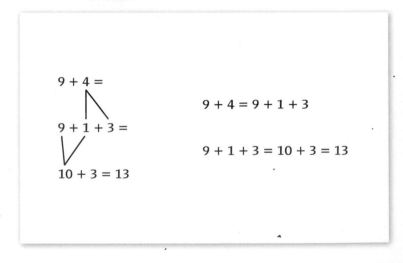

Teacher: Did anyone else change the order and think about it as 9 + 4 instead of 4 + 9?

Monisha: I started with 9, and then I went 10, 11, 12, 13.

Teacher: There's a tried and true strategy. You can start with the bigger number and count up.

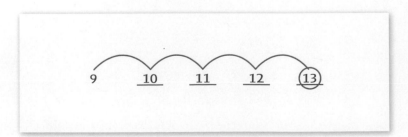

Teacher: Any other strategies for solving 4 + 9?

Simon: You could give one number from the 4 to the 9 and then you have 3 and 10 and that equals 13.

Teacher: What Simon is saying is that I can take 1 from the 4 and give it to the group of 9, and then I have 10 and 3, and that's 13.

The teacher draws the following on the chart paper as she speaks:

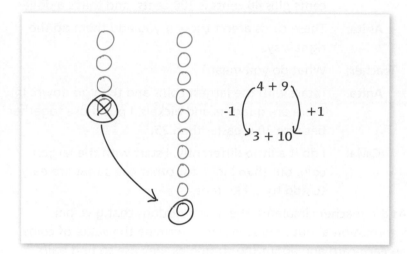

Teacher: Why do you think Simon wanted to make this group have 10?

Melissa: Because 10 is easy to work with. If you know your plus 10s, then it's easy because you can take 1 from the 4 and add it to the 9, and then you have 3 + 10.

Chen: You just take 1 from the other number and add it to the 9 for 10, and then those numbers are easy to add.

Teacher: Let's look at that with cubes. Here's 4 + 9. Can someone show us what happens with the cubes in Simon's strategy?

Notice the way students use what they know to solve 4 + 9. Some reason that if 4 + 10 = 14, then 4 + 9 must equal 1 less. Others create an easier, equivalent problem (4 + 9 = 10 + 3) by taking 1 from the 4 and giving it to the 9. Still others know that you can add numbers in any order and count on from 9 or add on the 4 in useful groups (9 + 1 + 3). Note that these strategies rely on the following generalizations that students have been discussing over the course of the year:

○ If you subtract 1 from one addend, the sum decreases by 1.

○ If you take 1 from one addend and add it to the other addend, the sum remains the same.

○ Order does not matter in addition.

○ You can break numbers into parts to add them.

Strategies for *Make a Dollar*

Students are playing *Make a·Dollar*. The teacher circulates, observing the students and asking them to articulate the strategies they are using as they play. She stops to talk to Jeffrey and Esteban to find out how they are choosing their cards.

Jeffrey: I am thinking about this one and something else (points to a card with 70 cents).

Jeffrey quickly finds the match to his card.

Jeffrey: 70 and 30. That makes a dollar.

Teacher: Are you using any strategies that help you while you are playing?

Jeffrey: I'm starting by finding the amount on one card and then looking for a card that helps it make one dollar.

Jeffrey finds a card worth 80 cents and then quickly notices another card that has four nickels. He grabs that pair.

Esteban: I don't see any more cards that match. Oh wait! I see one! I see one! Nope, only 90 cents!

The boys work together for about three minutes to try and find another pair. Then they replace the four cards Jeffrey used, and Esteban takes his turn.

Esteban: I found one. Wait. I want to count the coins and make sure it's right.

Esteban starts with the card that equals 50 cents (two quarters). Then he counts the card with one quarter.

Esteban: This doesn't work. It is only 75. We need to put the cards back.

The two boys continue working cooperatively to find matches for Esteban. At another desk, Carla and Anita are also playing *Make a Dollar*. Carla has a card with 60 cents on it.

Teacher: What are you looking for?

Carla: I knew that this was 60 because I counted the quarter and then the nickel, and that makes thirty. Then I counted the three dimes. It makes 60. So I knew that I had to find 40.

Teacher: So you used 60 plus 40 equals 100 to help you. How does 60 plus 40 equals 100 help you figure out how much to add to 60¢ to make a dollar?

Carla: I know that a dollar is equal to 100 cents, so 60 cents plus 40 cents is 100 cents, and that's a dollar.

Anita: These cards aren't tricky if you add them up the right way.

Teacher: What do you mean?

Anita: I start with the largest coins and then go down. If there are quarters and nickels, I put those together because 30 is easier than 25.

Carla: I do it a little differently. I start with the largest coin, but then I look for other coins that are easy to add to it, like tens.

As the teacher circulates, she asks questions that give her information about how students determine the value of coins on each card and about the strategies they use to find pairs of cards that add to a dollar. The students verbalize a range of strategies, such as starting with the largest coin and then adding 10s, combining coins such as a quarter and a nickel to make an amount that's "easier to work with," and using known combinations that add to 100 to find pairs of cards that add to a dollar. Asking students to articulate their approaches helps consolidate these strategies and also encourages learning from others as they work toward greater computational fluency and efficiency. Working cooperatively on each player's turn also encourages conversation about the coin combinations and thus supports the learning.

Strategies for *Capture 5*

After playing *Capture 5* in Math Workshop for several days, the teacher brings the class together to discuss their strategies (at the beginning of Session 1.5). Students are discussing the Change Cards they can use to move a game piece on 35 to capture a chip on 52. The class has shared the following combinations:

$$35 + 30 - 10 - 3 = 52$$

$$35 + 20 - 3 = 52$$

1	2	3	4	5	6	7	8	9	10
11	12	13	14	15	16	17	18	19	20
21	22	23	24	25	26	27	28	29	30
31	32	33	34	◼	36	37	38	39	40
41	42	43	44	45	46	47	48	49	50
51	(52)	53	54	55	56	57	58	59	60
61	62	63	64	65	66	67	68	69	70
71	72	73	74	75	76	77	78	79	80
81	82	83	84	85	86	87	88	89	90
91	92	93	94	95	96	97	98	99	100

Teacher: You've been playing *Capture 5* for a few days now. What are some strategies you are finding useful when playing this game? How did you decide which cards to use for this round?

Juan: I tried different cards to see where I could move my game piece. So I started with the +30 card. I know 35 + 30 = 65. But then I saw that I had gone too far, so I used the −10 card, which would put my piece on 55. 55 is 3 more than 52, so I used the −3 card to move back 3.

Teacher: So Juan tries different cards to see which combination of cards will help him capture a chip.

The teacher asks Juan to demonstrate his moves on the 100 chart. As he demonstrates, the teacher asks the class to consider which equation matches Juan's moves.

Teacher: So we agree that the equation 35 + 30 − 10 − 3 = 52 matches Juan's moves on the 100 chart. Who used a different set of Change Cards to capture the chip on 52?

Holly: I used the +20 and the −3 cards. My strategy is a little different. I saw 52. In my head, I thought: How far is it from 35 to 52? I know that 35 + 10 = 45 and 7 more would get me to 52. Together that's 17, so I knew I needed to move the game piece 17 spaces.

Teacher: So Holly found the distance between the game piece and the chip. Did anyone else use this strategy?

A few students nod in response.

Teacher: Do you agree that the distance between 35 and 52 is 17? How do you know?

Roshaun: I thought about it in stickers. 35 + 1 strip of 10 is 45. 5 more singles would be 50, and 2 more would be 52. Together that's 17.

Amaya: I can see it on the 100 chart. 35 + 10 is 45. Then you count up 7 to get to 52.

Teacher: It would be easy if we had a +10 and a +7 card to get the game piece from 35 to 52. But we don't have those cards. Holly, can you explain what you did next?

Holly: I looked at the cards. I thought about which ones equaled 17. I used the +20 and the −3 card.

Teacher: Do people agree that a +20 card and a −3 equals 17?

Many students nod in agreement.

Teacher: What about the Change Cards Juan used? Do you think he moved the game piece the same number of spaces? Do you agree that +30 − 10 − 3 is 17? Turn and talk to someone next to you about this.

After giving students an opportunity to talk with each other, the teacher asks students to share their thinking.

Juan: I know I moved the same number of spaces as Holly because we both started on 35 and landed on 52.

Tia: +30 − 10 − 3 equals 17 too! 30 − 10 = 20 and then 20 − 3 = 17.

Teacher: So Juan and Holly both moved the same distance to capture the chip on 52, but they used different strategies to do so. As you continue to play this game, think about the strategies you are using to choose the cards you need to capture a chip. Is it helpful to figure out the distance between your game piece and a chip before you choose cards?

The teacher focuses this discussion on two strategies for playing *Capture 5:* trying out different combinations of Change Cards to reach the target number and first determining the distance between the game piece and a chip and then selecting Change Cards that total that amount. While the latter strategy may be more efficient, it is clear from Juan's description that he is able to efficiently add and subtract groups of 10 to test out different combinations of Change Cards. As the teacher observes students during subsequent sessions, he will continue to work with students who may be counting on or back ones to develop strategies for adding and subtracting with greater efficiency.

Playing *Close to 100*

In Session 2.1, the teacher observes students as they play *Close to 100* for the first time. She notes that some students are developing useful strategies for finding combinations that are close to 100, while other students are selecting cards at random. She decides to focus the first strategy discussion (in Session 2.2) on one strategy that she would like students explore: starting with a known combination and adjusting the numbers.

Teacher: Starting with a combination you know makes 100 can be a useful strategy. I know 80 + 20 = 100. I wanted to use that fact in a round of *Close to 100*, but I didn't have the right cards. I had a 7 and 9, so I chose to make 79. What number do I need to get to 100? Can I use the fact 80 + 20 = 100 to help me?

Carolina: 79 is close to 80. So I think you can use 80 + 20 = 100, but I'm not sure how.

The teacher takes out 80 red cubes and 20 blue cubes arranged in towers of 10 and asks Carolina if she would like to use the cubes to think through the problem. Carolina counts the 80 cubes and removes one cube to make 79. She then places the 20 blue cubes beside the 79 red cubes. She looks at the teacher unsure of what to do next.

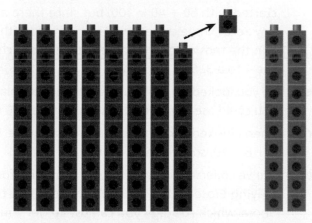

Teacher: I see 79 red cubes and 20 blue cubes. How is 79 + 20 related to 80 + 20? Does 79 + 20 equal 100? What would we need to add to 79 to get to 100?

Leo: You started with 80 + 20 = 100. Then Carolina took one away, but if you take one from the 80 to make 79, then you would have to add the one to the 20 to make it even.

Teacher: Can you say more?

Yama: I think I know what Leo means. If you take one from the group of 80, then you have to give one to the group of 20, or you will end up with 1 less than 100.

Carolina counts the cubes and determines there are 99 in all. She takes the cube she originally removed and places it beside one of the towers of 10 blue cubes.

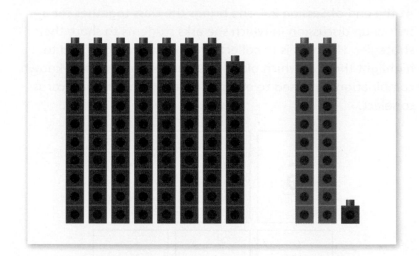

Carolina: So you're not really adding or subtracting anything. You're just removing the one from the 80 and giving it to the 20?

Chen: I think about it differently. 79 is one less than 80, so it puts you one more away from 100. 79 + 20 would be 99, so you need one more. 79 + 20 + 1 = 100.

The teacher models the problem on the number line.

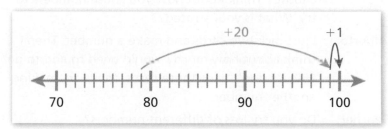

Teacher: This is another way we can show this strategy. Can someone use the number line to explain why 79 + 21 = 100?

Travis: I can see on the number line that 79 is one jump to 80. Then I know that 80 + 20 = 100, so it's 21.

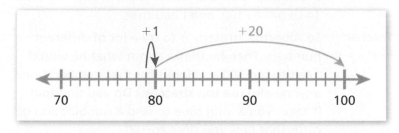

The teacher is aware that there are several students who are still working to make sense of this strategy. Over the coming days, she continues to observe students as they play and takes note of who in the class is using a combination of 100 and then adjusting the numbers to get as close to 100 as possible. She also notes the other strategies students are developing as they gain more experience with the game.

At the end of Session 2.4, she brings the class together for a follow-up discussion in which she asks students to share their strategies. Her goal is to collect a range of strategies and to highlight those in which place value understanding and known combinations are used to efficiently determine the best cards to select.

6	8	2
4	3	1

Teacher: You've gotten a lot of experience playing *Close to 100*. Imagine you are playing a round, and these are your cards. Which of these cards would you choose? Think about how you chose numbers to try. What is your strategy?

Alberto: I just pick two cards and make a number. Then I think about how much I would need to add to get 100. If I don't have those cards, then I try making another number.

Teacher: Do you try lots of different numbers?

Alberto: Sometimes I have to try a lot of numbers to find one that will help me get close to 100. Like for this round, I tried 48 first, but there weren't any numbers I could use that would get me close enough to 100. Then I tried 86 because that was the biggest number I could make. I knew I needed 14 to get to 100, and I had that.

Teacher: So Alberto's strategy is to try a lot of different numbers. Then he thinks about what he would need to get 100 and looks for that number. Does anyone else use this strategy? Do you find that it takes you a long time to find a combination of cards that gets you close to 100?

Juanita: I used that strategy for a while, but it was hard. I kept getting a high score. Then I realized I could look for cards that make 100. Like I know 8 + 2 = 10, so 80 + 20 = 100, and 4 + 6 = 10 so 40 + 60 = 100. I used the numbers that make 10 in the tens

place. Then I looked for zeros or small numbers to use in the ones place. I would do either 81 + 22 or 61 + 42.

Teacher: So you use a combination you know and then make the numbers as close to that as possible. How close to 100 is Juanita's score?

Leo: I think it's pretty close. 80 + 20 = 100. Then 2 + 1 = 3, so it would make 103. 42 + 61 would be the same answer. So the score would be 3.

Teacher: Did anyone else use a similar strategy?

Jacy: I started with 60 + 40 = 100, but since there aren't any zeros, I knew whatever I put in the ones place would be too much, so I changed the numbers. I know 39 + 61 = 100, but there isn't a 9 so I kept going. 38 + 62 = 100, and we have an 8 and a 2. So I used those.

Teacher: So you started with a combination you knew, and then adjusted the numbers to get as close to 100 as possible. Did anyone else choose these numbers?

Gregory: I got the same numbers as Juanita, but I did it differently. I looked for the tens place digits first. I started with 60 + 40 = 100, but since there aren't any zeros, I knew that whatever I made with 6 and 4 in the tens place would be over 100, so I changed the 4 to a 3. 60 + 30 = 90.

Teacher: So you looked for two numbers in the tens place that you could use to make 90. Then what did you do?

Gregory: Then I looked for a combination that made 10. 2 + 8 = 10, so I made 62 + 38.

Teacher: We've collected many different strategies for playing *Close to 100*. As you play, continue to think about which strategy you can use to get you as close to 100 as possible without having to try lots of different cards. Is there a strategy you heard a classmate share today that you might try? Did any of these strategies help you think about how to play the game differently?

After giving students the opportunity to explain their strategies in their own words, this teacher names and then restates each strategy for the class. After this discussion, she posted a chart showing the strategies shared for students' reference as they continue to play. In the coming days, she will continue to observe students as they play. She will check in with students who are still selecting cards randomly and help them select an appropriate strategy from this chart to practice with her support.

Addition Strategies

Students begin Investigation 3 by solving a 2-digit addition problem on *Student Activity Book* page 335. The teacher brings students together to share their solution strategies. She focuses the discussion on two strategies in particular: adding one number on in parts and adding tens and ones, because students will be practicing these two strategies throughout the investigation. She also wants them to begin to consider the efficiency of various strategies for adding and notating their work.

Kira had 48 balloons. Jake gave her 33 more balloons. How many balloons does Kira have now?

Teacher: What equations did you write?

Anita: 48 plus 33 equals blank.

Nadia: Or 33 plus 48 equals blank.

Chen: Or you can do it the stacking way, up and down.

The teacher records these suggestions on chart paper. Beneath them she writes "Adding Tens and Ones" and "Adding One Number in Parts."

Teacher: Who used strips of 10 and singles to solve the problem?

Henry: I did 4 lines, and then I put 3 more lines. And then I put 8 singles and then 3. I counted the strips first, and I got 70. And then I did plus 8 equals 78. Then I knew that 78 + 3 = 81.

Teacher: Where should I record Henry's strategy? Did he keep one number whole and add the other on in parts? Did he add tens and ones? Did he use another strategy?

Monisha: Tens and ones.

Teacher: How many people agree?

The class agrees. The teacher rephrases Henry's strategy as she records it beneath the heading "Adding Tens and Ones."

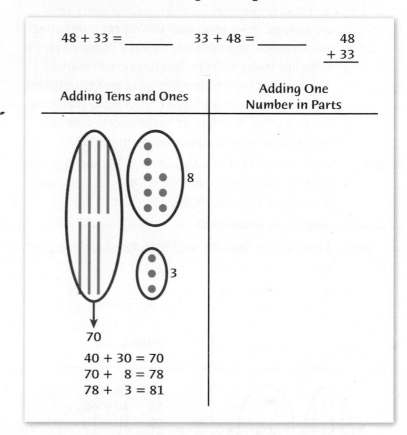

Paige: I did it similar to Henry. I did 40 + 30 = 70. 8 + 3 =11. And you take the 10 and add it to the 70. That's 80. And then 80 plus 1 is 81.

Teacher: Which of our strategies would that go under?

Paige: The tens and ones.

The teacher records Paige's strategy under Henry's.

40 + 30 = 70
8 + 3 = 11
70 + 10 = 80
80 + 1 = 81

Teacher: Henry, do you agree that this is similar to yours? [Henry nods.] Henry used stickers in strips of ten and singles, and Paige used numbers and equations. Who else used adding tens and ones? [Eight students raise their hands.] Those of you who are using stickers, like Henry, can start to think about how to use numbers and equations to record when you add tens and ones. Did anyone try this other strategy of keeping one number whole and adding the other on in parts?

Rochelle: I broke the 33. Then 48 and 10 is 58, and then 58 and 10 is 68, and 68 and 10 is 78. So it's 78, and then the 3 more is 79, 80, 81.

Teacher: Any other strategies?

Leo: I did 48 plus 30 is 78, and then 78 plus three is 81.

$$48 + 33 = \underline{\hspace{1cm}} \qquad 33 + 48 = \underline{\hspace{1cm}} \qquad \begin{array}{r} 48 \\ + 33 \\ \hline \end{array}$$

Adding Tens and Ones	**Adding One Number in Parts**
	$48 + 10 = 58$
	$58 + 10 = 68$
	$68 + 10 = 78$
	$78 + 3 = 81$
	$48 + 30 = 78$
	$78 + 3 = 81$

$40 + 30 = 70$
$70 + 8 = 78$
$78 + 3 = 81$

$40 + 30 = 70$
$8 + 3 = 11$
$70 + 10 = 80$
$80 + 1 = 81$

Teacher: Leo's strategy reminds me of another one on our chart.

Students: Rochelle's!

Teacher: How are they similar?

Lonzell: They both kept 48 whole and added on 33.

Teacher: How are they different?

Juanita: Leo did the 30 altogether. Rochelle did 10 plus 10 plus 10.

Teacher: Yes, Leo did it in two steps. People who are using this strategy can push themselves to add on the other number in fewer and fewer steps. I have one last question. The problem was 40 something plus 30 something. Why wasn't the answer in the 70s?

Luis: Because the somethings made more than 10. That put the number in the 80s.

Tia: It wasn't just 40 and 30. The 3 from the 33 and the 8 from the 48 made it go over into the 80s.

Teacher: Why did that happen?

Lonzell: Three and 8 is 11. And 70 plus 11 equals *eighty*-one.

Holly: The 10 from the 11 made it bump from 70 to 80. And then the 1 made it go to 81.

Discussing the similarities and the differences between the work of students who used the same strategy gives the teacher an opportunity to highlight more efficient approaches and methods of notation. Recording the strategies discussed provides students with concrete examples they can reference as they work toward more efficient approaches.

Counting by 5s and 10s

At the end of Session 3.3, the teacher brings her class together to practice skip counting by 5s and 10s and to discuss the patterns they notice. After counting around the class by 5s from 400, the class launches into a discussion about the patterns they notice in the skip counting sequence. In doing so they focus on important ideas about the place value of 3-digit numbers.

Teacher: Take a moment to look at the list of numbers we said when we counted around the class by 5s. Turn and talk with someone beside you about what you notice.

After students have had an opportunity to talk with one another, the teacher asks them to share their observations.

Henry: All the numbers we counted end in a 5 or a 0. See, it goes 0, 5, 0, 5, 0, 5, and on like that.

Teacher: Raise a hand if you also noticed this pattern.

Many students raise their hands.

Teacher: Why do you think it works like that? Why do we say a number that ends in either a zero or a five when we are counting by fives?

Simon: Well, when you count by fives, you add on 5 each time. So 400 + 5 = 405. Then 405 + 5 = 410. You land on 10s numbers like 410, 420, and 430 when you count by 5s. That's where the zero comes from.

Katrina: I can see it on the list. When we are counting by 5s, we say the 10s numbers too. We say a number in the tens every other number. That's why it goes 5, 0, 5, 0.

Teacher: What other patterns do you notice?

Carla: I noticed that the tens number, the one in the middle, has a pattern. It goes 0, 0, 1, 1, 2, 2, 3, 3, 4, 4, 5, 5, 6, 6, and on like that.

Teacher: So Carla is noticing a pattern in numbers in the tens place. Why do you think that pattern happens? Let's look at an example a little more closely. What does the 2 represent in the number 420? In the number 425?

Carla: It represents 2 tens.

Katrina: I think I see how it works. It's like with stickers. 20 is two strips of 10. When you add on 5 more singles, the number of strips doesn't change, but if you add on 5 more singles to 25, then you have 30, which is 3 strips. The number of 10s changes every other number.

The teacher asks Katrina if she could represent her idea with a set of cubes.

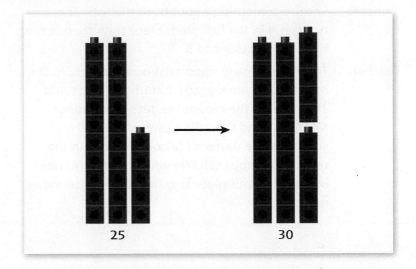

25   30

Teacher: What do people think? Does anyone else have an idea about why this pattern happens?

Nate: I think I agree with Carla, but I think about it like this: We're counting by fives, and it takes two fives to make a ten. So you say two numbers before the number in the tens place changes.

Teacher: You've noticed interesting patterns and have thought carefully about why those patterns happen. Let's count around the class again. This time, let's count by 10s. We'll start at 400 again. Do you think we will say 465 when we count by 10s? Talk to a neighbor about this, and then we will count.

Students count around the circle by 10s. The teacher lists the numbers students say, starting with 400.

Teacher: We didn't say 465 this time. Why not?

Leigh: Because when we count by 10s we only say the 10s numbers, and 465 comes between 460 and 470.

Teacher: What patterns did you notice this time we counted?

Henry: I notice that all the numbers we said this time end in 0, and I know why, because the tens numbers end in zero, and we were counting by tens.

Malcolm: I notice that the tens numbers go 1, 2, 3, 4, 5, 6, 7, 8, 9, 0, and then they repeat.

Teacher: So Malcolm is noticing a different pattern in the tens place this time.

Lonzell: I notice something about both the lists. The number 4 in the hundreds place stays there a long time then changes to 5.

Teacher: These are all very important observations. In the coming days we'll practice counting by 5s and 10s more. In the meantime, let's think about Malcolm's and Lonzell's observations. Why do you think the pattern Malcolm noticed in the tens place happens? And why does the number in the hundreds place stay the same for so many numbers?

In this discussion, the teacher asks students to identify patterns and to articulate why those patterns appear. This is a challenging task, and the teacher is aware that while some students are able to easily grasp and explain how the digits in the ones, tens, and hundreds place change when skip counting by 5s and 10s, there are other students who are still developing these understandings. As the class practices skip counting, the teacher continues to ask students to share observations about the patterns they notice and to think about why those patterns occur.

INDEX IN THIS UNIT